Introduction to the Atmosphere

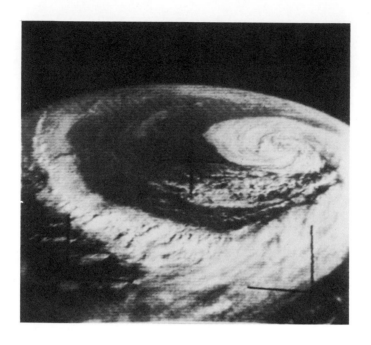

Launching of the weather satellite TIROS I in 1960 inaugurated a new era in exploring the atmosphere. The cameras and radiation sensors aboard satellites hundreds of miles above the earth inform the world's weather services about storms in the atmosphere far from the shore of continents and weather-observing networks. Cloud systems often have the shape of huge spirals. Here we see a spectacular case, photographed by TIROS VI over the western Atlantic on May 29, 1963. (Courtesy U.S. Weather Bureau and National Aeronautics and Space Administration.)

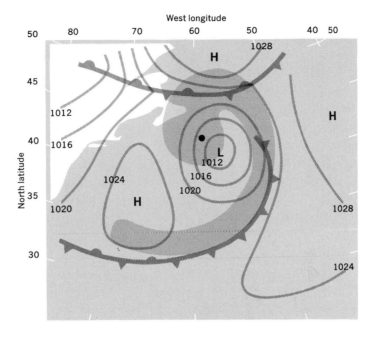

Surface weather map for May 29, 1963. A slowly decaying low-pressure center, or cyclone, lies southeast of Newfoundland. The spiral cloud mass revealed by TIROS VI (shaded) strikingly shows the position of the surface cold front. The core of the spiral is associated with the center of the cyclone in the upper atmosphere (heavy dot). (Isobars are drawn at intervals of 4 millibars; the frontal symbols are explained in Appendix I.)

Introduction

McGraw-Hill Book Company

to the
Atmosphere

Herbert Riehl
PROFESSOR OF ATMOSPHERIC SCIENCE, COLORADO STATE UNIVERSITY

new york, st. louis, san francisco, toronto, london, sydney

Introduction to the Atmosphere

Preface

During the years that have passed since about 1940, the advances in knowledge of the atmosphere have been rapid and exciting. In part, they have come about through increasing understanding of the physical processes, in part through great expansion of observing networks and development of instruments to measure the atmosphere. When the author took his first meteorology course, telemetering of pressure, temperature, and humidity aloft to the ground from rising balloons was the latest technological advance. Nowadays, we take it in stride when weather satellites bring news about storms over distant oceans, when rockets report jet-stream winds at great heights, and when large computers grind out weather forecasts for large parts of the world in minutes.

The advances in knowledge have brought, as a corollary, ever-increasing interest in Atmospheric Science and its relation to other branches of science. Widening use is made of information about weather in public and private enterprises. At many universities instruction in Atmospheric Science has been started as part of geophysics curricula; numerous non-specialist "terminal" courses have become part of science offerings. It is for the students in such instruction programs, desiring a concise yet thorough view of the field, that this book is primarily intended. The author hopes, further, that it will prove useful as a volume for study and reference to engineers and other professional men and women whose work requires some understanding and judgment about the atmosphere.

With these objectives, the book is short and nonmathematical. Subject matter has been held to a limited range of topics, with emphasis on the basic aspects of the science.

Even so, considerable room remains for an instructor's selection and, of course, for enlargement in areas of his choice. At Colorado State University, the course is offered for students with general science background.

The modern views about the atmosphere, and the problems for the future, are stressed throughout the book. The author has not hesitated to present subjects such as large-scale wave motion in the upper air under the influence of the earth's rotation. This is a most important topic for understanding daily weather changes, warm or cold winters, and even climates. Controversial subjects like weather modification are also included. Further, the author wishes to convey that, although Atmospheric Science is a field for rigorous and useful inquiry, it is also fun, and exciting in its future prospects.

The author is grateful to the several copyright holders and to his many friends who have placed illustrations at his disposal. He also wishes to express thanks to his colleagues, especially Dr. Patrick Squires, of the National Center for Atmospheric Research, Boulder, Colorado, for critical reading of parts of the text, and to Ann Ewing and Jamia Cone for editorial assistance.

Herbert Riehl

Contents

1

A Survey of the Atmosphere

For five years before the French revolution began in 1789, Thomas Jefferson, in Paris, observed at close range the fermentation that led to the conflict. After noting that all attempts at progressive measures were nullified by the influence of Queen and Court, he commented (in his autobiography) about the 1788–1789 winter:

But the hand of heaven weighed heavily indeed on the machinations of this junto [Queen and Court]; producing collateral incidents, not arising out of the case, yet powerfully co-exciting the nation to force a regeneration of its government, and overwhelming with accumulated difficulties, this liberticide resistance. For, while laboring under the want of money for even ordinary purposes, in a government which required a million of livres a day, and driven to the last ditch by the universal call for liberty, there came on a winter of such severe cold, as was without example in the memory of man, or in the written records of history. The Mercury was at times 50° below the freezing point of Fahrenheit, and 22° below that of Reaumur. All out-door labor was suspended, and the poor, without the wages of labor, were, of course, without either bread or fuel. The government found its necessities aggravated by that of procuring immense quantities of fire-wood, and of keeping great fires at all the cross streets, around which the people gathered in crowds, to avoid perishing with cold. . . .

Jefferson, in these lines, has made a powerful analysis of how weather, especially extreme weather, affects the affairs of men. What causes temperatures of −18°F at Paris? The pattern of air flow that brings very cold winters to Europe is well known today from records taken since weather-observing networks were established in the nineteenth century. Air is persistently channeled westward from Russia and Siberia, and this must have occurred during the winter of 1788–1789.

The roots for such abnormal, as well as for normal, air motions lie in the reactions of the atmosphere to the sun's radiation, to the earth's rotation, to large bodies of water, and to mountain ranges, among many factors. These reactions determine the variations, in space and time, of temperature, wind, precipitation, and other variables. Atmospheric science is the branch of physics concerned with understanding of atmospheric processes. When the atmospheric variables are considered as a whole at an instant of time, that particular state of the atmosphere is termed *weather*. When the weather is observed for a sufficiently long time to show features such as mean annual temperature and rainfall, their seasonal changes, and the differences among the various parts of the world, we speak of *climate*.

The atmospheric processes and the weather and climate they produce are the substance of this book. Most observations of the atmosphere are meaningful only when related to their large-scale climatic setting. Therefore we begin with a survey of the world's major wind and thermal patterns.

GENERAL CIRCULATION

Principal Controls. Earth and atmosphere receive heat from the sun; they radiate the same amount of heat into space. But this heat balance applies only to the globe as a whole and not to any specific area. The equatorial region absorbs more heat than it loses, while the polar zones give off more heat than they receive. Nevertheless, the equatorial belt does not become warmer during a year, nor do the poles become colder. Heat flows from the warm to the cold regions, maintaining the observed average temperatures. This exchange of heat implies motion of the atmosphere, and this motion, when summarized over the earth as a whole, is called the *general circulation.*

The flow of heat toward the poles increases from the equator to about latitude 35° (Fig. 1.1). From there it decreases as some of the imported heat remains in each belt of the higher latitudes. Outside the tropics, the wind systems of large storms carry out most of the heat exchange. These storms travel mainly from west to east. They form a never-ending succession of low-pressure

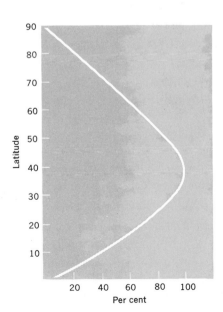

Fig. 1.1 Poleward flow of heat, in per cent of maximum.

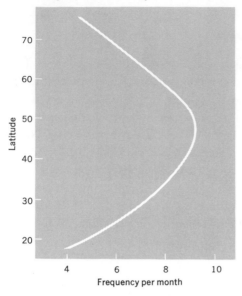

Fig. 1.2 Average frequency of traveling weather disturbances per month in the Northern Hemisphere winter plotted against latitude. The number of storms decreases quickly both northward and southward from the peak near 45°.

centers, or cyclones, with winds revolving counterclockwise, followed by high-pressure centers, or anticyclones, with clockwise circulation.[1] The number of traveling storms is highest near latitude 45° where, during winter, an average of two bad-weather periods occur per week (Fig. 1.2). Ahead of the cyclones, southerly winds carry warm air northward to heat the higher latitudes. Behind them, north winds carry cold air from the polar zones toward the tropics (Fig. 1.3). Such large-scale mixing of warm and cold air prevents the temperature difference between equator and poles from becoming more extreme than it is.

Inequalities in heating start the basic north-south motion from warm to cold air. But the rotation of a body the size of the earth, turning about its axis once every 24 hours, also generates east-west motions of the atmosphere. Chapter 6 will describe how air moving toward the pole is deflected to the right in the Northern Hemisphere (left in the Southern Hemisphere), looking along the direction it is moving, so that its path curves eastward. Air moving to-

---

[1] In the Northern Hemisphere. The circulation is in the opposite direction in the Southern Hemisphere. This book refers to the Northern Hemisphere, unless otherwise stated.

ward the equator also is deflected to the right, and it turns toward the west (Fig. 1.3). Thus we encounter winds near the earth's surface from the east in the tropics, the *trade winds,* and winds from the west in middle latitudes, the *polar westerlies* (Fig. 1.4). Ground friction holds average wind speeds to low values near the earth's surface. However, since there are no continents exerting strong frictional drag between latitudes 40° and 60° in the Southern Hemisphere, the westerlies there—the "roaring forties"—are much faster than in the Northern Hemisphere.

Centers of Action. On a globe with uniform surface, low- and high-pressure centers should march with equal frequency across all longitudes at one latitude. Because of the distribution of oceans, continents, and mountain ranges, however, high- and low-pressure centers are consistently found over some regions and, just as consistently, not over others. Thus the average flow during one season contains cellular patterns. These centers are called *centers of action* because their strength over a week, month, or season, compared to long-term averages, indicates how far weather departs from the

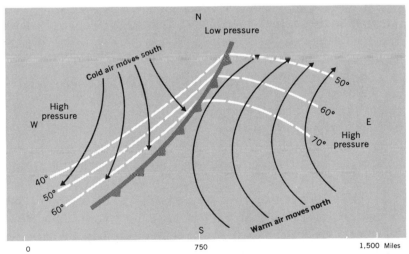

Fig. 1.3 *Cold front with streamlines (solid lines with arrows pointing along direction toward which wind blows) and isotherms (dashed, labeled in °F), showing northward transport of heat and turning of wind direction with latitude.*

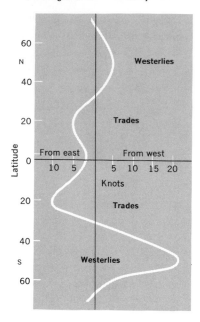

Fig. 1.4   The major east-west (zonal) wind systems of the globe.

average. Jefferson observed an extreme departure in France during the winter of 1788–1789.

In the climatic average, above a typical ocean basin, a low-pressure center with counterclockwise revolving winds lies over the high latitudes, while a high-pressure center with clockwise circulation is situated over the subtropics (Fig. 1.5). The trade winds, on the equatorward side of the subtropical highs, blow with a component toward the equator and are therefore called *northeast trades* in the Northern Hemisphere. They meet the trades from the Southern Hemisphere, the *southeast trades*, along a belt or *trough* of low pressure in the equatorial zone. This trough lies near latitude 5°N in the annual average, and this latitude is termed the *meteorological equator*.

The meeting of the two trade-wind streams along the equatorial trough produces rising air currents. As the air moves upward, its high moisture content condenses, resulting in the world's heaviest rainfall (Fig. 10.4). A second belt of bad weather and heavy precipitation lies where traveling storms are most frequent in middle latitudes. Between these two rainy belts, in the region of the subtropical high-pressure cells, large-scale sinking of air takes place. Cloudiness and precipitation are very scant in most parts of the subtropics, and large portions of the land areas are deserts.

In many ways, the flow of the surface waters in the oceans resembles the flow of the atmosphere (Fig. 1.6). In an ocean basin of the Northern Hemisphere, we see a large clockwise circulation centered in the subtropics and a counterclockwise circulation in the subpolar zone. In the lower latitudes, a cold current flows equa-

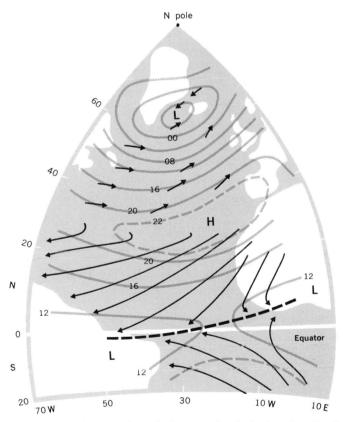

Fig. 1.5 Mean surface isobars and winds for the North Atlantic during winter showing model of the general circulation in an ocean basin. Isobars labeled in millibars, first two digits omitted; for instance, 20 denotes 1020 millibars. Heavy dashed line is equatorial low pressure trough. Drawn-out streamlines show trade winds.

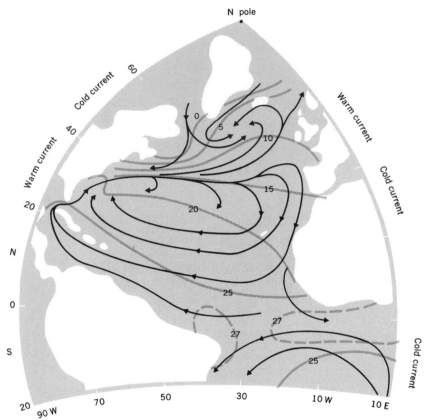

Fig. 1.6 Isotherms (°C) of the sea surface and approximate flow of the surface water of the North Atlantic during winter, showing model of oceanic general circulation and similarity with Fig. 1.5.

torward in the eastern part of the ocean, while a warm current moves poleward along its western edge.[2] In higher latitudes, the warm current, after crossing the ocean to the east, flows toward the pole along the eastern side of the basin; cold water is carried to lower latitudes in the west. The direction of water flow is reversed in the Southern Hemisphere, with counterclockwise circulation in the subtropics. Thus, the position of warm and cold currents with

[2] "Cold" and "warm" are used here with respect to the average water temperature at any particular latitude.

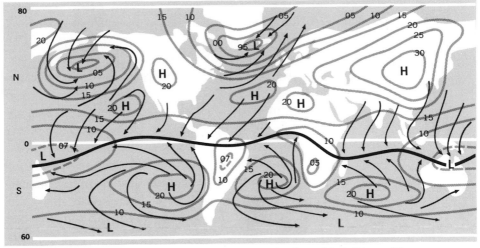

Fig. 1.7 World distribution of sea-level pressure (isobars labeled in milli-bars) and wind during January. Heavy black line is equatorial low pressure trough.

respect to the adjoining land areas is identical to that of the Northern Hemisphere, at least to the southern limit of the continents.

Charts of the world's surface pressure and winds during January and July (Figs. 1.7 and 1.8) show cellular high-pressure centers above the subtropics of all oceans, three in the Southern and two in the Northern Hemisphere. A broad belt of westerlies circles the Antarctic continent. Where there are no land barriers, the average circulation does become simple. In the Northern Hemisphere, the belt of low pressure below the North Pole is split into two cells, the Icelandic and Aleutian Lows. Between the subtropical highs and the subpolar lows lies the main zone of traveling cyclones and anticyclones. Situated about 10° latitude farther south in the Pacific than in the Atlantic Ocean, the center of the storm tracks resembles a gigantic spiral that starts south of Japan and ends in the polar sea north of Siberia (see Fig. 1.9).

Seasonal Changes. In winter, the belt of middle-latitude westerlies broadens, and the high-pressure areas over the subtropics dip toward the equator by 5 to 10° latitude. This permits middle-latitude storms near 30° and occasionally even near 20°, which are very important for the water supply in the subtropics. Both the frequency and the intensity of cyclones are greater in winter than in summer; the climatic Icelandic and Aleutian Lows are much stronger in the cold than in the warm season.

Despite these variations, the general circulation has the same pattern over the oceans throughout the year. But over large land masses, especially over Asia, North America, and Australia, much greater changes occur. Land surfaces become hot in summer and cold in winter, while the temperature of the oceans changes comparatively very little (Chapter 9). Under the influence of winter cooling, high pressure develops in the atmosphere over the continents; warm temperatures and low pressure develop during summer.

The continental effect is most marked over Asia, the world's largest land mass. In winter, air flows outward in a wide arc from the area of the Siberian anticyclone toward the tropics. The flow reverses during summer. This reversing circulation bears the name *monsoon*, from an Arabic word denoting seasonal wind. The south-

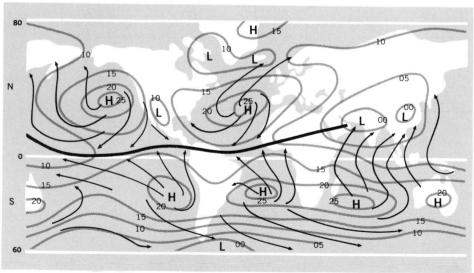

Fig. 1.8 World distribution of sea-level pressure and wind for July.

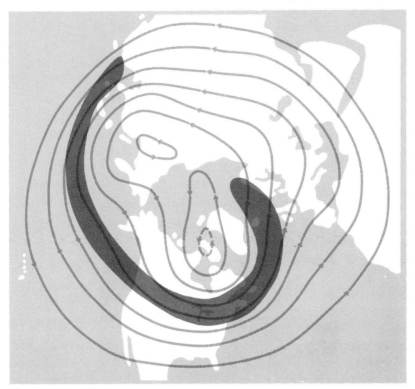

Fig. 1.9 *Average streamlines around the Northern Hemisphere near 18,000 ft (500 millibars) during winter; close spacing of streamlines denotes high wind speed. Pattern of three long waves is apparent. Shading marks approximate spiral of most frequent cyclone paths and of jet stream.*

west monsoon blows during the northern summer, and the northeast monsoon during the winter.

Upper-air Winds and Temperatures. In a deep layer of the atmosphere above the influence of surface friction, the *free* atmosphere, the westerly winds encircle the globe from latitudes 20 to 25° poleward. As seen from above, the westerlies move on a wavelike path, especially in their central portion in middle latitudes. In winter, three standing long waves occur between the subtropical and subpolar zones (Fig. 1.9). They are called "standing" because troughs and ridges of the wave train recur in certain locations and hence appear on charts such as Fig. 1.9, and "long" because the distance or *wavelength* between them is no less than one-third of the planet's circumference, or about 6,000 miles at latitude 40°. Troughs are found in winter over eastern North America, over eastern Europe, and near the Asiatic east coast. Ridges, not so clearly seen on the polar map projection of Fig. 1.9, lie above the eastern Atlantic and Pacific Oceans, and over central Siberia.

Despite the tendency of long waves to remain in preferred positions, their location and intensity at any time undergoes frequent variations. Within a few days, any part of the atmosphere in middle latitudes will respond to changes in the upper-air circulation halfway around the globe. A narrow, high-velocity core within the westerlies, the *jet stream,* is one of the atmosphere's main links in communicating such changes. Winds frequently reach speeds of 150 mph in the jet stream, carrying air around one-fifth of the world in one day at latitudes 40 to 50°.

The jet stream cannot be found on climatic charts, because its position and strength vary too much from day to day, and because the atmosphere often contains more than one jet stream. However, the average westerly winds contain a core in which air moves most rapidly from west to east. This core is approximately 40,000 ft (12 km) above sea level (Fig. 1.10). Westerly wind speed increases from the ground to these altitudes. Above the core, wind speed again decreases. The average latitude of the strongest westerlies in Fig. 1.10 approximately coincides with that of the surface subtropical Highs and with the latitude where heat transfer from equator to pole is strongest.

Temperature differences between polar regions and the equatorial zone are closely related to the changes in west wind speed as height increases. Up to 36,000 to 40,000 ft (11 to 12 km) temperature decreases toward the pole (Fig. 1.11) and the west wind speed increases upward. Above this level, the temperature difference is reversed; temperature is higher over the poles than over the equator, and the west wind speed decreases upward. At 50,000 ft (15 km) temperatures are 20 to 40°F (about 10 to 20°C) higher in polar latitudes than they are in the tropics. Comparing Figs. 1.10 and 1.11 we see that the level of strongest speed of the westerlies is also the level at which the north-south difference of

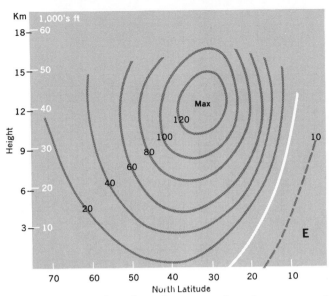

Fig. 1.10 Vertical north-south cross section of average west-wind speed (knots) during winter in the Northern Hemisphere. E denotes winds from east in tropics; white line marks separation between west and east winds.

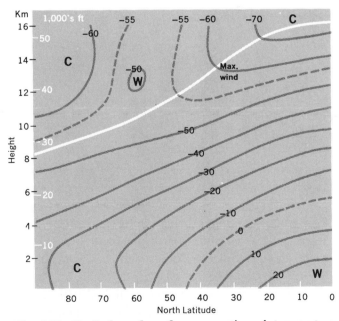

Fig. 1.11 Vertical north-south cross section of temperature (°C) during winter for the Northern Hemisphere. W denotes warm and C cold areas at one level. White line is tropopause. The core of strongest wind from Fig. 1.10 is situated at the height where the temperature difference between high and low latitudes reverses—higher up, temperature is warmer in north than in south.

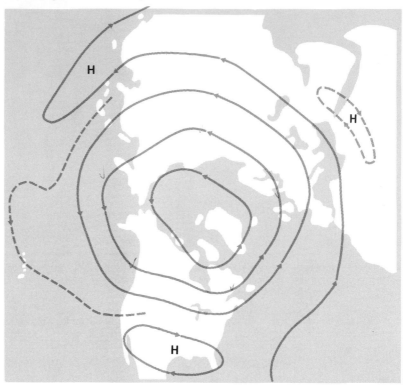

Fig. 1.12 *Average streamlines around the Northern Hemisphere near 18,000 ft (500 millibars) during summer. Wide spacing of streamlines indicates that flow is much weaker than in winter; dashed lines show where flow is very weak. There are five long waves in the westerlies compared with three in Fig. 1.9.*

temperature reverses its sign. This close connection between temperature and wind fields is a fundamental part of the general circulation.

The upper westerlies vary in strength and extent according to the season. In summer their mean velocity is only half that of winter. Moreover, the westerly belt expands far into the tropics in winter, while, in summer, subtropical high-pressure cells are situated near latitude 30°N at 33,000 to 40,000 ft (10 to 12 km) (Fig. 1.12). These variations in circulation are linked with the seasonal changes in the atmosphere's temperature below about 33,000 ft. In winter the temperature difference between pole and equator for this layer is 80°F (45°C); in summer it is only 36°F (20°C).

VERTICAL STRUCTURE

Before about 1900, temperature was assumed to decrease with height to the atmosphere's outer limit, because it was known to do so in the lower atmosphere. Then the first high-altitude balloon soundings were made, upsetting this simple picture. Temperature was found to be constant, or to increase with height, beginning at an altitude varying from 30,000 to 33,000 ft in polar regions to 50,000 ft in the tropics (Fig. 1.13). The point at which temperature stops decreasing upward is known as the *tropopause*—the boundary between the *troposphere,* or mixing layer, underneath and the *stratosphere* above. In the troposphere the upward temperature decrease facilitates overturning; hence its name, from the Greek word *tropos* (turn). The stratosphere is so called because it strongly tends to remain layered, or stratified, without rapid upward and downward mixing.

The location of heat and cold sources for the atmosphere determines to a considerable extent the remarkable profile of temperature

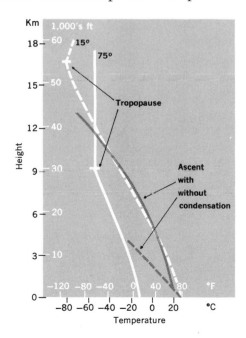

Fig. 1.13 Average temperature distribution with height at latitudes 15° and 75° in the Northern Hemisphere, showing difference in temperature structure and base of the stratosphere between high and low latitudes. The solid and dashed gray lines show the ascent path of individual masses of air rising with and without condensation in the tropics.

with height. The atmosphere consists of 78 per cent nitrogen and 21 per cent oxygen. These gases largely transmit the sun's radiation without interception. Most absorption takes place at the earth's surface, which, in a sense, acts as the immediate heat source for the low layers. The atmosphere also contains a small amount of ozone, concentrated most strongly near 15 miles (24 km) height. Although ozone constitutes only a variable, minute fraction of the atmosphere, this is enough to produce serious problems for high-flying aircraft because of danger from ozone poisoning and decay of such materials as rubber. A small fraction of the incoming sunlight is absorbed almost completely at the top of the ozone layer near a height of 31 miles (50 km). At this altitude the temperature of the air, measured by rocket instruments, is almost as high as it is at the surface (Fig. 1.14); here, the main heat source for the stratosphere is located.

From these two locations, the earth's surface and the top of the ozone layer, heat is transported upward and downward into the bulk of the atmosphere. The tropopause, where the temperature is lowest, marks the approximate boundary between heat flow from these two sources.

In the troposphere, above a shallow surface layer a few thousand feet deep, clouds account for most of the upward heat transport. The atmosphere contains water in gaseous form—water vapor—in variable amounts, ranging from nearly zero to about 3 per cent. When air rises, it cools and the water vapor begins to condense. During condensation, heat is released to the atmosphere; the air retains this heat when the condensed water falls to the ground as precipitation. Inside a tall tropical cloud, towering from a base 2,000 to 4,000 ft above the ground to 40,000 ft, the condensation process creates a temperature distribution very close to that shown by the solid gray curve in Fig. 1.13. This curve is almost identical with the actual average temperature-height curve over the tropics, the dashed white curve for latitude 15° in Fig. 1.13. Thus condensation mainly determines the temperature structure of the tropical troposphere.

Standard Atmosphere. The average vertical structure of the atmosphere in middle latitudes has been formalized in terms of a

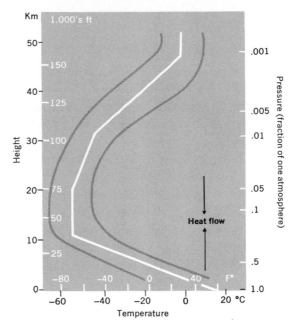

Fig. 1.14 Temperature distribution against height (and pressure) to the top of the ozone layer in the 1962 United States Standard Atmosphere. Gray: range of temperature about the mean, determined from average temperatures in individual months. Arrows show direction of heat flow along the vertical.

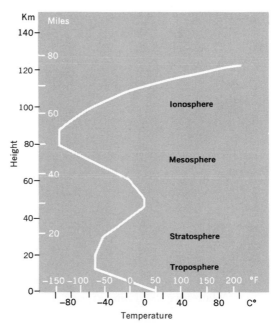

Fig. 1.15 The four principal layers of the atmosphere, according to the 1962 United States Standard Atmosphere.

standard atmosphere, a very useful tool. The standard atmosphere is a good guide to the different layers of the atmosphere. It also provides designers of aerospace vehicles with a rough indication of conditions in the layers through which, and in which, they propose to fly their craft.

As a plot of the 1962 United States Standard Atmosphere shows, there are two layers in which temperature decreases upward and two layers in which it increases upward (Fig. 1.15). Above the second temperature minimum near a height of 50 miles (80 km), electrically charged particles are primarily responsible for the reactions there. This part of the atmosphere is named *ionosphere.* High-energy radiation from the sun, intercepted in this layer, mainly produces the ionization. Reflection of radio waves gave the first clues to the existence of the ionosphere. Since then, it has been explored by rockets and satellite measurements.

The ionosphere, as well as the whole atmosphere above about 40,000 ft (12 km), serves a highly important function for life on the ground. These upper layers shield us from most of the high-energy radiation and from highly charged particles from space, both deadly to life. Adequate protection against these dangers is essential for travelers into space.

Pressure and Density in the Standard Atmosphere. The average pressure exerted by the entire mass of the air on the earth's surface at sea level is defined as "one atmosphere"; it corresponds to the pressure of a mercury column 29.92 in. high. Using this definition, all other pressures can be expressed in percentages of 1 atm. As shown in Fig. 1.14, pressure is $\frac{1}{10}$ atm at 53,000 ft (16 km), $\frac{1}{100}$ atm at 102,000 ft (31 km), and only $\frac{1}{1,000}$ atm at 158,000 ft (48 km) near the top of the ozone layer. As height increases about 53,000 ft (16 km), pressure decreases by a factor of 10.

Air density, or mass contained in a given volume, can be computed from the pressure and temperature of a gas, such as the atmosphere's mixture of nitrogen and oxygen (Fig. 1.16). If the temperature is constant, density will increase as pressure increases, and decrease as pressure decreases. If the pressure is constant, density will be high at low temperatures and low at high temperatures. Therefore cold air at one level, such as near the earth's

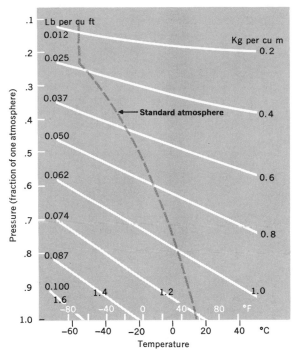

Fig. 1.16 *Density of air as a function of pressure and temperature. Dashed: standard atmosphere.*

surface, is called "heavy" compared with warm air at the same level.

In the standard atmosphere, and quite generally in the air, density mainly varies with pressure as height increases. At $\frac{1}{10}$ atm, for instance, density is less than 11 per cent of sea-level density; the air is very "thin." The space between 102,000 and 158,000 ft (31 and 48 km) holds only 1 per cent of the mass of air located between sea level and 53,000 ft (16 km).

More than 75 per cent of the atmospheric mass in middle latitudes, and 90 per cent in the tropics, lies in the troposphere. Pressure decreases by nearly 10 per cent per 3,300 ft (1 km) up to 10,000 ft (3 km) where standard atmosphere pressure is 0.7 atm. Most people can live quite well at this height after becoming accustomed to it. Leadville, Colorado, the highest town in the United

States, is situated at close to 10,000 ft above sea level. In the Andes of South America and in Tibet, human habitations extend to 0.6 atm.

Around the halfway mark of the atmosphere by weight, near 18,000 ft (5,400 m), extra oxygen becomes necessary for sustained activity, for instance in unpressurized aircraft. Climbing high mountains is strenuous because of the low air density. Only after lightweight oxygen containers were developed was the world's highest peak, Mt. Everest, conquered in 1953. Modern air travelers in subsonic jets fly at altitudes where air pressure is only 0.3 to 0.2 atm; however, cabin pressure usually is kept at about 0.85 atm. Supersonic aircraft usually fly at pressures below 0.1 atm.

The average depth of the troposphere, 6 miles, is 1,000 times less than the pole-to-equator distance of 6,000 miles. Thus we can visualize the atmospheric layer, in which nearly all weather occurs, as a very thin shell encircling the world.

PRINCIPAL VARIABLES

The principal atmospheric variables, which have already been introduced, are:

Temperature
Pressure
Wind
Humidity
Clouds
Precipitation

Nowadays there is much justification for adding gaseous and particle pollutants in the air to these factors.

Together, these variables describe the state of the atmosphere. They must be accurately observed, if we are to understand what is happening in the air. For this purpose reliable instruments are required, and measurements must be made often enough from stations sufficiently close to one another.

Time and Space Scales. How often observations are made, and how widely they are spaced, depends on the *scale* of the atmospheric events about which information is desired. Time and space scales are connected. The general circulation has a distance scale of several thousand miles and a time scale from season to year. Cyclones in middle latitudes have a scale of about 1,000 miles and of 1 to 5 days. Large thunderstorms cover 10 miles with durations of 1 to 6 hr, and small clouds $\frac{1}{10}$ mile during 10 to 30 min.

The observing networks are designed primarily to provide information on the scale of the general circulation and the cyclone. For this purpose, upper-air observing stations make balloon soundings twice a day. The average distance between stations is about 200 to 500 miles over North America, Europe and Russia, China, Japan, India, and Australia. Very large gaps remain over all oceans. Ground observing stations are spaced more closely where the population is more dense. Near major airports they may be only a few miles apart and may report weather at intervals of an hour or even less to warn of approaching weather dangers, such as thunderstorms, fog, or heavy squalls. Special networks, such as operate over the western plains of the United States during the tornado season, furnish additional information about occurrence of severe local weather. For research purposes, networks with stations spaced only $\frac{1}{10}$ to 1 mile apart have been maintained for limited periods in small areas.

We now turn to a brief discussion of the individual weather elements.

Temperature. Since temperature may increase or decrease several degrees in the lowest few feet, standard temperature observations are made in most countries in well-ventilated thermometer shelters about 5 ft above the ground. The shelter is needed to protect the instruments against heating by the sun. Shelters should not be placed next to buildings or in low spots where local winds drain up or down a slope.

Temperature is usually measured with a thermometer having a bulb filled with mercury just like a clinical thermometer. The mercury expands and contracts with warming and cooling, and the length of the mercury column indicates the temperature on a graduated scale. Another method is to use a strip of two metals that expand and contract at different rates. During heating and cooling, the shape of the strip changes as one metal contracts or expands more than the other one, and the change is recorded by a pen moving on a chart mounted on a revolving drum. Such a chart gives a record of how temperature varies with time (Fig. 2.8).

Averages, or means, of temperature and other variables occur often in the course of this book. Such averages are usually taken over a period of time, such as an hour, a day, a month, or a year. A good daily average temperature is obtained when a thermometer is read every hour; the twenty-four hourly values are then added and the sum is divided by 24. Quite often, only four values at 6-hr intervals are available, or highest and lowest (maximum and minimum) temperatures for the day alone. The monthly average is determined by adding the daily average temperatures and dividing by the number of days.

A mean monthly temperature can be computed when the average temperature for an individual month, such as January, has been recorded for at least 30 years in middle latitudes. The average January temperatures are added over the length of record, and the sum is divided by the number of January's on the record. The procedure is the same for any desired time interval of averaging.

Pressure. Pressure is a weather element without the direct impact on life that temperature has. During 24 hr, pressure seldom changes by more than 1 per cent, rarely by 3 per cent. A secretary riding the elevator to the upper floors of the Empire State Building in New York takes such changes in stride each day. The building is 1,000 ft (300 m) tall, so the pressure from the ground floor to the top floor decreases by 0.03 atm. Interest in pressure, therefore, is due to other reasons, mainly its close link with the wind field and periods of good and bad weather.

Pressure is the force exerted on a surface, usually expressed as the force exerted on a surface of standard or "unit" area. In modern meteorological practice an area of 1 sq cm is used as unit surface; pressure then is expressed conveniently in millibars.[3] Weather maps published by weather services and in newspapers

---

[3] One millibar is 1,000 dynes per square centimeter. Dyne is the unit of force in the centimeter-gram-second system of measurements. The equivalent weight (English units) is 0.0145 pound per square inch.

usually express pressure in millibars, or in inches or millimeters of the height of a mercury column.

In 1643 the Italian physicist Torricelli made an experiment which demonstrated the barometric principle. He found that the force exerted by the atmosphere at sea level will support a column of mercury almost 30 in. high in a vacuum tube. The vacuum assures that there is no pressure on the top of the mercury column; thus, in effect, the atmosphere is weighed in the experiment.

This method of measuring pressure is so simple that it is used to the present day. Mercury is chosen for convenience. By international agreement, one standard atmosphere is defined as the pressure to support a mercury column 760 millimeters, or 29.92 inches, high.[4] This pressure is 1,013.25 millibars. For most purposes of this book, it is entirely permissible to make a 1 per cent approximation and assume that 1 atm has a pressure of 1,000 millibars. The corresponding weight of the atmosphere is 1 kg per sq cm, or 14.5 lb per sq in. Air is anything but light! The mass of the atmosphere above an average house with an area of 1,500 sq ft weighs 1,400 long tons. Even the mass of air in a room is considerable. As shown in Fig. 1.16 air density near the ground is, roughly, 1 kg per cu m, or 0.062 lb per cu ft. A room 20 ft long, 10 ft wide, and 8 ft high ($6 \times 3 \times 2.5$ m) contains 100 lb (45 kg) of air.

The mercury barometer is the standard instrument for measuring pressure. As in the case of temperature, an instrument for continuously recording pressure is also available, the *aneroid* (without fluid) barometer. In a flat metal container, usually round, pressure is reduced to a low value; an inside or outside spring keeps the container from collapsing. The shape of the container changes as air pressure increases or decreases; this change can be recorded by means of a pen arm on a revolving drum. The instrument is therefore called a *barograph*. Figure 8.15 shows an excellent example of a barograph trace.

Wind. Wind observations differ from those of temperature and pressure in that two quantities must be observed: direction and speed. Close to the ground, wind speed increases quickly with

---

[4] At latitude 45° and at a temperature of 32°F (0°C) around the measuring instrument.

height. Both direction and speed are sensitive to the influence of buildings, trees, and other obstacles. It is therefore difficult to obtain a wind measurement representing air flow over a distance of several miles from the observing point.

Wind direction, from old times, has been measured with a wind vane. The rate at which air moves past the observing site is measured by the rate of revolution of a small propeller driven by the wind or by three or four rotating cups on a turnstile. Wind is often gusty; direction and/or speed may fluctuate widely in just a few seconds. A recording instrument giving a continuous trace of direction and speed on a revolving drum (Fig. 3.9) permits reading averages of direction and speed over time intervals such as 1 or 5 min. Such averaging makes the measurement useful for determining the pattern of air motion from station networks.

In modern practice, wind direction is reported on the 360° compass (Appendix I). However, the 16-point compass also remains in use. All numbers and letters giving wind direction are defined to indicate the direction *from* which the wind blows. A north wind blows from the north, not toward north. This practice is not always followed in nonmeteorological writing, so that it is advisable to check the definitions when using information not from standard weather sources.

Wind speed as a rule is stated in knots (nautical miles per hour), in statute miles per hour, or in meters per second (Appendix II). Other units, such as feet per second or kilometers per hour, are also used.

Humidity and Clouds. Humidity and cloud observations are discussed in Chapter 4. However, a spectacular development of modern technology should be mentioned here. Since 1960, weather satellites of the TIROS series have scanned the skies around the globe from above and radioed photographs of cloud masses over continents and oceans, as well as other important information about the atmosphere, especially radiation. These photographs have increased the scale of cloud observation from the ground observer's local horizon to the cyclone and even the general circulation scale.

The information gathered by numerous ground observers may not reveal the large-scale structuring of clouds apparent, for example, in the frontispiece of this book. A substantial advance in understanding large-scale weather systems can be achieved with satellite observations. This expansion of the horizon does not downgrade the value of ground observers. Satellites cannot measure such important features as the height of cloud bases above ground and the percentage of sky covered by low clouds when higher cloud layers are also present.

Figure 1.17 shows a typical satellite track. Many other types of orbits are employed, for instance, a path oscillating between the polar circles of Northern and Southern Hemispheres.

Precipitation. Precipitation is another element difficult to measure accurately over any area. It may, however, become measurable with new techniques. Especially during showery weather, precipitation often varies widely over the different parts of just one city. In hilly or mountainous country, large differences in precipitation almost always occur within very short distances. A measurement using the standard equipment, the rain or snow gauge, will seldom represent precipitation accurately beyond a few miles, often much less, around the observing site.

Most rain gauges have a diameter of 8 in. at the top. The water flows through a narrow opening (to prevent evaporation) into a container. Some remote stations have large containers for accumulation over a week, a month, or even a season. A more refined instrument is the weighing rain gauge that records precipita-

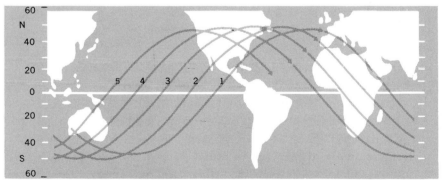

Fig. 1.17 Sample of satellite track orbiting between latitudes 50° North and South. One orbit takes about 90 min at the heights at which weather satellites are flown.

Fig. 1.18 Weather radar installations on plateau near 12,000 ft height in
central Colorado Rockies. This instrument is an SO-4 Marine Beech radar
which sees rain or snow clouds up to 60 miles distance. The radar has been
modified so that it also measures the height of clouds. (Courtesy L. O. Grant,
Colorado State University.)

tion continuously on a revolving drum. Its record permits the
determination of such quantities as extreme rain intensity for 1,
5, 10, or 60 min, which is very important for the design of drainage
systems.

Buildings and other obstacles so channel the wind that precipitation gauges must be freely exposed. A special problem exists on
shipboard, where there are no ways of eliminating deflection of
the air stream by the ship, which is also subject to wave action. A
satisfactory solution to shipboard measurements has not been
found, and a reliable precipitation record does not exist over the
oceans. During World War II certain radar waves were found
to be reflected by water and by ice particles in clouds, especially
by large drops typical of precipitating clouds. This fact, an un-

suspected by-product of radar operation, caused a sensation at the time. Radar (Fig. 1.18) can map precipitating clouds up to distances of 100 to 200 miles (180 to 360 km) and more from the antenna (Fig. 8.12), depending on the type of instrument used. The brightness of the radar image is related to the amount of reflecting water or ice in the clouds except near the radar site, where reflection from the ground and nearby buildings produces *ground clutter*, seen as a large white area in the center of the picture. Thus, size and brightness of the echo may indicate precipitation rate. If so, total precipitation over large areas, land and sea, could be measured. This would advance our knowledge of world precipitation substantially.

Upper-air Observations. Soundings of the upper air as high as 0.1 atm, even 0.01 atm, are generally made by balloon; for exploration of greater heights, rockets are used. Balloons normally rise at 1,000 ft (300 m) per min, completing the measurement of troposphere and lower stratosphere in 1 hr. A small box, trailing the balloon, contains instruments to record pressure, temperature, and humidity and to telemeter this information to a ground receiving station. The whole installation, therefore, is called *radiosonde*.

Upper-air observations are much more informative if wind is measured with the other elements. For this purpose, radiosonde balloons are tracked by radar-type equipment. This World War II development ended the long period when upper winds could be measured only by following balloons visually from the ground with a small telescope, called a theodolite. Such balloon soundings could be made only during good weather, which introduced a strong and systematic bias into all upper-wind records. With increasing use of radar, the importance of these *pilot balloon* observations has declined. But they still provide quick information on low-level winds at airports, when the cloud bases are high enough.

Meteorological rockets measure temperature, density, and other variables above a height of about 12 to 13 miles (20 km). The instrument package is released at the top of the rocket flight, say 38 miles (60 km), and the measurements are made and telemetered during its fall. Radar tracking of chaff released by the rockets is one method of determining wind at very high altitudes.

part one

Physical Processes

2

Radiation Heating and Cooling

SOLAR CONTROL OF CLIMATE

Radiation from the sun is the main source of energy for the atmosphere, for the oceans, and for life on earth. Differences in radiation, both in time and space, give rise to weather and climate. Consider Fig. 2.1, which shows the average variation of temperature through the year at New York City (latitude 41°) and at Singapore (latitude 1°). Temperatures at Singapore are almost uniform; no seasons can be distinguished. New York, in contrast, has a large annual temperature range of 45°F (25°C). The highest average temperature occurs in July, the lowest in January.

Figure 2.2 shows how the sun's altitude at noontime changes

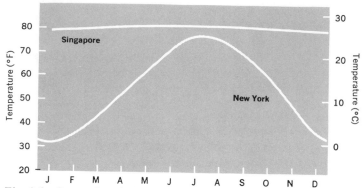

Fig. 2.1   Seasonal variation of surface temperature, measured about 5 ft above the ground, at New York City and at Singapore (1°N, 104°E), at the tip of the Malayan peninsula.

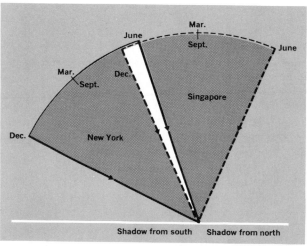

Fig. 2.2   The seasonal march of the sun's altitude in the noon sky at New York City and at Singapore.

at these two locations. On the equator the elevation of the sun in the sky is always within $23\frac{1}{2}°$ of the zenith; twice, in March and September, the sun is overhead. At New York the highest path the sun takes across the sky is 17° from the zenith. The lowest, in December, is 64° from the zenith, or 26° above the horizon, which makes shadows long in winter.

Average temperature and solar elevation evidently are connected. At the equator, where the sun stays close to overhead, temperature is constant over the whole year. At New York the temperature changes with the variation in the sun's altitude. Also, the average temperature there is only 54°F (12°C), compared with over 80°F (27°C) at Singapore. Of course, solar altitude does not explain all features of the annual march of temperature. New York, Chicago, Rome, and Peking do not have identical temperatures, though they all lie near latitude 40°N. Factors such as proximity to the ocean also influence climate. These cities, however, all have warm summers and cold winters, while near the equator most locations have a uniform mean temperature as Singapore does.

SHORT– AND LONGWAVE RADIATION

Emission of energy from a body in electromagnetic waves is called radiation. One characteristic of waves is their wavelength, the distance from crest to crest of succeeding waves. Most commercial broadcasts are made on wavelengths of several hundred meters, whereas radar waves used in weather work are measured in centimeters.

Most radiation emitted by any body is concentrated in a very small fraction of the whole range of electromagnetic wavelengths. The preferred wavelength depends on the temperature of the body; it decreases as the temperature of the body increases. Radiation from the sun, as well as from the earth's surface, approximates quite closely *blackbody* radiation, the highest theoretical value that a body can possibly emit at a given temperature. The corresponding wavelengths, at which sun and earth radiate most strongly, are so short that it is difficult to discuss them in length units such as centimeters or inches. Usually, their length is stated in microns; one micron is $\frac{1}{10,000}$ of one centimeter, or $\frac{1}{25,400}$ of one inch, a very short distance indeed.

Strongest radiation from the sun occurs near 0.5 microns, which corresponds to a mean temperature of about 12,000°F, or 6000°C. The earth's surface radiates most intensely near 10 microns at a mean surface temperature of 60°F (15°C). Thus the length of the waves that mainly transmit radiation from the sun is about 20 times less than the length of those from the earth. Comparing sun and earth alone, we speak of *shortwave* solar radiation and of *longwave* radiation from the earth.

Radiation sent out by the sun at wavelengths from 0.4 to 0.7 microns—that is, the bulk of the solar radiation—is visible to the human eye. Colors of the visible radiation are as follows in order of increasing wavelength: violet, indigo, blue, green, yellow, orange, red. Rainbows give a fine natural display of this array of colors. They appear when the sun shines on falling raindrops, which bend the solar beam.

Radiation with wavelengths shorter than those producing the visible colors is called *ultraviolet* (beyond the violet); radiation with wavelengths longer than the visible range, *infrared* (below the red). The intensity with which a black body radiates[1] depends strongly on temperature. Even at the temperatures found on earth, the blackbody radiation ranges by a factor of 10, from 0.1 to 1.0 cal per sq cm per min (Fig. 2.3). The sun, however, radiates no less than about 100,000 cal per sq cm of *solar* surface per minute at *its* temperature. Because of the great distance of the earth from the sun, roughly 93 million miles (150 million km), only a tiny fraction of this radiation reaches the earth.

A surface placed perpendicular to the solar beam intercepts the largest possible amount of radiation (Fig. 2.4). When located at the outer limit of the atmosphere, it will receive 2.00 cal per sq cm per min. This quantity is called the *solar constant*. In the past,

---

[1] Radiative energy flow is usually stated in calories per square centimeters per minute; a calorie is the heat needed to raise the temperature of one gram of water by one degree centigrade, under specified laboratory conditions.

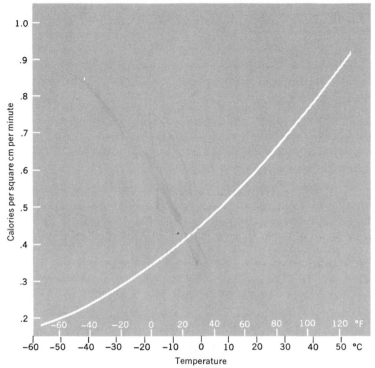

Fig. 2.3 Radiation emitted by a black body over the temperature range occurring near the earth's surface.

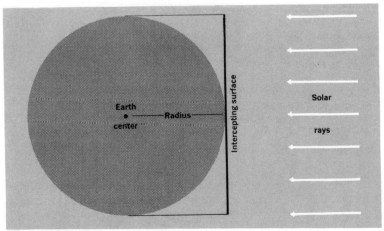

Fig. 2.4 Illustrating the total intercept of solar radiation by the earth. Area of intercepting surface is one-fourth that of earth's surface.

much speculation has centered on the question of whether the solar constant varies slightly about its mean value, since even small variations could produce large-scale changes in weather patterns. Although this is an intriguing possibility, the evidence indicates that solar radiation is constant, except for the ultraviolet radiation that contributes very little to total solar radiation.

When the sun is overhead, an area of given size on the ground will intercept a maximum amount of solar energy (Fig. 2.5). When the sun is 23½° from the zenith, the largest angle at the equator, this area will catch less of the solar beam, but only a little less. The reduction in heat received compared to that from overhead sun is about 8 per cent. At an angle of 64°, however, a unit surface intercepts only 44 per cent of the incoming radiation. Therefore the solar energy intercepted in the middle of the day is almost

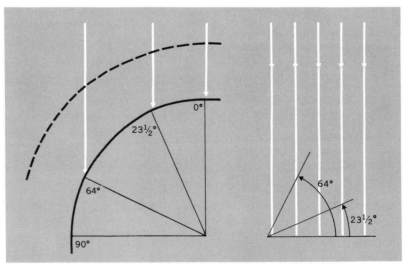

Fig. 2.5   The decrease of solar radiation intercepted by a surface of unit area with decreasing altitude of the sun in the sky. Numbers are latitudes on earth; sun is pictured overhead on the equator. Dashed: outer limit of atmosphere.

constant through the year near the equator, while a large seasonal variation takes place in middle latitudes. At New York, the earth intercepts 44 per cent of the solar beam in winter and 95 per cent in summer, when the sun is 18° from the zenith.

Figure 2.5 illustrates the main cause for the connection between seasonal temperature change and solar altitude. Of course, factors such as length of day also must be taken into account. The solar beam, moreover, travels through one atmospheric thickness when the sun is overhead while its oblique path through the air at a solar elevation of 26° above the horizon is much longer. *Depletion* of the solar beam on the way from space to earth, largely through scattering and reflection of radiation, increases with length of travel through the atmosphere. At low solar altitudes the radiation reaching the ground is relatively low not only because of the large angle between incoming solar beam and surface, but also because of the long path the solar rays travel through the atmosphere. These two factors are correlated; they act to increase the difference between the radiation received at the ground at high and low altitudes of the sun in the sky.

SCATTERING, REFLECTION, AND ABSORPTION OF SOLAR RADIATION

Scattering. If the solar beam reached the surface of the earth without any interference in the atmosphere, and if the earth's surface absorbed the incident radiation completely, we would not experience daylight and sky colors as we know them. Rather, the sun would appear as a fiery disk in an otherwise dark sky. Actually, a portion of the sunlight is scattered on its path from the outer limit of the atmosphere to the ground by the intervening air molecules. Scattering is most effective for the shortest wavelengths. When the sun is overhead and the atmosphere cloudless and dust-free, more than 50 per cent of the "blue" radiation is scattered, while nearly all the "red" radiation is transmitted. This is the reason for the sky's predominantly blue color.

When the sun is near the horizon during sunrise and sunset, the number of air molecules in the path of the solar rays is highest.

This long path explains why the winter sun often is called "weaker" than the summer sun, and why the noon sun is more brilliant over the tropics than it is in high latitudes.

Very fine dust or smoke haze in the atmosphere creates an abnormal sky appearance, because the particles scatter the solar beam. Industrial areas or large population centers discharge various combustion products into the air. With intense air pollution the sun may appear as a dull red ball in the sky over cities even at noon. Pollution has decreased the net solar radiation reaching the ground in many areas, adversely affecting such branches of agriculture as the fruit-growing industry.

Reflection. Unless they are very small, solid particles in the atmosphere—water droplets, ice crystals, dust, and combustion products—*reflect* the solar rays. That is, there is no discrimination between different wavelengths of the incident light as there is with scattering. Nearly the entire solar beam is reflected; only a small portion is absorbed by the particles. Therefore reflection does not affect sky color, only total light intensity.

Locally heavy concentrations of pollution aside, solar radiation is reflected mainly from clouds. The difference between a bright day and one covered with low overcast is obvious. When the sun is higher than about 30° above the horizon, the radiation transmitted through an overcast sky ranges from 80 per cent for thin high clouds down to 25 per cent or even less for thick low clouds. Thickness of clouds is very important. Surprisingly, very little of the space occupied by a cloud contains water. If a cloud *volume* has one part of liquid water per million parts of air, this is considered a high ratio. Evidently, only a tiny fraction of the solar radiation is intercepted by the cloud tops. As the solar beam penetrates into the cloud, an increasing percentage of the radiation is reflected. If the cloud is thin, the diffusely reflected light passing downward through the cloud base gives the cloud a whitish appearance. The thicker a cloud, the blacker it looks. In the extreme, during passage of heavy thunderstorm clouds, the sky may become nearly dark even on a midsummer afternoon.

A startling example of how clouds reflect solar radiation is the change in brightness experienced when taking off in a plane on a dark, overcast day. Well before the plane passes through the top of the overcast, light intensity begins to increase. The light becomes brilliant, often blinding, as the plane climbs into the clear air above the clouds and meets the reflected radiation.

The Albedo of the Earth's Surface. The solar radiation that reaches the ground after passing all the obstacles just cited is largely absorbed by the earth's surface. But still another fraction is reflected from the earth back to space. This fraction is called the earth's *albedo* (degree of whiteness or reflectivity); it is the ratio of light reflected to light received by the earth. Albedo varies widely from place to place, depending on the composition of the surface. Table 2.1 contains a few typical values.

Over the earth's surface as a whole the albedo is very low, about 8 per cent, because more than two-thirds of the globe is covered by water. But most vegetation also absorbs radiation efficiently. Glare from a cultivated field is almost nil. Upon entering a dense forest in the noon hours of a hot summer day, the sudden darkness and cool air bring welcome relief; nearly all radiation is absorbed in the treetops (Chapter 11). Sand has a high albedo. Sand deserts have formed precisely in those regions on earth where the general atmospheric circulation inhibits the formation of clouds and rain. The fraction of solar radiation that reaches

Table 2.1

Surface type	Albedo, per cent
Forests	3–10
Fields (green)	3–15
Fields (dry, plowed)	20–25
Grass	15–30
Bare ground	7–20
Sand	15–25
Snow (fresh)	80
Snow (old)	50–70
Ice	50–70
Water, solar elevation greater than 40°	2–4
Water, solar elevation 30° to 5°	6–40

the ground there is large; but the high reflectivity helps to prevent temperatures from rising even higher. We see here one of the checks and balances of nature that prevent the unlimited growth of climatic extremes.

Snow and ice have a very high albedo. When snow first falls at the beginning of winter, the amount of sunlight reflected suddenly increases. The varying extent of snow cover has given rise to much speculation about climatic changes. If the polar ice sheets were to expand or shrink a little, a substantial change in the heat budget would follow as the size of the high-albedo area changed.

The Albedo of Earth and Atmosphere. There are three major mechanisms for returning solar energy to space.

> Reflection from dust, salt, and smoke particles in the air
> Reflection from clouds
> Reflection from the ground

These produce the total albedo of earth and atmosphere.

Only the reflection from the ground has been estimated with fair reliability, by extrapolating measurements made at numerous observation sites over the earth. The light rays reflected by solid particles in the air are returned to space in part only; some of them eventually find their way to the surface, making it difficult to determine the albedo of the atmosphere. Historically, much effort has been expended to measure, as far as possible, and to estimate the total albedo of earth and atmosphere. Knowing the albedo is essential for understanding not only weather and climate, but also the motions of the oceans and the biological balances.

Past methods for determining albedo were rendered obsolete in 1961 when the weather satellite TIROS III began to observe albedo on a world-wide basis. TIROS III and subsequent satellites have indicated that the albedo may be lower than the best pre-satellite estimate, which is 35 per cent. Besides determining the total albedo, which is of high interest, satellite observations may reveal *variations* of the albedo over the earth at large, or over smaller areas such as the tropics or polar zones. If they exist, these variations may be connected with longer-period weather changes. Without doubt, meteorological satellites have opened new and exciting avenues for exploring some of the most puzzling questions about the atmosphere.

Absorption of Solar Radiation. If the albedo is 30 per cent, the fraction of incoming sunlight which earth and atmosphere absorb is 70 per cent. The troposphere itself absorbs about 15 per cent, mainly by water vapor and dust, a little by clouds. About 3 per cent is taken up in the ultraviolet part of the spectrum in the stratosphere, mostly by ozone. Therefore the earth's surface absorbs about half of the solar beam arriving at the outer limit of the atmosphere. This interesting result suggests, together with the upward decrease of temperature, that the atmosphere may be heated primarily from the ground. Before exploring this possibility further, we must examine the radiation sent from earth and atmosphere to space.

RADIATION FROM EARTH AND ATMOSPHERE

The plane perpendicular to the solar rays (Fig. 2.4) intercepts 2.00 cal per sq cm of *its area* in every minute. From geometry, the area of this plane is one-fourth that of the earth's surface. Thus, we can also express the solar constant as 0.5 cal per sq cm of *earth's surface* per min, averaged over the whole globe. If the ground absorbs 50 per cent of the solar radiation, it will receive 0.25 cal per sq cm per min.

The earth radiates very nearly as a black body at a mean temperature of 60°F (15°C), or 0.55 cal per sq cm per min, as shown in Fig. 2.3. But this is more than twice the solar radiation absorbed. We see at once that blackbody radiation from the ground does not complete the heat balance at the earth's surface. For a balance, the surface temperature would have to be −40° (C or F), and life as we know it could not exist on earth. Clearly, the atmosphere must act in some way to prevent escape of the blackbody radiation from the ground to space. It acts as a gigantic greenhouse.

The Greenhouse Effect. Ordinary glass has a remarkable property. It permits radiation at the wavelengths of solar radiation to pass unhindered. But it completely absorbs radiation emitted at the long wavelengths typical of the earth's radiation. As a result,

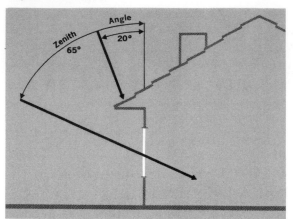

Fig. 2.6 Protection against, and utilization of, the greenhouse effect by the solar house during summer and winter.

a room exposed to sunshine will heat up rapidly. This property of selective absorption is used in constructing greenhouses; hence the term *greenhouse effect*. It is very important to be aware of this effect when constructing houses, offices, and factories. Design of the "solar house" allows for the changing altitude of the sun in middle latitudes. An expanse of windows, facing south, has an overhang (Fig. 2.6), so that windows are in the shadow from the summer sun, yet are unshaded in winter.

The atmosphere contains a small and variable amount of water in gaseous form, the water vapor. There is also a minute amount of carbon dioxide, with about 0.05 per cent of the mass of the principal gases. Water vapor and carbon dioxide, although they are only a tiny fraction of the atmosphere's mass, decisively influence the heat balance of atmosphere and ground, since they possess the same property as glass: they are transparent to solar radiation but opaque to radiation from the earth, at least within certain limits. These gases do not intercept all infrared radiation; they absorb in certain *bands*, or ranges of wavelength, selectively. Water vapor absorbs the earth's radiation in a band with wavelengths shorter than 10 microns and then again at longer wavelengths. Between these bands there is a "window" in which water vapor is transparent.

The center of the window occurs near 10 microns, where radiation from the ground is strongest. Therefore a satellite which measures radiation near 10 microns can "see" the surface. Ground temperature can be determined from its observations, even when the satellite is several hundred miles above the earth. However, if the measurement is to ascertain the earth's temperature accurately, the intervening atmosphere must be cloudless and not contaminated by dust, salt, and smoke particles. Unfortunately, the window often is very "dirty." The solid particles within the atmosphere absorb radiation so strongly that ground temperature is not properly measured by the satellite.

Water vapor and carbon dioxide prevent appreciable radiation from the ground directly to space, except for wavelengths near 10 microns. When the effect of clouds on outgoing radiation is also taken into account (see below), we find that only about 20 per cent of the blackbody radiation from the ground, or 0.10 cal per sq cm per min, escapes to space. The entire residual radiation from the ground is intercepted and in large measure reradiated downward from the atmosphere.

Variability of Water Vapor. Both the total amount of water vapor in the atmosphere and the distribution of vapor content with height affect the longwave radiation to space. Total vapor content, also called *precipitable moisture* or *optical thickness* of water vapor, ranges from almost nil in cold air masses of winter to 2 to 3 in. (5 to 8 cm) in humid tropical air. An atmosphere with high moisture will intercept and reradiate downward more heat than will a column with little moisture. This is one main reason that the daily range of temperature is greater in dry than in humid air; it is, for instance, 15 to 20°F (7 to 10°C) over the land areas of the humid tropics and twice as large in the subtropical deserts.

Distribution of moisture with height is also important. Reradiation from the atmosphere to the ground is largest when the moisture is concentrated in the lowest few thousand feet above the surface, since temperature normally is highest in the atmosphere in this layer. Nevertheless, even a thin, high, moist layer at quite low temperatures interposes a large obstacle to outgoing radiation, compared to a dry atmosphere. A marked reduction in the nighttime temperature drop near the surface follows arrival of a high moist layer after a dry period.

Variability of Carbon Dioxide. In the mean, the amount of carbon dioxide in a unit mass of air, or mixing ratio of carbon dioxide, is constant in the troposphere, so that radiation is affected only by its total mass. This mass is usually assumed to be constant in radiation calculations.

The role that long-period variations in the amount of carbon dioxide in the atmosphere may have had in changing climate has attracted much interest. During the last century the temperature of the atmosphere near the earth's surface has risen by perhaps 1°F on the average. This increase, though apparently small, marks a major climatic change, especially in the higher latitudes where temperature rise has been greatest. Now, the last century is exactly the period when, owing to industrial expansion, the total carbon dioxide in the atmosphere is estimated to have increased by at least 10 per cent. Can these two events be connected? An assured answer cannot be given, since climatic changes on the time scale of centuries have occurred many times, and since industrial emission is by no means the only factor governing the carbon dioxide content of the air. Nevertheless, an intriguing possibility exists that the connection is real. If true, it is the *major weather modification* accomplished by man.

The Effect of Clouds. Cloud layers, even thin ones of perhaps no more than a few hundred feet thickness, absorb radiation at earth's temperatures almost completely. They themselves radiate as a black body, just as the earth's surface does. Thus, when the sky is overcast, the radiating surface is effectively transferred from the ground to the top of the overcast. As a rule, cloud-top temperatures are colder than ground temperatures. A satellite sees overcasts as areas with lowered 10-micron (window) radiation, compared to clear areas. This is illustrated in Fig. 2.7, in which radiation measured by TIROS III has been converted to *effective radiation temperature* using Fig. 2.3. The satellite sees a hurricane in the Caribbean Sea. Close to the center, high clouds must extend at least to the temperature typically found near a height of 45,000 ft in order for the radiation to be so low. The effective radiation temperature

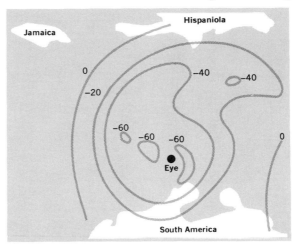

Fig. 2.7 Distribution of effective radiation temper-
ature (°C) in the water vapor window as seen by the
satellite TIROS III passing over a Caribbean hurri-
cane on July 21, 1961. The low radiation temperatures
close to the center show that it was surrounded by a
very high cloud mass. (After T. J. Fujita.)

increases with distance from the hurricane, indicating that the cloud
mass of the storm gives way to small cumulus clouds (Chapter 4)
with large patches of clear sky.

Overcasts restrain the heat flow from the earth and act to
reduce radiation cooling at the earth's surface and in the air below
cloud base. Yet, as we have seen, the clouds also reflect a large
fraction of the incoming sunlight, reducing temperature increases
of ground and atmosphere in daytime. On balance, the net effect
of clouds on the average temperature over 24 hr may be quite small.
When skies are clear, daytime temperatures are high and nighttime
temperatures low (Fig. 2.8). Cloudy skies keep the temperature
at a uniform value day and night.

Snow cover on the ground has properties similar to those of
clouds. It reflects sunlight with a high albedo, but it radiates heat
at its temperature as a black body. Therefore, temperatures at the
top of a snow surface readily fall to very low values during winter
nights, and this leads to low minimum temperatures in the air near
the ground, if the sky is clear and the atmosphere dry. The lower

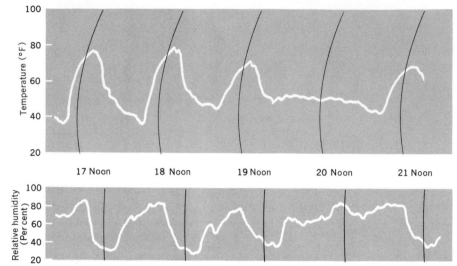

Fig. 2.8   Traces of temperature (°F) and of relative humidity (per cent) at Colorado State University, October 17–21, 1963. A diurnal temperature range of over 40°F on October 18 during clear skies was succeeded by virtual suppression of the daily temperature and humidity cycle on October 20, when the sky was overcast with intermittent rain. (Courtesy Arnold Finklin).

snow boundary also acts as a black body. It absorbs radiation from soil and vegetation and largely returns it. Therefore snow is very effective in keeping frost from intruding into the ground.

HEAT BALANCE AT THE GROUND

At the beginning of the last section we found that, on the average, the earth's surface absorbs 0.25 cal per sq cm per min of solar energy and that it radiates about 0.55 cal per sq cm per min. Water vapor and carbon dioxide return most of this radiation; the net infrared radiation from the earth to space is only 0.10 cal per sq cm per min. This is considerably less than the solar energy absorbed; again our calculations fail to achieve heat balance by a wide margin, since we have a source of 0.25 and a sink of only 0.10 cal per sq cm per min.

If the ground gains 0.15 cal per sq cm per min, the atmosphere must lose the same amount of heat in order for incoming and out-going radiation to be equal at the outer limit of the atmosphere. The atmosphere is thus a *radiational cold source.* Its cooling amounts to not less than 2.0°F (1.1°C) per day, which, if continued through one year, would make the air very frigid indeed. Clearly, processes other than radiation must transfer heat from ground to air. These are heating by conduction of air near the ground (Chapter 3) and evaporation from land and water surfaces (Chapter 4).

Table 2.2   Radiation Balance at Surface (cal per sq cm per min)

Solar radiation absorbed by earth's surface	.25	
Longwave radiation from earth's surface	.55	
Back radiation from atmosphere	.45	
Net radiation from surface		.10
Heat transfer from surface to atmosphere by conduction (est.)		.05
Heat transfer from surface to atmosphere by evaporation (est.)		.10
Net heat loss from surface		.25

3

Vertical Mixing
of Air
Below the Clouds

FORCE OF GRAVITY

All life on earth and the structure of the earth itself are adjusted
to the gravitational attraction toward the vicinity of the earth's
center. The acceleration resulting from the force of gravity is very
large. If there were no atmosphere, an object dropped from the
height of the tropopause in the tropics (50,000 ft or 16 km) would
fall freely to the ground. The object would accelerate by 32 ft per
sec (10 m per sec) *each second.* After 10 seconds, it would travel
at 220 mph (100 m per sec); after 40 seconds, it would have covered
the whole distance, hurtling into the ground with a speed of close
to 900 mph.

Physical Processes

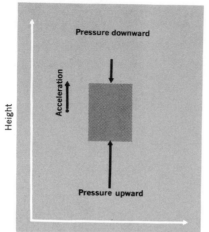

Horizontal distance

Fig. 3.1 Vertical acceleration of air produced by decrease of pressure with height.

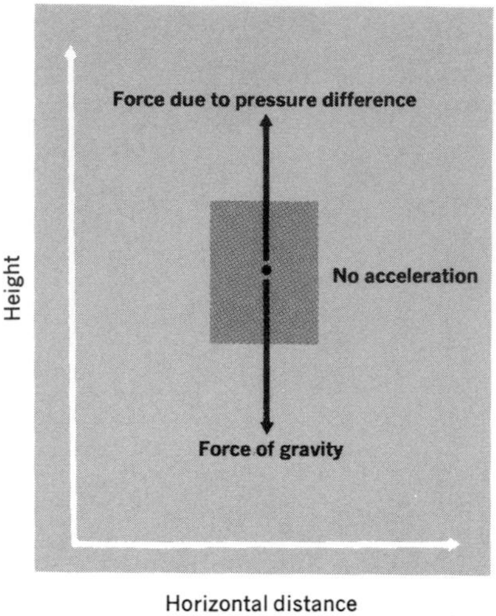

Horizontal distance

Fig. 3.2 Illustrating hydrostatic balance.

This example shows the strength of the earth's gravitational attraction. Yet, on the whole, air remains suspended. Therefore the air must experience an equal and opposite force away from the earth. This force comes from the decrease in air pressure with increasing height. An object having high pressure on one side and lower pressure on the other side experiences a net resulting force accelerating it from higher toward lower pressure (Fig. 3.1). If air remains suspended without rising or falling, the upward acceleration due to the pressure decrease must balance exactly the downward acceleration due to the force of gravity (Fig. 3.2). Such balance is called *hydrostatic*.

Hydrostatic balance is demonstrated by the fact that the earth has an atmosphere. The opposing forces are so nearly equal at almost all times and places that hydrostatic balance is considered an atmospheric "ground state" and is used in many computations, such as that estimating the height of aircraft above the earth's surface (Chapter 13) by computing the vertical distance over which pressure decreases by a specified amount. The greater the density of the air, the more rapidly must pressure decrease upward to hold the air at constant height against the force of gravity. Therefore pressure decreases quickly with height at low altitudes, where density is high, and slowly at high altitudes where density is low. Further, the thickness of the layer between two pressures will decrease with increasing density or, referring to Fig. 1.16, with decreasing temperature. As an example, Fig. 3.3 shows how the thickness of the layer between a pressure of 1,000 millibars and pressures of 700, 500, and 300 millibars varies with the mean temperature of each layer. In each case thickness and temperature decrease together, least for the layer from 1,000 to 700 millibars, whose average thickness is smallest (9,510 ft or 2,900 m in the standard atmosphere), and most for the layer from 1,000 to 300 millibars, whose average thickness is largest (29,680 ft or 9,770 m in the standard atmosphere).

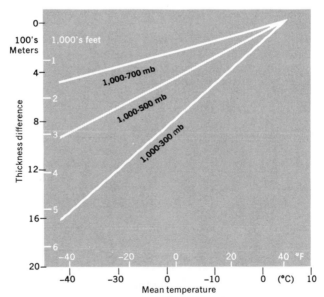

Fig. 3.3 Variation of the thickness of the layers between 1,000 and 700, 1,000 and 500, and 1,000 and 300 millibars pressure with the mean temperature of the layer. The ordinate indicates decreases of thickness compared with the thickness of each layer when the mean temperature is 41°F (5°C). The colder the temperature, the smaller the thickness of each layer.

VERTICAL ACCELERATION

Although hydrostatic balance prevails over the atmosphere as a whole, individual masses of air frequently experience upward or downward accelerations. These seldom amount to more than 1 per cent of the acceleration due to gravity. If really strong accelerations occurred, as they do on the sun, particles would leave the earth's gravitational field and escape into space. Since the mass of the atmosphere remains constant, very few, if any, air particles escape. Even so, the comparatively small accelerations which do occur bring about many important weather events. For instance, clouds and rain would not exist without ascending motions of air. Therefore, it is important to know how these slight departures from the balance of upward- and downward-acting forces originate.

Buoyancy. The warming of air near the ground during a summer morning furnishes an outstanding example. Heating progresses from the ground upward (Chapter 2), so air particles nearest to the ground are the first to warm up as the sun's rays hit the surface. But warming rarely proceeds at a uniform rate, even over horizontal distances of only hundreds of feet, because the ground has many irregularities—slight changes in slope, soil type, or moisture, and often large changes in vegetation. As the sun rises, temperature differences of perhaps 1°F (0.5°C) develop over short distances. As shown in Fig. 1.16, gases, such as those which the atmosphere contains, are less dense at high than at low temperatures, if the pressure remains constant. Thus particles heated most strongly near the ground also expand most and become less dense than all other particles around them.

More than 2,000 years ago the Greek mathematician Archimedes showed that a body immersed in a liquid is accelerated upward if its density is less than that of the fluid; it will sink if it is heavier than the fluid. This "principle of Archimedes" is easily observed when air bubbles rise in water.

In the heated layer of surface air, particles will be accelerated upward, i.e., become *buoyant,* when they are less dense than their surroundings. Quite often the updrafts are not randomly distributed, but consolidate into columns of rising air, called *thermals* (Fig. 3.4).

In the space between thermals, compensating downward motion occurs—there are no holes in the atmosphere.

Conservation of Heat. As these buoyant particles rise in a thermal, we may assume that they do not mix initially with the surrounding air. When they are only a few feet from the ground, their heat supply is cut off. Thus, during the few minutes to be considered now, the air particles in a thermal *conserve their heat.*

Outside of the rising column, pressure decreases upward. As the buoyant stream ascends, it enters surroundings with successively lower pressure. If a particle starts with pressure of 1,000 millibars, it will soon be adjacent to air with pressure of 999 millibars. The particle then has an excess pressure of 1 millibar; it expands against the surroundings until this excess pressure is lost. The pressure adjustment takes place so quickly that the rising air can be considered to assume the pressure of its surroundings everywhere on its upward journey.

To expand against the surroundings, the air inside the thermal

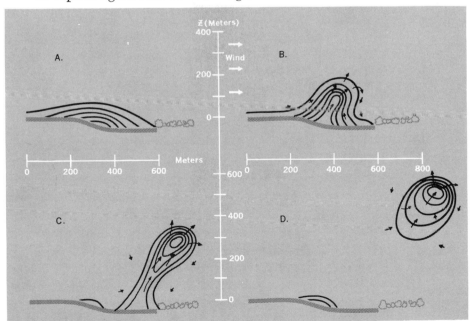

Fig. 3.4 Organization of ascent of air heated near the ground into a "thermal." (From Betsy Woodward, in Cumulus Dynamics, *Pergamon Press, New York, 1960.)*

does work. Performing work always requires an expenditure of energy. The rising column, having lost contact with the ground, no longer has a heat supply. Therefore, the *internal energy* of the gas must become the source of energy for work done by the gas. The internal energy of air is proportional to its temperature. When air expands, the temperature therefore decreases; when air is compressed, as it is during downward motion toward higher pressure, the temperature increases.

Decrease of temperature during expansion and increase during compression are called *adiabatic*, which means without addition or loss of heat. Air expanding adiabatically cools at a rate of 5.5°F per 1,000 ft (1°C per 100 m) of ascent with minor assumptions. When air is compressed, its temperature increases at the same rate.

Limit of Buoyant Ascent. The adiabatic temperature decrease of air rising in a thermal normally differs from the rate at which temperature decreases with height in the surroundings. The latter rate may be determined by sending up a balloon with temperature-measuring equipment. We call the temperature variation with height, so measured, *temperature lapse rate*. In general, this lapse rate is considerably smaller than the adiabatic rate. In the standard atmosphere, temperature is assumed to decrease at 3.5°F per 1,000 ft (0.65°C per 100 m) in the troposphere.

An environmental temperature-height distribution according to this lapse rate has been drawn in Fig. 3.5. The air in a column with a temperature that is 2°F (1°C) higher than other air near the ground will undergo the adiabatic cooling during ascent which the broken line with arrows shows. Evidently, the rising air cools faster than the surroundings. Therefore, the acceleration, which depends on the temperature difference between rising air and environment, decreases upward and becomes zero at 1,000 ft (300 m). The upward velocity, however, produced by acceleration from the ground to the height at which the buoyancy vanishes, is greatest at that point. Hence the air will continue upward, now colder and denser than its surroundings, and decelerating. Soon the upward motion will cease and the particles will start to sink. After a few oscillations about the 1,000-ft level they will settle near that height as they are slowed down by friction with other air particles.

Figure 3.5 demonstrates that the prevailing lapse rate in the atmosphere controls the height to which particles heated near the ground can rise. Two additional cases are illustrated in Fig. 3.6. On the left side the lapse rate of the surroundings is 1.6°F per 1,000 ft (0.3°C per 100 m). The temperature difference between rising air and environment decreases quickly so that the limit of penetration is only 460 ft (140 m); this atmosphere is much more "stable" than that of Fig. 3.5. On the right side of Fig. 3.6 we see a rather different but quite common occurrence. Temperature decreases with height at the rate of 4.3°F per 1,000 ft (0.8°C per 100 m) to a height of 1,000 ft (300 m); then it increases through a layer 330 ft (100 m) thick. In this layer, the temperature lapse rate is inverted from the normal state of upward decrease; we speak of *temperature inversion* or *inversion layer*. Penetrating into this layer, the ascending air

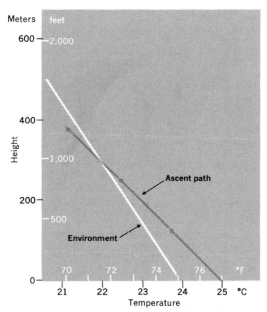

Fig. 3.5 Illustrating buoyancy. The solid white line is the temperature-height curve of the standard atmosphere. The line marked with arrows is the ascent path of air in a thermal starting with a surface temperature of 77°F (25°C). Air in the thermal is buoyant up to 1,000 ft (300 m).

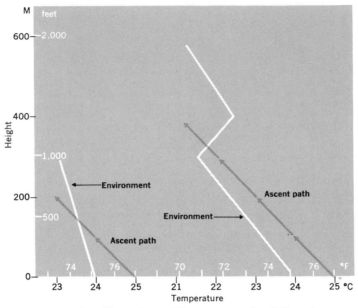

Fig. 3.6 Further illustrations of buoyancy. Left: shallow buoyant layer in stable environment. Right: deep buoyant layer in unstable environment, topped by temperature inversion.

quickly becomes colder than the environment and stops moving upward. Temperature inversions act as very strong lids against penetration of air from below, trapping the surface air layer underneath the inversion base.

VERTICAL MIXING

During a summer day, an area of 50 to 100 acres may experience hundreds of large and small thermals. Close to the ground, unrest because of buoyancy becomes pronounced during the forenoon. Figure 3.7 illustrates the growth of this unrest in the lowest 6.6 ft (2 m)—the height of a tall man—on a spring morning. After 10 A.M. the surface layer becomes turbulent. Air particles are accelerated upward after variable heating at the ground, so that their temperatures differ considerably. Rising, consequently, at different speeds, the particles do not fully retain their identity as the ascent paths of

Figs. 3.5 and 3.6 assume. *Mixing* occurs with the air displaced during ascent; the relatively warm particles coming from the ground give up some of their heat to colder particles higher up.

Since such mixing reduces the buoyancy, most ascending columns or "bubbles" do not reach the equilibrium heights of Figs. 3.5 and 3.6. If the air particles in the ascending columns cool more rapidly than when they are rising without mixing, they must settle at lower elevation. Because of the mixing, however, the environment gains heat. Balloons sent up every hour during the forenoon show the pattern of temperature change in the low atmosphere depicted by Fig. 3.8. At the end of the night, the coldest air is situated next to the ground; we observe a *ground inversion*. After heating sets in, the layer nearest the ground responds first (curve for 9 A.M. in Fig. 3.8). Gradually the heating spreads upward, transforming the temperature lapse rate. A limit or final state is reached when the lapse rate becomes adiabatic (3 P.M.). Then the whole low atmosphere is said to be mixed, the end product of *turbulent exchange*, or mixing.

Upward Heat Transport. Up to this point we have examined only the history of ascending air. However, for each particle that

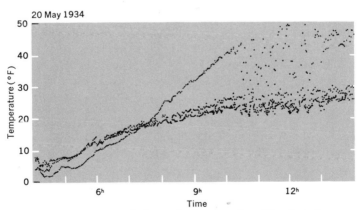

Fig. 3.7 *Onset of turbulence during morning. The dotted curves portray temperature measurements (°C) at several levels between 23 cm (coldest at sunrise) and 2 m (6.6 ft) height. General overturning, destroying the continuity of the curves, begins between 10 and 11 A.M. (From R. Geiger,* The Climate near the Ground, *Harvard University Press, Cambridge, Mass., 1950.)*

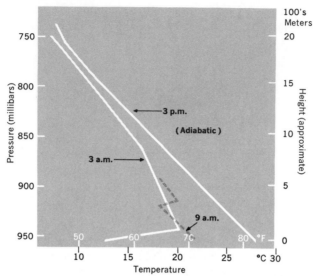

Fig. 3.8 Variation of temperature in the lowest 200 millibars (2,000 m) at O'Neill, Nebraska, on August 19, 1953, under the influence of diurnal heating and cooling. Temperature-height curves labeled to nearest hour. Before sunrise (3 A.M.), there was a large ground inversion. At 9 A.M., this inversion was wiped out and a shallow adiabatic layer had become estab-lished. A deep mixed (adiabatic) layer was observed in the afternoon. The area on the diagram between the 3 A.M. and 3 P.M. soundings shows the temperature increase due to ground heating; the temperature difference is largest near the ground and vanishes near 750 millibars.

goes up, another must be found to take its place. In the setting we are examining, the replacement must come from higher levels near the place where the buoyant ascent also occurs. Later chapters will discuss other means for maintaining continuity of mass in the atmosphere. If the environment has the lapse rate of the standard atmosphere (Fig. 3.5), air particles cannot descend far. Any particle starting to do so moves toward higher pressure and is heated by compression at the adiabatic rate. It will immediately become warmer than the air around it and return to its starting altitude.

As soon as the mixed layer has formed, however, particles can move readily to the surface in downdrafts. Then vertical exchange gradually thickens the mixed layer during the day. Thus, heat re-ceived from the ground is distributed over an increasing mass of air and the warming per *unit mass* becomes less. It eventually stops in the late afternoon, when heating from the surface declines and the mixed layer is at its greatest thickness.

During the night, air particles close to the ground are cooled; their density increases and they tend to remain next to the surface. The nocturnal temperature drop is limited to a shallow layer giving rise to ground temperature inversions. Thus heat loss by conduction is not distributed by up- and down-moving columns over a deep layer, in contrast to heating. During the daytime, heat is added to the air above the ground inversion by turbulent transport; because thermal stability restrains turbulence, a corresponding loss does not occur at night.

Thus the low atmosphere experiences net heating over land through the variable action of turbulence during day and night. The heat so gained balances in part the net radiation heat loss of the atmosphere, discussed at the end of Chapter 2. There we noted that heating of the air immediately adjacent to the earth by conduction from the ground is one of two processes counteracting the imbalance of radiation on the earth and in the atmosphere. The preceding description has shown how this heat is next distributed upward, over the land masses. Over the oceans, where the daily variation of temperature is almost nil, vertical mixing by turbulence continues day and night wherever the sea surface temperature exceeds the air temperature. Such mixing maintains the observed temperatures below the height of the cloud bases over the wide expanse of the tropics and also in many parts of higher latitudes. Over the tropical oceans the height of the cloud bases averages 2,000 to 3,000 ft (600 to 900 m); over continental deserts, especially in the subtropics, the heating through turbulence may extend to 13,000 ft (4,000 m) height.

DAILY WIND VARIATION

Near the ground, air tends to be calm at night, and relatively strong and gusty winds tend to blow during daytime (Fig. 3.9). Based on the preceding analysis of how temperature changes with height during day and night, the wind trace of Fig. 3.9 can be explained

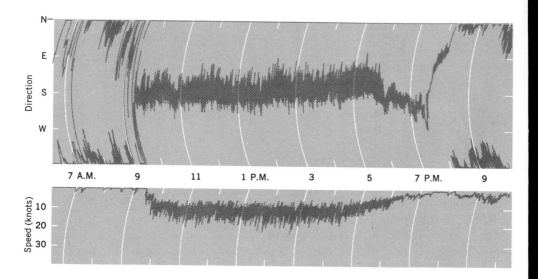

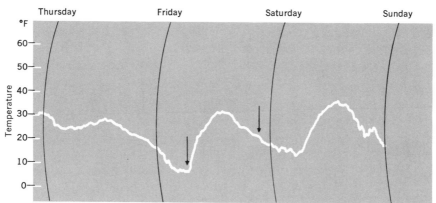

Fig. 3.9 *Daily wind variation at Colorado State University on February 15, 1964. Lower diagram: temperature; arrows show period over which wind record is reproduced. During the night, with low temperatures, wind speed is very light and direction fluctuates irregularly. When temperature had risen by 15°F about 9:30 A.M., an adiabatic layer had formed and overturning began, marked by sudden increase in wind speed and nearly constant wind direction. After sunset, with falling temperatures, the wind again subsided.*

if the wind, averaged over the entire day, increases upward (Fig. 3.10). Because of ground friction, wind speed approaches zero quite close to the ground, though of course not always—for instance, when dust is blown high up. Wind speed increases upward most rapidly in the lowest few feet, while, higher up, the rate of increase diminishes (see also Fig. 11.18).

Let us now reexamine the thermal of Fig. 3.4 with regard to wind structure. The particles in this column travel from a layer with low *horizontal* wind speed toward a layer with higher wind speed. Just as we initially assumed that the air particles in the column conserve their heat, we shall now assume, again only initially, that they conserve their momentum. The lower diagram of Fig. 3.10 shows the vertical distribution of momentum per unit mass of air, when the wind direction is constant.[1]

Conservation of horizontal momentum would hold strictly if there were no other forces acting on the particles in the column— especially frictional drag by the surrounding air. Rising particles would arrive at the top of the mixing layer with the same horizontal wind speed they had when leaving the layer with ground obstructions, perhaps 30 m or 100 ft above the ground (particle *A* in Fig. 3.10). Of course, the surroundings do exert drag. Nevertheless, the air in a thermal will have relatively low horizontal momentum compared with the surroundings. Air pockets, where the wind speed suddenly drops, are often encountered by aircraft during take-off or landing. Sudden change in wind speed is one factor leading to bumpiness.

Particles descending from upper levels toward the ground in a thermally mixed layer should also conserve their momentum in the absence of drag and other forces (particle *B* in Fig. 3.10). The downward transport of high momentum from the upper air mainly produces the high wind speed and gust structure near the ground in the noon hours. Through turbulence, a continuing supply of momentum from above maintains the surface wind against friction. When turbulence stops near sunset, the surface wind dies quickly. The low-level air is confined near the ground during the night,

---

[1] Momentum is defined as mass times velocity; momentum per *unit mass* is simply the velocity.

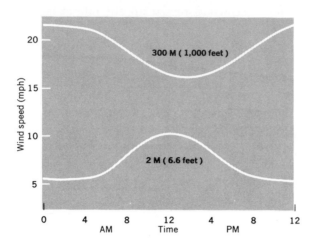

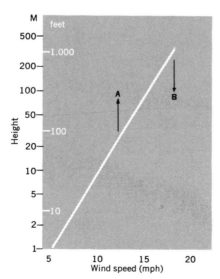

Fig. 3.10   Typical daily wind variation near the ground and at 300 m (1,000 ft) height (top); variation of wind with height, averaged over 24 hr (bottom).

and stagnation develops, unless the terrain slopes, causing drainage winds (Chapter 11). General winds of about 10 mph and even a little more are suppressed in the surface layer because of thermal stability and friction.

An observer at 1,000 ft (300 m) height should find that the daily wind variation at his altitude is opposite that near the surface. During the day, arrival of slow particles from below would act as a brake on the upper wind. When the surface air stopped rising, horizontal air movement would become smooth and fast. This reverse daily cycle really occurs (Fig. 3.10); the wind varies least with height during daytime and most at night.

From this analysis, the vertical wind profile, averaged for a day, determines whether the wind is strongest during the day or the night at a given level. As long as the wind increases upward, as shown in Fig. 3.10, wind speed rises during the day at low and decreases at high levels in the layer through which the mixing extends. If, however, the 24-hr average wind decreases upward, the opposite course of daily wind variation should be expected. In the Midwestern United States the general wind often decreases upward in summer above about 1,000 ft (300 m) height. Figure 3.11 shows a typical case from an experimental site in the flatlands of Nebraska where, during 1953, many observations were made. The mean wind, averaged from 8 P.M. on August 18 to 8 P.M. on August 19, decreased upward above 1,000 ft (300 m). During the night, wind speed decreased from 28 mph at 1,000 ft (300 m) to only 6 mph near 6,000 ft (1,800 m). By the afternoon of August 19, however, a constant momentum profile had been nearly established. Above 3,000 ft (900 m) the wind increased from night to day; below this level it decreased.

The normal pattern of daily temperature and wind variation for quiet-weather days changes completely during passage of strong low-pressure areas. Then the winds accompanying the large-scale pressure distribution easily override local frictional control; wind speed remains high throughout the night and temperature decreases just slightly. Fast air motion over all such "rough" terrain features as trees and buildings furnishes the energy to create turbulence. This turbulence is *mechanical*, in contrast to *thermal* turbulence.

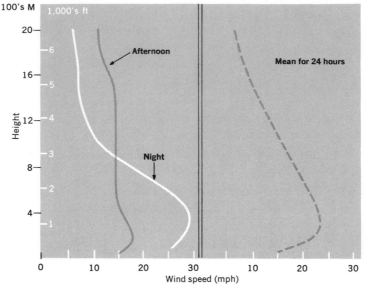

Fig. 3.11 Variation of wind speed with height averaged over 24 hr on August 18–19, 1953, at O'Neill, Nebraska (right.) The two wind profiles on the left correspond in time approximately to the 3 A.M. and 3 P.M. temperature-height curves of Fig. 3.8. In the afternoon, when a mixed layer had been established for temperature up to 750 millibars (2,000 m above ground), the horizontal wind speed had become almost uniform. Since wind speed decreased upward in the 24-hr average, the change from night to day showed increases of speed above 900 m (3,000 ft) and decreases below.

But the effect on the temperature distribution with height is identical: a mixed layer is produced near the surface. Over the depth of this mixed layer, which may be only a few hundred feet (or m), active up and down motions take place.

DAILY VARIATION OF POLLUTION

The distance to which buildings, mountains, trees, and other objects are clearly visible is called the *horizontal visibility*. In and near population centers with pollution sources, combustion products in the air restrict visibility. Visibility is normally lowest during the early morning and improves during the later forenoon.

The daily variation in pollution is easily explained, if we disregard local wind currents (Chapter 11). At night, when vertical mixing is suppressed and when the horizontal motion also dies out, combustion products accumulate near the ground. During the morning, as turbulence caused by the sun's warming increases, pollutants are mixed farther and farther upward. When downdrafts begin to import horizontal momentum from the upper layers toward the ground, the pollution is also removed horizontally by the strengthening winds. In a city where pollution sources extend over more than 10 miles, very little of the pollution will leave the source region when nighttime winds are only 1 or 2 mph. But with winds of 10 to 20 mph, the material escapes downwind from the city during the day in only $\frac{1}{2}$ to 1 hr.

The change in concentration of pollutants in the air throughout the day may be only weakly related to the variation of source strength. City life accelerates during the early morning—factories open and traffic increases—and these sources may become very intense. However, because the air mixes vertically and because the horizontal wind speed picks up, the city atmosphere normally becomes cleaner during the late morning. In suburban and rural areas nearby, to which the polluted air is carried, the opposite is often true.

4

Evaporation,
Condensation,
and Clouds

MOISTURE IN THE ATMOSPHERE

The amount of water vapor air can hold varies; we speak of dry and moist air masses. Yet the moisture content of air cannot increase without limit. Water vapor, like other gases, exerts a pressure, called *vapor pressure*. Air is considered saturated when its vapor pressure equals that directly over a level water surface. The saturation vapor pressure depends strongly on temperature. Over the range of air temperature, it fluctuates from less than $\frac{1}{10}$ millibar to over 100 millibars, or by a factor of 1,000 (Fig. 4.1). At the boiling point of water, it equals the total atmospheric pressure.

Relative Humidity. Relative humidity, a familiar quantity given

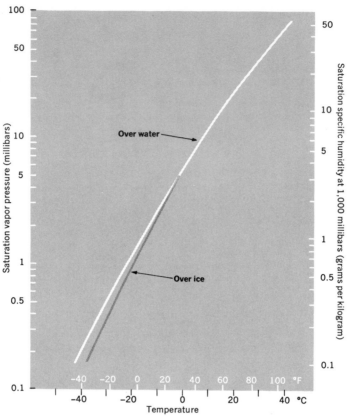

Fig. 4.1   Relation between saturation vapor pressure and temperature. Right: saturation specific humidity at pressure of 1 atm.

in weather reports, is the ratio of the amount of water vapor actually measured to that which air could hold at saturation. Normally, the moisture in air is well below saturation, especially, of course, in dry climates. Strangely, perhaps, human comfort depends on relative humidity rather than on the actual moisture content of air. When the relative humidity is above 80 per cent, even air with low moisture content feels clammy. Human hair reacts to changes in relative humidity by expanding and contracting, so that it can be used to measure relative humidity directly. The length of hair changes by about 2½ per cent between 0 and 100 per cent relative humidity.

Specific Humidity. The moisture content of air is usually expressed in terms of weight of water vapor per unit weight of air, such as grams of water per kilogram of air. This ratio is known as *specific humidity.* At levels below 10,000 ft (3 km), unless the temperature is extreme, a space of 1 cu m contains about 1 kg of air. Therefore, in the low atmosphere, specific humidity indicates the moisture content in a volume of 1 cu m within 10 to 15 per cent. A single room may hold surprisingly large amounts of water in vapor form. A lecture room 10 ft (3 m) high and 33 ft (10 m) wide and long, with a volume of 300 cu m (11,000 cu ft), will contain 1,500 g (3 pt) of water vapor, if the specific humidity is 5 g per kg, which is rather low.

The specific humidity corresponding to saturation vapor pressure can be computed for any value of air pressure. It is shown in Fig. 4.1, in parts per thousand, at a pressure of 1 atm. We see a very large difference in the capacity of warm and cold air to hold moisture. At a temperature of 77°F (25°C) and a relative humidity of 50 per cent, 1 kg of air contains about 10 g of water vapor. At 0°F (−18°C) and 50 per cent relative humidity, the moisture content is only about 0.5 g per kg. When such air is heated to room temperature, the relative humidity falls to 2½ per cent! Such a low value seldom occurs naturally, even in deserts.

On days with a normal temperature range, the saturation specific humidity varies considerably. If temperature rises from a low of 50°F (10°C) to a high of 77°F (25°C), the saturation specific humidity at pressure of 1 atm increases from 8 to 20 g per kg. The actual moisture in air, however, remains nearly constant. If the specific humidity is 6 g per kg, relative humidity decreases from 75 per cent near sunrise to 30 per cent in the early afternoon. Thus, at noon, the air feels much drier than in the early morning.

Dew-point Temperature. Relative humidity rises during the night as temperature and saturation humidity decrease. When the relative humidity reaches 100 per cent, the air has attained its *dew-point temperature.* This is the lowest temperature to which air can be cooled, at constant pressure, before condensation begins.

Often, only a thin layer of air just above the grass, or in contact with such rapidly cooling surfaces as automobiles, reaches the dew point. Then a little water vapor condenses on grass or car. This deposit is called *dew,* leading to the term dew-point temperature. In arid regions, dew may be an important source of water for both human beings and animals. Dew formation can be accelerated by covering the ground with flat metal sheets placed along an incline, with a cistern at the bottom to catch the water.

EVAPORATION

Moisture enters the atmosphere mainly through evaporation from oceans, lakes, rivers, and reservoirs, and through transpiration from plants. Evaporation occurs when the vapor pressure at the earth's surface exceeds that in the atmosphere. An energy expenditure is required to change water from the liquid to the vapor phase. This energy is usually supplied by the body from which the evaporation takes place and which is, as a result, cooled. Upon stepping out of a shower or bath, for instance, we suddenly feel cold. The vapor pressure of the water clinging to the skin exceeds that of the air, and heat from the body supplies the energy to evaporate the water. Such cooling of the body becomes most important when air temperature exceeds body temperature. Heat conduction from the body then ceases and evaporation alone regulates the body temperature.

Evaporation also occurs when raindrops fall through air, as long as their vapor pressure is higher than that of the air. In this case the atmosphere gives off most of the heat required for evaporating the water and becomes colder. This is the principal reason why summer showers bring relief from heat. Evaporation has a powerful effect on temperature. At summer temperatures, nearly 600 cal must be expended to evaporate 1 g of water. If this gram of water evaporates into 1 kg of air, the air will cool 4.5°F (2.5°C). In a room with temperature of 86°F (30°C) and relative humidity of 10 per cent, such an increase is easily achieved. The relative humidity of the air will rise only slightly. Such air conditioning through evaporation has long been practiced in hot, dry climates—for instance, in cooling houses in the Middle East.

Wet-bulb Temperature. Evaporation can be used to determine the specific humidity. Consider air at a temperature of 83°F (28.5°C), relative humidity of 40 per cent, and pressure of 1 atm. The specific humidity then is 10 g per kg and the dew point 57°F (14°C). Figure 4.2 shows how this information can be obtained. Water sprayed into the air will partially evaporate, decreasing the air temperature at the rate shown by the straight slanting line from lower right to upper left in Fig. 4.2. At the same time, the dew point increases, indicated by the almost straight line marked "increase in dew point." Relative humidity increases, because of both the rise in actual specific humidity and the decrease in saturation specific humidity. Where the two lines meet, the relative humidity is 100 per cent. We have cooled the air to the lowest possible temperature that can be attained by evaporation.

Virtually the same temperature can be reached by wrapping muslin cloth around the bulb of a mercury thermometer, soaking it with distilled water, and then swinging it vigorously. When the temperature stops falling, usually after about 3 min, the thermometer indicates the *wet-bulb* temperature (66°F, or 19°C, in Fig. 4.2).

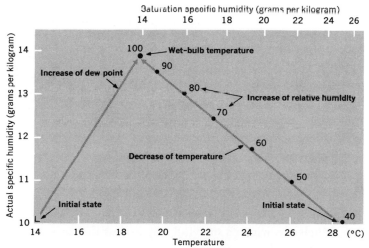

Fig. 4.2 Illustrating the cooling of air to the wet-bulb temperature.

From the difference between air and wet-bulb temperatures, the *wet-bulb depression,* the specific humidity can be computed from tables. In Fig. 4.2 the wet-bulb depression is 17°F (9.5°C).

Evaporation Rates. Because vapor pressure depends strongly on temperature (Fig. 4.1), evaporation is highest when the water or other types of surfaces are warmest; the vapor-pressure difference between the evaporating body and the air then reaches a maximum. Usually, this happens in the middle of the day and in summer. Conversely, evaporation is least at night and during winter, when it may cease altogether. Since temperature normally also decreases upward, less water is lost by evaporation from storage reservoirs at high than at low altitudes, as discussed in Chapter 12.

Wind is another important factor in controlling evaporation rate. When winds are very light, a thin layer of air just above the surface becomes saturated, or nearly so; because of the small difference in vapor pressure between ground and air, evaporation will be very slow. However, when the air flow is turbulent, individual air particles remain in contact with the ground for only a short time, to be succeeded by drier particles from above. Moisture evaporating from the ground is mixed upward, and the vapor-pressure difference between the surface and the atmosphere remains large.

Regions with persistently strong winds of perhaps 15 to 20 mph, especially the trade-wind belts, have high evaporation rates. Disastrous evaporation over land follows a combination of strong wind, high temperature, and very low humidity, for instance winds of 30 to 40 mph, a temperature of 80°F (27°C), and relative humidity of 10 per cent or less. A few hours of such conditions, often recurring east of the Rocky Mountains during spring, can dehydrate the soil to a depth of several inches. When such extreme weather recurs without relief by 1- or 2-in. rainfalls, whole spring plantings are lost and dust bowl conditions arise.

Even at temperatures well below freezing, a snow cover will evaporate quickly when the wind is strong and relative humidity low. Much of a winter's snowfall may be lost that way, never passing through the soil.

Latent Heat of Vaporization or Condensation. We found in Chapter 2 that the earth gains and the atmosphere loses heat through radiation over the year. The mixing, through turbulence, of air heated near the ground with colder air from above reduces the earth's net radiational heat gain by about one-third (Chapter 3). Evaporation, then, must account for two-thirds of the heat exchange between ground and atmosphere. To maintain the heat balance both in earth and atmosphere, 30 to 40 in. of water (75 to 100 cm) must evaporate, and also precipitate, per year over the world. This computation agrees well with world rainfall estimates (Fig. 10.4).

Evaporation from the earth does not heat the atmosphere directly, as conduction does. The water vapor must condense in the atmosphere, and the water must then fall back to the ground, before the heat exchange is complete. It is important to remember, however, that heat release through condensation need not, and seldom does, take place near the site of evaporation. Water vapor may travel thousands of miles without condensing. We therefore speak of *latent heat* of evaporation or condensation. For example, the subtropical oceans supply most of the moisture for the atmosphere. This happens because in these latitudes general subsiding air motion takes place, producing a minimum of cloudiness and permitting a maximum amount of solar energy to reach the oceans.

CONDENSATION

Condensation Nuclei. Water vapor nearly always condenses at relative humidities very close to 100 per cent. It is not obvious, however, why this is so. We have defined saturation of air with respect to the vapor pressure over a flat water surface. This definition is important for evaporation from the oceans, but not necessarily for condensation within the atmosphere. The vapor pressure over droplets with highly curved surfaces is very much higher than that of a flat water surface. Such droplets would therefore evaporate into air having a relative humidity of 100 per cent.

Experiments near the end of the nineteenth century showed that, in pure air, condensation does not occur anywhere near 100 per cent relative humidity. If the air is carefully filtered to remove

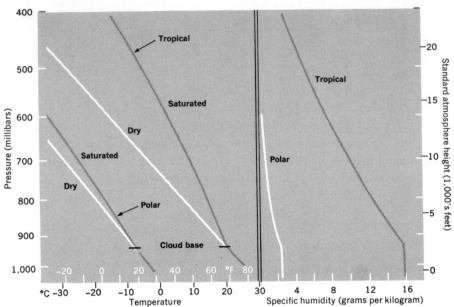

Fig. 4.3   Temperature variation following rising tropical and polar air above indicated cloud base (left). White lines show unsaturated ascent for comparison; clearly, condensation heating is much greater in the tropical than in the polar air. Decrease of specific humidity along these ascents (right).

all particles normally present, the relative humidity can rise to around 400 per cent before this happens. The very small particles which are practically always present in the air provide a starting point for water to condense, and supersaturation of air to a relative humidity greater than 101 per cent rarely, if ever, occurs.

If these particles have a diameter of $\frac{1}{10}$ micron ($\frac{1}{100,000}$ of a cm), water vapor will condense on them at a relative humidity very slightly above 100 per cent. Often condensation nuclei are appreciably larger than the minimum size required. Many particles have a diameter of 1 micron, some of even 10 microns—*giant* nuclei. Salt particles, carried over the continents from the oceans by the winds, are thought to be the most effective condensation nuclei. Dissolved in a droplet, these salt particles greatly reduce the vapor pressure of the drop. Condensation may begin at relative humidities as low as 75 per cent. Visibility then decreases and the landscape takes on a dull, grayish appearance. We speak of *wet haze,* a frequent precursor of bad weather.

Release of Latent Heat. When air cools adiabatically as it rises, that is, without any heat being added or taken away from it (Chapter 3), the dew point is easily reached, often only minutes after air starts to ascend. Then cloud formation begins, and the rising mass of air no longer cools at the dry-adiabatic rate of 5.5°F per 1,000 ft (1°C per 100 m) but at a very variable lower rate. During condensation, approximately the same amount of heat is released to the atmosphere per gram of moisture condensed that was needed to evaporate the water. In tropical air, which has high temperature and moisture, the heat released during condensation is much greater than in polar air, which has low temperature and specific humidity (Fig. 4.3). Therefore, the temperature of rising tropical air decreases more slowly with height than that of polar air. Most water vapor in

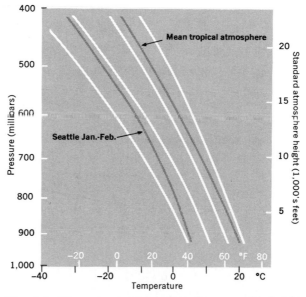

Fig. 4.4 *The average temperature decrease with height, or pressure, as determined for tropical oceanic and middle-latitude marine climates by radiosonde balloon observations. See also Fig. 1.13. White: samples of the temperature curves rising air would follow when condensation is occurring.*

both types of air masses is condensed in the lower troposphere. Above 500 millibars (18,000 ft), the rate of cooling again becomes nearly adiabatic, since less and less moisture is available to condense.

Average Temperature Lapse Rates. Condensation is the mechanism releasing latent heat gained through evaporation of water from the surface. Through cloud formation, the condensation heat is mixed through the troposphere, up to 50,000 ft (15 km) in the tropics. Balloon soundings made over most parts of the earth, especially the oceans, show that the average temperature lapse rate, determined from these soundings, is close to the ascent path of cloud-producing air (Fig. 4.4). Condensation, therefore, *determines* the average temperature lapse rate above the lowest few thousand feet and is a key factor in shaping the atmosphere's structure.

CLOUDS

Stratus and Cumulus. We can compare the temperature lapse rate in cloud-forming ascent with the temperature structure of the environment, just as we did in Chapter 3 for cloud-free air; the comparison shows whether or not the ascending mass will be buoyant. Despite the release of latent heat of condensation, tem-

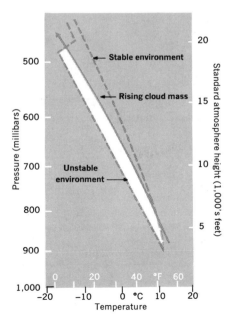

Fig. 4.5 *Illustrating formation of cumulus and stratus clouds. The solid curve with arrow shows the temperature curve that rising air follows. Stratus will form when the temperature of the environment is warmer than that of the rising air,* marked stable; *cumulus will form when the environment is colder,* marked unstable.

perature may decrease upward more quickly in a cloudy updraft than in the surrounding clear air (Fig. 4.5). Under such circumstances, a cloud should not grow or even persist. Nevertheless, cloud growth often occurs because other factors, mainly large-scale mass flow toward a cyclone center (Chapter 7), will enforce ascent of air. Such forced ascent leads to formation of cloud sheets spread over a large area horizontally compared to their depth; appearing as thin, stratified layers, these clouds are called *stratus* (Fig. 4.6).

An entirely different type of cloud forms during buoyant ascent, when the surrounding temperature is colder than the cloudy updraft. In Fig. 4.5 cloud temperatures exceed those of the environment marked "unstable" by 5.5°F (3°C) up to 500 millibars. The upward acceleration is powerful, favoring the formation of clouds with great vertical and small horizontal extent compared with stratus clouds. Because of their "heaping" appearance, these clouds bear the name *cumulus* (Fig. 4.7).

Air in a buoyant updraft, forming a cumulus cloud, is not likely to rise very far without mixing with the surrounding air. Such mixing, or *entrainment*, into the updraft severely curtails cumulus growth as a rule. Normally, the surrounding air is not only colder than the updraft; it is also comparatively dry. Buoyancy inside the cloud is reduced by entrainment, as is the amount of water, since

Fig. 4.6 Stratus extending forward from cumuliform clouds in the background. (Courtesy Maxwell Parshall, Colorado State University.) A solid stratus deck is difficult to show; the page just would look uniformly gray.

Fig. 4.7   *Cumulus of fair weather.* (*Courtesy Maxwell Parshall.*)

Fig. 4.8   *Trade-wind cumulus sky over the tropical Pacific Ocean.* (*Courtesy Dr. Joanne S. Malkus. Photo by C. F. Ronne.*)

droplets will evaporate into the unsaturated admixture. We can observe this desiccation clearly from the ground, when cloud towers first push upward vigorously and then suddenly fade away; this means that the cloud has penetrated into a dry upper layer.

Cumulus clouds rising in a very narrow column are most likely to undergo this kind of erosion. Over an area with thousands of cumulus clouds, some have stronger updrafts and their base covers a wider area than others; these are most favored to grow. A cumulus sky, most dramatically seen in summer or over the tropical oceans, has cloud tops that are far from uniform (Fig. 4.8). The entire range of cloud histories is on display. Some cumuli live only for a few minutes; they may evaporate after acquiring a depth of only 2,000 ft (600 m) or less. A few may become 10,000 ft (3,000 m) thick and last for half an hour.

Towering Cumulus and Cumulonimbus. The larger the area covered by the base of an updraft, the more likely it is that the cloud will have a "protected core"—an inner updraft area to which the mixing from the sides does not reach during the few minutes needed by the air in the cloud to pass through the lower troposphere. Rising air in such cores may have upward speeds of 1,000 to 2,000 ft per min (300 to 600 m per min), and thus may arrive at 10,000 ft (3,000 m) above cloud base after 5 to 10 min. If surrounding conditions do not inhibit cloud growth severely—that is, if relative humidity is high—the cloud columns grow to 15,000 to 20,000 ft (4,500 to 6,000 m) or more. They are then called *towering,* or *swelling,* cumuli. Their tops are cauliflower-shaped, and the cloud edge appears sharp or hard, indicating that, despite temperatures well below freezing, the cloud drops have remained in the liquid phase (Fig. 4.9).

When ice does begin to form, the tops assume a soft, milky appearance; they often become anvil-shaped, clearly revealing the outflow pattern of the air that has risen in the cloud (Fig. 4.10). Such clouds bear the name *cumulonimbus.* They are the most imposing of all clouds, the producers of thunderstorms and other forms of severe weather.

In middle latitudes, cumulonimbi normally have tops at 30,000 to 40,000 ft (9 to 12 km), the base of the stratosphere; radar ob-

Fig 4.9   Towering cumulus. Observe cauliflower structure and hard appearance of cloud top. (U.S. Weather Bureau.)

Fig. 4.10   Cumulonimbus, with rain shower. Observe fuzzy, unstructured appearance of whole upper part of cloud when contrasted with Fig. 4.9. (Courtesy U.S. Weather Bureau.)

servations occasionally indicate much higher tops. In the tropics, especially over land, 50,000-ft (15-km) tops often occur. Cumulonimbi may become tremendous cloud masses covering 10 to 100 sq miles (or km) and lasting one to several hours.

Cloud Classification. Although stratus and cumulus are the basic cloud forms, there is an infinite variety of cloud patterns. This renders complete cloud classification impossible. Nevertheless, different observers can usually agree on some outstanding features of clouds. A cloud composed entirely of ice crystals is called a *cirrus.* It is also called a *high cloud,* because, in middle latitudes, it seldom occurs below 25,000 ft (7,600 m). *Low clouds* exist mainly in the layer below 10,000 to 12,000 ft (3 to 4 km); clouds at intermediate heights are labeled *middle clouds.*

In the following table, the basic cloud types are listed according to phase, buoyancy, and height.[1]

Table 4.1   Principal Cloud Types

	Low	Middle	High
Stratus	Stratus	Altostratus	Cirrostratus
	Cumulus	Altocumulus	Cirrocumulus
Cumulus	Towering cumulus		
	Cumulonimbus		

Cirrostratus (Fig. 4.11), when followed by altostratus, often heralds the beginning of a day or two of bad weather. The sky becomes overcast with a high-altitude cloud mass that appears whitish and streaky. Gradually the cloud thickens and the sky assumes a uniform gray color as the water drops of the altostratus

[1] Readers desiring more detailed cloud descriptions will find them in the International Cloud Atlas. (See Appendix III.) Table 4.1 slightly simplifies the classification of the cloud types given in the atlas, which is based mainly on a scheme put forward in the year 1803.

Fig. 4.11   Cirrocumulus and streaky cirrostratus extending above low cumuli. (Courtesy Maxwell Parshall.)

Fig. 4.12   Altocumulus. (Courtesy Maxwell Parshall.)

replace the ice crystals of the cirrostratus. Cirrocumulus and alto-cumulus (Fig. 4.12) provide some of the most picturesque skies. In spite of their cumuliform shape these clouds may be only a few hundred feet (or m) thick. Combinations of cumulus and stratus also occur, especially of altocumulus and altostratus. Stratocumulus, a low cloud cover with bulging tops as seen looking down from an airplane, is another such combination (Fig. 4.13).

Cloud Streets. Rockets and satellites have revealed the frequent organization of clouds into *streets*, or bands, hundreds of miles (or kilometers) long. The frontispiece of this book shows a spectacular street over the Atlantic Ocean, emanating from a cyclone center along its cold front. Though it was not until cloud pictures from satellites became available that the existence of cloud bands on such a large scale was proved, the tendency for cumuli to align in streets or rows (Fig. 4.14) has been observed for many years.

Fig. 4.13   Stratocumulus overcast, seen from above. (Courtesy U.S. Weather Bureau.)

Fig. 4.14 *Cumulus cloud streets over the tropical Pacific. (Courtesy Dr. J. S. Malkus. Photo by C. F. Ronne.)*

Fig. 4.15 *Trade-wind cumulus leaning with height under the influence of wind shear. (Courtesy Dr. J. S. Malkus. Photo by C. F. Ronne.)*

Often the distance between the rows is about twice their height. Although the formation of cloud streets is not fully understood, they are thought to occur mainly when the wind changes strongly with height; the direction of the cloud streets usually lies along the direction of the *shear* of the wind.

The shape of an individual cloud also can reveal much about wind structure. A trade-wind cloud, moving from the east and leaning backward toward the east as it rises, indicates that the speed of the east wind decreases upward (Fig. 4.15). The shear then is from west toward east as the photo shows. If the cloud is vertical in the lower portion, but has a pronounced slope near the top (Fig. 5.2), we may assume that the cloud has penetrated into an upper layer with flow from west. The appearance of the cloud portrays beautifully where the shearing layer in the atmosphere begins.

FOG

A cloud with base at or very close to the ground is called *fog*. Fog interferes with transportation, whether by land, sea, or air. It can restrict visibility to a mile or so or to a few hundred feet, or it can be the proverbial "pea soup," in which a flashlight is of little use.

Stratus and cumulus clouds form when the pressure of a rising mass of air decreases; the temperature then lowers at the adiabatic rate until it reaches the dew point. In contrast, most fogs, though not all, originate when air cools to the dew point at constant pressure. Stratus and cumulus formations are preceded by cooling under conservation of heat. Fog formation involves actual withdrawal of heat from the air, mainly through radiation cooling and movement of air over cold ground.

Radiation Fog. Radiation fog forms when a night is long, the sky clear, the wind light, and the relative humidity near sunset high. A clear sky permits radiation from the earth to escape to space through the "window" at 10 microns. When relative humidity is high near sunset, only a little cooling will decrease temperature to the dew point. High winds would prevent nocturnal cooling (Chapter 3); the turbulence generated even by winds of 15 mph will hinder fog formation completely. A light wind of 2 to 3 mph, how-ever, is favorable; the small amount of turbulence it brings mixes the air particles cooled at the ground upward, thus ensuring a solid fog layer up to 30 to 100 ft (10 to 30 m). In completely still air, radiation fog will be patchy and often only waist-deep.

Because cold air drains downhill, radiation fog is thickest in valley bottoms, with the surrounding hillsides rising above it. If low foggy and high clear stretches alternate when driving through rolling country near sunrise on a quiet morning, radiation fog and cold-air drainage are the causes. As soon as the sun has warmed the ground sufficiently, in 1 to 3 hr after sunrise, radiation fog normally disappears.

Autumn and winter are the most favorable seasons for radiation fog. During autumn moisture is still high in the air, and during winter, the nights are longest. The center of a high-pressure area is a favorite spot for radiation fog, since winds are light and skies usually clear. When a high-pressure center stagnates during winter, the same air will be cooled by radiation during several successive nights. When moist air is trapped in valleys, as in the San Joaquin Valley of California, east of the coastal mountain range, a solid fog cover may form that persists through the day and will not clear until a pronounced weather disturbance with strong winds arrives.

Advection Fog. When warmer air blows, or is *advected,* over a colder surface, fog develops under conditions very different from those causing radiation fog. The air gives off heat to the ground, and this cools the air temperature to the dew point.

The temperature of the earth's surface normally decreases north-ward; thus advection fog forms mainly when air currents blow from the south, especially when they carry high moisture. During winter, tropical air entering the Central and Eastern United States from the Gulf of Mexico is likely to encounter ground with temperature near freezing, often covered by snow. Turbulence at wind speeds of 15 to 20 mph distributes the cooling through a layer some 1,000 ft (300 m) thick. This shallow layer will be mixed; the temperature lapse rate will be adiabatic and the moisture constant through the layer. At the top a temperature inversion forms that gradually strengthens (Fig. 4.16). Relative humidity first reaches 100 per cent

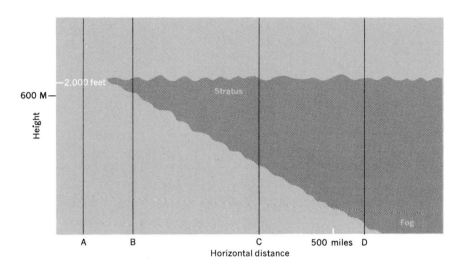

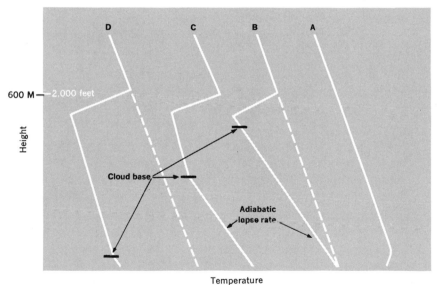

Fig. 4.16   Thickening of stratus to fog during movement of tropical air over cold land or water (top). Schematic temperature-height curves illustrating changes in temperature structure, as fog forms, for the indicated locations A–D (bottom). Dashed line is same as initial sounding at point A, showing the subsequent distribution of cooling with height.

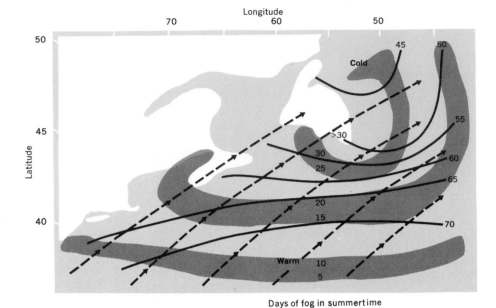

Longitude

Days of fog in summertime

Fig. 4.17 The foggy climate over the Atlantic Ocean in summer. Numbers in middle refer to average number of days with fog June–August in the western Atlantic off Newfoundland (shadings); average sea-surface temperatures (isotherms labeled on right in °F) and streamlines (dashed with arrows) of prevailing surface air flow.

near the top of the mixed layer, where a stratus deck forms. Underneath, the air becomes very hazy: water vapor begins to condense on sea salt and combustion particles at relative humidities of 90 per cent and less.

When the tropical air continues northward, the mixed layer becomes saturated at lower and lower levels, and the base of the stratus approaches the surface. The fog layer is very thick and will persist day and night, in contrast to radiation fog. Warm rain falling through the evaporating into the fog layer often contributes to fog density.

During summer, advection fog is rare when tropical air is flowing northward over the United States, because the sun heats the northern tier of states. Over the Atlantic and Pacific Oceans, however, tropical air will advance northward to latitude 50° and beyond, where water temperatures remain relatively low through the summer, and will lead to extensive and persistent fog. Around

Newfoundland, fog will occur throughout as much as a third of the summer. Water temperatures decrease northeastward along the American coast (Fig. 4.17); winds from south or west predominate, bringing air with dew point of 60 to 70°F (15 to 20°C) and higher over water with temperatures of 50°F (10°C) or less.

Dense fog often extends across the congested shipping route between Europe and North America. The route is farther south in summer than in winter because of the fog and because icebergs drift southward at that time of year. Nevertheless, modern radar warning devices on shipboard did not prevent the ramming and sinking of the liner *Andrea Doria* on July 25, 1956, with loss of fifty-one lives.

Expansion Fog. When air moves upslope for a long time over rising terrain, the decrease in temperature it undergoes due to adiabatic expansion may lead to fog. Across the Great Plains of the United States, the standard atmosphere pressure decreases from about 980 millibars near the Mississippi to 850 millibars at the eastern margin of the Rockies. Surface air traversing this distance from east to west would have an adiabatic temperature decrease of 23°F (13°C). Such westward motion occurs mainly in late winter and spring. Then the difference between temperature and dew point in the lower plains is sufficiently below 23°F (13°C) that the air crossing the slowly rising land will form expansion, or *upslope,* fog about 100 to 200 miles east of the mountains.

Steam Fog. During early morning in summer, long columns of steam, or *mist,* often rise over small lakes and even river valleys. At that time of year water temperature and vapor pressure over water are at their highest. Air draining down the slopes toward the water may be 18°F (10°C) colder. Water evaporating from the surface may supersaturate this air at once. The evaporated water recondenses and rises with the air that is heated from below.

When cold air in winter moves from a land mass out over water perhaps 45°F (25°C) warmer than the air, or when polar air travels from the Arctic ice shelves onto the open ocean, the steaming is so intense that it consolidates into a "fog" called *Arctic sea smoke.*

5

Precipitation, Severe Storms

FORMATION OF PRECIPITATION

After condensation starts, the water droplets go through an initial growth stage and reach sizes that vary from 2 to 20 microns in diameter. The water vapor content of the air surrounding them is reduced, and water vapor pressure diminishes to that on the surface of the droplets, preventing their further growth. Moreover, they begin falling. Even with high humidity just below cloud base, such small drops evaporate within a minute or less, when they have gone a few inches or, at most, a few feet below cloud base.

For a cloud to persist, the air must ascend at least slightly, lowering the dew point. Then water lost when the falling drops evaporate below the cloud can be regained through formation of new drops. Since the vast majority of clouds do not precipitate but drift across the sky in seeming suspension, such slight ascent is the rule rather than the exception. Clouds constantly change in appearance; lighter and darker areas appear, indicating that many small-scale up and down motions are taking place. The air traveler nearly always encounters some turbulence when flying in clouds or even in clear air adjacent to clouds.

Water drops must acquire a diameter of well over 100 microns ($\frac{1}{10}$ mm), even in humid air, if they are to resist evaporation and to arrive at the ground with realistic speed. A drop that retained a 10-micron diameter, falling from a cloud base 3,300 ft (1,000 m) above the ground, would require 140 hr to reach the surface because of frictional slowing down by the atmosphere. A drop which retained a 500-micron (0.5-mm) diameter would arrive after less than 10 min of fall. It would have evaporated to some extent, but would still be considered a raindrop. A diameter of 500 microns has been adopted conventionally as the minimum raindrop size; below this size, drops are called *drizzle drops*. In contrast, raindrops, such as those from cumulus clouds, may have an average diameter of more than 1,000 microns (1 mm).

It has been difficult to learn how droplets grow to precipitation size, and the task is still unfinished. We know that in situations of active weather, especially when air is ascending over large areas during the passage of cyclones, nearly all condensed moisture falls as rain or snow. But the heavy precipitation tends to be concentrated in only a small portion of the ascent area, perhaps one-tenth. Often the precipitating clouds form lines or bands, as radar echoes have shown. It is necessary to relate these larger-scale aspects of precipitation to the processes in the minute area around individual drops—that on a scale of 1 sq in. (or cm) or less. Two mechanisms have been proposed for explaining the growth of cloud drops to raindrops and to ice crystals, of which snowflakes are composed.

Coalescence Process. In a cloud mass containing many small droplets of uniform size, each drop competes for the available water vapor. None will attain raindrop size, because condensation tends to make all drops grow at the same rate, and there is not enough water available to let them all grow into raindrops. But there are differences among them, due in part to the different sizes of the condensation nuclei on which they grew, and this results in their having different fall speeds. The larger drops will fall faster, or ascend more slowly, than the smaller ones, collide with some of them, and draw others into their wake from the rear. Through such *coalescence* the number of drops is decreased.

The speed with which raindrops form and fall out as precipitation depends on the amount of liquid water in the cloud and on how far the drops are able to fall within the cloud. Only a tiny fraction of the cloud volume contains water. A liquid water content of 1 g per cu m is high even for tropical cumuli. In middle-latitude stratus clouds, it may be only $\frac{1}{10}$ g per cu m. Since the volume of 1 g of water is 1 cu cm, only one part per million to one part per ten million of the cloud volume contains water! Clearly, a relatively large drop must travel a considerable distance through the cloud in order to intercept enough small drops to attain a diameter of 0.5 to 1 mm. This travel may be upward as well as downward, since it is the speed of the large drop *relative* to the small ones which matters. Prolonged updrafts and a large vertical cloud extent are favorable conditions for forming rain-sized drops.

Mixture of Water and Ice. Clouds composed only of liquid water must have drops with diameters of at least 50 to 100 microns in order to grow through coalescence. Condensation on very large, or *giant*, nuclei produces such drops; their fall velocity relative to small drops will be large enough that the time needed for growth to raindrop size will not be excessive. When water and ice crystals coexist at temperatures below freezing, another mechanism may initiate the growth of cloud particles.

Over ice, the saturation vapor pressure is lower than it is over water (Fig. 4.1). In a mixed cloud, there are often many more water drops than ice crystals, and then the vapor pressure of the air will be practically equal to that over the surface of the water drops, and consequently larger than that over the surface of the ice crystals. In this case, vapor diffuses rapidly from the air to the ice crystals. Consequently, the vapor pressure of the air is decreased and becomes lower than that over the water drops. These begin to evaporate and thus restore the vapor content of the air. In this way the vapor pressure in the air remains higher than that of the ice crystals, until all water is evaporated. The larger crystals acquire substantial fall velocities; *accretion* of small crystals on the large ones leads to further growth, producing the snowflakes we see falling to the ground.

Until the 1940s, all precipitation was thought to originate through the ice phase. If this were true, only clouds situated at, or extending to, heights with temperature below freezing could produce precipitation. However, copious rain often falls from cumulus clouds, where temperatures at the top are above freezing, so ice crystal growth due to the mixed phase cannot be the only process leading to precipitation. Nevertheless, it is still regarded as an important mechanism, especially for altostratus precipitation.

The circumstances that lead to freezing of small water drops have been studied in laboratory experiments that are by no means concluded. Spontaneous freezing of water has been observed to begin at temperatures below about $-28°F$ ($-33°C$). At $-40°$ (C or F), virtually all water is frozen, though reports persist of aircraft encountering water drops at lower temperatures. Cloud drops usually freeze at much warmer temperatures, and such ice crystals often contain a tiny solid nucleus of about 1 micron in diameter, a *freezing nucleus.* These nuclei have the property of causing any droplet with which they collide to freeze, provided of course that the droplet is cold enough. Some nuclei can cause freezing at $14°F$ ($-10°C$), but they are rare. Often when temperature drops to $-4°F$ ($-20°C$) there are enough "active" nuclei available to cause the cloud to change from water to ice.

Since water drops do occur at very low temperatures, freezing nuclei cannot be as abundant as condensation nuclei. Cloud observation can help one appreciate this fact qualitatively. Just east of the Rocky Mountains, for instance, the cumuli on many days have the "hard" appearance of water clouds. On other days, with the same air mass and winds, virtually all clouds take on the soft milky look of ice-crystal clouds; *virga,* or trails of evaporating precipitation, protrude from many of the clouds, giving the sky a weird appearance.

What is the origin of the freezing nuclei? Some have been

identified as soil particles, others as combustion products. In the lee of the Rockies, solid particles may well initiate the ice phase. A strong west wind over the high plateaus and mountain ranges farther west may whirl up dust and carry it eastward across the continental divide. When this happens, freezing nuclei are abundant; otherwise, they may be scarce. It is difficult, however, to generalize about the origin of nuclei over the earth as a whole, because of its large expanse of water. Particles from dust storms and volcanic eruptions have been tracked across whole oceans, but such long journeys do not often occur. Further, winds often carry freezing nuclei in the upper troposphere at altitudes of 30,000 to 40,000 ft (9 to 12 km), where cirrus clouds form. It is not easy to explain how the nuclei get there from the ground. In the face of such difficult questions it has even been proposed that cosmic dust from meteor showers is a possible source of freezing nuclei.

ARTIFICIAL MODIFICATION OF CLOUDS

The scarcity of freezing nuclei, well recognized in the 1930s, led researchers to speculate about introducing nuclei into clouds. In 1946, Irving Langmuir and Vincent Schaefer performed the first conclusive experiment. They dropped dry ice from an airplane into supercooled stratus over New England. Within minutes, a hole developed in the "seeded" portion of the cloud (Fig. 5.1). Dry ice pellets produce extreme local cooling in the area through which they fall. Presumably, the temperature of part of the water drops was depressed below −40°; the drops then froze, started to fall, and grew, first through the mixed-phase process and then by accretion. Falling out as snow, the crystals evaporated below cloud base.

Search for freezing nuclei disclosed that the particles of silver iodide smoke, because of their structure, act as freezing nuclei at temperatures as high as 21°F (−6°C). This activation temperature is higher than that of most natural freezing nuclei found in air; thus the mixed phase can be initiated in growing clouds much sooner than it occurs naturally. Further, silver iodide does not require an airplane for delivery into clouds; it may be introduced

Fig. 5.1 Effect produced by seeding stratus clouds over New England with dry ice. Hole developed over entire affected area within 1 hr. (Courtesy Dr. Vincent J. Schaefer.)

from the ground, provided the air is ascending. For these reasons, silver iodide has become a favorite tool in cloud-seeding experiments. Of course, it can also be dispersed from burners in aircraft; canisters have been developed which, released near cloud top, will fall through clouds of great vertical extent in perhaps a minute, seeding them in depth.

Water clouds have been successfully transformed into ice-crystal clouds many times. One August day, the author witnessed a conclusive demonstration by Vincent Schaefer in the mountains of western Montana. With numerous cumuli based near freezing, and with natural nuclei count near zero, Schaefer introduced silver iodide smoke at a high point along a mountain range, where cloud-forming updrafts could be expected to develop. The wind blew across the range, so that clouds developing from the updrafts were clearly visible over the broad valley downstream. Monitoring the experiment from an airplane of the U.S. Forest Service, the author inspected several thousand cumuli during a 2-hr flight in the operating area and over adjoining valleys. All of these had the hard configuration of water clouds; only downwind from the operating site did the clouds develop the fuzzy appearance of ice clouds.

Schaefer's experiment can be useful for airport operation. During radiation fog, the acceptance rate of aircraft will be very low; in dense fog, the airport must be closed. However, if winds are light and the fog occurs at temperatures below about 23°F (-5°C), silver iodide seeding may clear away the fog sufficiently to permit the airport to remain open. This scheme will not work, of course, during advection fog, when the wind constantly and rapidly transports new droplets over the airport.

Hopes for cloud seeding extend far beyond this one limited application. If the mixed-phase process could be started, a chain reaction might follow which could increase precipitation. The addition of even a small amount of precipitation would benefit not only arid regions, but also such areas as the Eastern United States, where droughts lasting several months sometimes occur. Experiments near Sydney, Australia, in 1947 first succeeded in stimulating the growth of several towering cumuli to cumulonimbi. In the summer of 1963, several similar experiments over the Caribbean produced such growth. The clouds began rising very quickly a few minutes after seeding, suppressing smaller clouds around them and producing heavy rain (Fig. 5.2). Conversion of liquid water to ice in the upper cloud portion is thought to have started the growth. During this change of phase, a quantity of heat, about 13 per cent of the heat of condensation, is released to the atmosphere; it is known as the *latent heat of fusion*. In marginal situations, when the buoyancy of a cloud is just balanced by the drag of the environment, this small increase may be enough to revitalize the upthrust.

Aims in weather modification have ranged from the modest

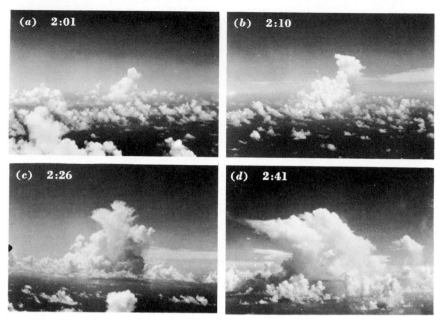

Fig. 5.2   Effect produced by seeding a cumulus cloud with silver iodide over the Caribbean Sea on August 20, 1963, in depth from U.S. Navy plane using device developed by Pierre St. Amand. Upper left shows cloud at time of seeding; it was 18,000 ft tall, top at 20,000 ft. In the next half-hour cloud grew to about twice this size, became full of ice and leaned eastward in its upper portions. Pictures are reproduced from viewpoint of observer looking toward south. (Courtesy Drs. Joanne S. Malkus and Robert H. Simpson.)

one of transforming individual clouds, to the possibility of influencing large middle-latitude cyclones and even world weather. If objectives are chosen reasonably, cloud modification may make a contribution to human welfare. The general circulation forces air currents to cross mountain ranges. On the windward side, the upward motion persistently produces clouds; this is a natural setting for experiments. The Colorado Rockies may serve as illustration. Oriented approximately north-south, the mountain chains lie perpendicular to the prevailing west wind. In winter, stratus clouds and, occasionally, cumuli are banked along the windward side at temperatures of 14°F (−10°C) and lower. When cyclones and troughs in the upper air pass (Chapter 7), heavy snowfall occurs.

But this happens normally on just a few days of the winter season. On 80 to 100 other days, the clouds, composed of water drops, form on the windward side and dissipate in downdrafts on the lee side, yielding little or no precipitation. The background count of natural nuclei is very low. If cloud seeding produced an average of only 0.05 in. of water on these days, the increase in seasonal precipitation would add a sizable fraction to the average winter precipitation because of the large number of days involved.

FORMS OF PRECIPITATION

The meteorologist makes an emphatic distinction between *rain* and *rain showers.* Cumulus clouds produce showers; these last a short time only, usually minutes, but the rainfall rate is heavy. A large fraction of this rain runs off into rivers; soil cannot accept water at precipitation rates which often exceed 1 in. per hr.

Steady *rain* is derived mainly from altostratus clouds associated with middle-latitude cyclones. If the mixed-phase process initiates the rain, the ice crystals melt before they reach the ground. Rain usually persists for several hours, sometimes for a day. The precipitation rate is low or moderate, perhaps 0.05 in. per hr, assuring maximum opportunity for the water to sink into the soil.

In winter, when temperatures are below freezing in the whole atmosphere, the ice crystals falling from altostratus do not melt. They reach the ground as *snow*, the wintertime counterpart of rain. The flakes form by coagulation of many crystals. *Snow showers* also occur, mainly to the rear of cold fronts.

Dangerous weather develops when raindrops or melted snowflakes fall through a layer with temperatures below freezing (Fig. 5.3). The drops then refreeze to form solid globes of ice, usually transparent. They are called *ice pellets, sleet,* and *grains of ice.*[1] Often they are not solidly frozen when they reach the ground. Interspersed, moreover, are drops that have barely started to freeze or that consist entirely of water. This mixture is *freezing rain,* a disastrous form of precipitation. When it strikes cold ground, it freezes to form a solid sheet of ice called *glaze.* Winter ice storms

[1] The meaning of these terms is not identical in all countries.

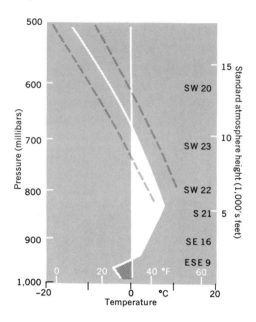

Fig. 5.3 Temperature-height sounding at Albany, New York, on January 6, 1962, showing atmospheric structure conducive to freezing rain. See Figs. 7.9 to 7.11 for general weather situation. Top of warm front is near 830 millibars (5,500 ft). In the warm air above the front, the sounding parallels the temperature-height curve of ascending saturated air (dashed curves). Wind directions and speeds (knots) indicated on right, showing turning of wind with height from lower cold to upper warm air through the front. The vertical line is for 0°C (32°F) and the shading shows the layers where the air is warmer or colder than freezing.

can break transmission lines and heavily damage forests and orchards by denuding trees of their branches with the weight of the ice.

Snow pellets, also known as *soft hail* or *graupel,* fall in showers from cumuli. Such showers develop regularly in the high mountains during summer, because temperatures are cold enough so that the pellets reach the ground before melting. Often they precede and accompany mountain thunderstorms. The pellets have circular or conical shape and consist of whitish ice particles formed when supercooled water drops coalesce with falling ice crystals.

Ice needles are long thin crystals forming on very cold winter days through *sublimation,* direct transition from vapor to ice. Floating leisurely in the air, they provide a magnificent spectacle when the sun is shining on them.

Drizzle is a type of rain consisting of many very small particles with diameters of less than 500 microns, as defined earlier in this chapter; it yields only traces or minute amounts of water. Drizzle forms in very low clouds with high water content but not subject to much, if any, lifting. Cloud base is not higher than a few hundred feet. Relative humidity in the shallow layer below cloud base is near 100 per cent, and this prevents the small drops from evaporating on their short journey from cloud base to ground. *Snow grains* are the frozen counterpart of drizzle.

THUNDERSTORMS

Lightning and Thunder. The problem of the origin of the lightning discharge has not been fully solved. However, lightning is thought to be part of a mechanism by which an electric current is conducted from earth to ionosphere. Normally—that is, during fair weather—the atmosphere conducts a current from the positively charged ionosphere to the ground, which carries a negative charge. This leakage would wipe out the earth's charge in about 10 min, unless a return or supply current from earth to ionosphere constantly restored the prevailing charge distribution. Observations of the electrical potential gradient between the earth and the ionosphere, made at widely different locations, have shown that this gradient varies daily in its intensity, reaching a peak simultaneously over the whole earth. This peak—referred to Greenwich Mean Time (GMT), which is the *local* time at longitude 0°—occurs during afternoon and early evening. But this is precisely the time that thunderstorm activity is greatest over the earth as a whole, because of afternoon maxima over equatorial Africa and South America.[2] The correlation suggests that thunderstorms may furnish the mechanism for the return current. If so, the potential gradient would be largest when thunderstorm activity is greatest. Because the earth and the ionosphere are both conductors, the peak occurs all over the earth simultaneously, irrespective of local time.

In order to provide an effective mechanism for the return current, a charge separation must take place inside the thunderstorm cloud. If the distribution of charge sketched in Fig. 5.4 is valid, a positive current can flow from the ground to the lower cloud

[2] Local time in Africa is 0 to 2 hr ahead of Greenwich and 3 to 5 hr later in South America. Afternoon thunderstorm maxima over these continents, in terms of local time there, will show up as a broad peak over 6 to 8 hr in terms of GMT.

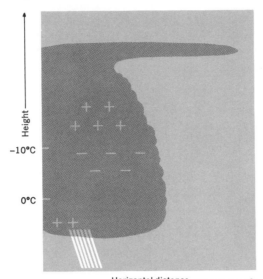

Fig. 5.4   Model of charge separation in thunder-storms acting as means for restoration of the earth's normal electric charge.

portions, partly through negatively charged lightning strokes from cloud to earth. Positive current will also flow from the upper cloud portion to the ionosphere. The charge separation is known to exist; the circumstances that produce it, however, have not been fully explored. A cloud with high liquid water content in its lower portion, and possibly with ice in the upper parts, provides a favorable setting. The average strength of the supply current from earth to ionosphere per thunderstorm and the average number of thunderstorms in progress over the globe at each instant—about three thousand when averaged over 24 hr—suffice to maintain the "fair weather" electrical field, according to the best estimates.

A lightning stroke heats the air along its path to as much as 18,000°F (10,000°C). Tremendous expansion of the air column follows, sending a vibrating pressure wave outward. This wave, moving at almost 1,000 ft per sec (300 m per sec), that is, at the speed of sound, makes the noise known as thunder. We can compute the distance of the lightning by measuring the number of seconds between the time when the lightning flash is seen and the time when the thunder is heard, at least up to 10 sec, which indicates a distance of 2 miles (3 km). At greater distances the sound may become refracted, so that it will be difficult to associate thunder-claps correctly with lightning strokes.

Updrafts and Downdrafts. The thunderstorm cloud is the cumulonimbus, which often extends to the tropopause. Cumulonimbi have a duration of at least 1 hr compared to 10 to 15 min for the smaller cumuli. Some thunderstorm cloud conglomerations with diameters as large as 30 miles have been tracked for a number of hours. The term "conglomeration" is appropriate: a cloud mass so large contains several updraft areas which, after some minutes, are replaced by others, all within the same massive envelope.

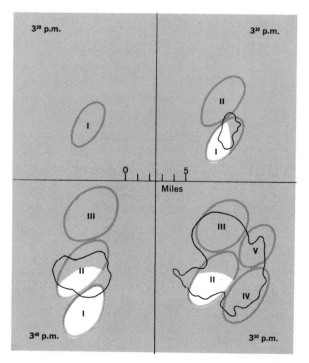

Fig. 5.5 Development of thunderstorm during afternoon of August 6, 1947, in Ohio. Cells are identified with roman numerals. Unshaded: updraft; white: downdraft. Irregular black curve outlines boundary of radar echo. (From The Thunderstorm, *courtesy H. R. Byers.)*

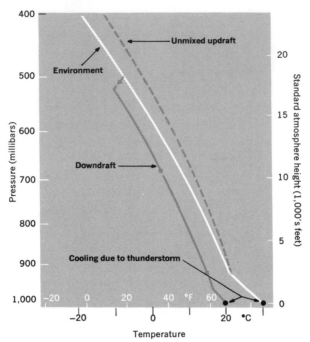

Fig. 5.6 Illustrating development of up- and down-drafts in thunderstorm. For details see text.

Shifting of active centers can be observed clearly at night from an airplane. There is hardly a finer weather sight than that enjoyed while traveling in quiet air under a starry sky beside a boiling thunderstorm mass and watching the lightning illuminate first one set of turrets, then another set in a different part of the huge, dark thunderstorm cloud. Some sections of this cloud suddenly come to life, while in others the lightning display dies out.

As the nighttime spectacle suggests, the updraft cells in a thunderstorm, which may be several miles in extent, go through a life cycle. Downdrafts develop, often violent ones, carrying the condensation product to the ground. After some minutes, the downdrafts encompass the whole cell, which then dies. A large thunderstorm can be expected to possess cells in various stages of the life cycle (Fig. 5.5).

To picture how the downdraft begins, consider a mass of

water or of water and ice mixed, carried upward in an updraft and then falling out into nearby air whose temperature is typical of the thunderstorm's environment (Fig. 5.6). The condensate evaporates into this unsaturated air, which cools, acquires negative buoyancy, and starts to sink. As long as water drops with sufficiently high vapor pressure are in the downdraft, the air will follow the path marked with the downward arrow in Fig. 5.6. In a typical summer situation, the downdraft air will arrive at the surface with relatively very cold temperatures of about 68°F (20°C). The drag of the falling rain also accelerates the downdraft.

Surface Weather. When it reaches the ground, the cold air spreads out on all sides, most rapidly in the direction toward which the thunderstorm is moving. At the approach of the cold mass the wind dies out, and the barometer, which usually has been falling slowly, levels off. Then a dark line of very low clouds approaches rapidly, often whirling up dust along its front. The wind shifts and begins to blow with gusts of 40 mph and more from the direction of the thunderstorm. Temperature falls suddenly by some 18°F (10°C) relieving the heat; the barometer starts to rise in jerks.

All this may happen a few minutes before the main thundercloud arrives overhead, carrying heavy rain. The extreme precipitation seldom lasts more than half an hour. But in that short time ½ to 1½ in. of rain may fall, with local flooding and runoff of most water.

Squall Lines. From time to time, most often in spring and early summer, thunderstorm cells form a line which can be as long as several hundred miles (or km), usually oriented north-south or northeast-southwest (Figs. 5.7 and 5.8). The line may persist for 6 to 18 hr; normally it travels toward the east. There is a large difference between an isolated thunderstorm on a hot afternoon and thunderstorms along a *squall line*. The latter tend to be much more severe. A *mammatus* sky often precedes a squall line—a dark overcast, usually of middle clouds, with downward bulging protuberances, or pouches. Virtually incessant lightning marks the arrival of the squall line. Winds become very strong and may attain hurricane force, with gusts to as much as 100 mph.

Squall lines sometimes are forerunners of cold fronts (Fig.

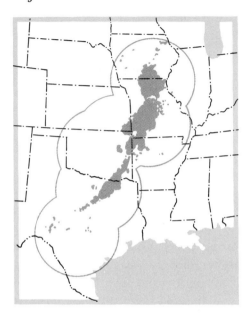

Fig. 5.7 Radar echo show-
ing squall line of 1,000-mile
length in Midwestern United
States on September 30, 1954.
The observations from five
radar sets were used to prepare this photo. (From S. G.
Bigler, in American Meteorological Society Monograph
No. 14, vol. 2. Photo courtesy
Dave Atlas, Air Force Cambridge Research Laboratory.)

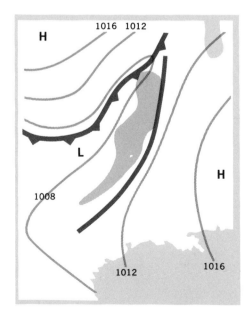

Fig. 5.8 Surface map on
September 30, 1954, show-
ing the radar observations in
relation to surface fronts and
isobars. Widespread thun-
derstorms were reported
throughout the area occu-
pied by the radar echo.
Heavy solid line denotes forward edge of squall.

5.8), and they then appear in the general setting of a traveling cyclone. While the lines often move more or less with the mean wind between 10,000 and 30,000 ft height (3 to 9 km), the author also has seen them develop in Minnesota and Wisconsin and travel from there on a wide clockwise arc to Florida, in the course of 18 hr, with the 40,000-ft (12-km) winds. Much remains to be learned about the squall lines, which are often referred to as *mesoscale* disturbances, because their size is between that of individual cloud masses and that of cyclones extending a thousand miles.

HAIL

Cumulonimbus, with its mixed phase and high liquid water content, is the only cloud which produces hail. Thunderstorms provide the setting for severe hail. Over many areas, for instance above the high plains east of the Rockies, hail shafts occur often without visible electrical activity.

The size of hailstones varies from a fraction of an inch to several inches in diameter. At Denver, Colorado, stones of about

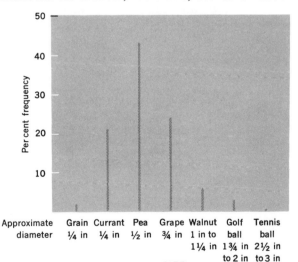

Fig. 5.9   Size distribution of hailstones at Denver, Colorado. (From W. B. Beckwith, United Airlines, Inc., in Physics of Precipitation, *American Geophysical Union Monograph No. 5.)*

½ in. predominate (Fig. 5.9), but 10 per cent have a diameter of more than an inch. Under the impact of hailstones, fields may be completely denuded in a narrow strip along the path of a hailstorm. Preferred *hail streets* exist near mountainous regions. Along these streets, channeled by the topography, hailstorms form and travel again and again.

Upon dissection, a large hailstone is found to consist of a series of more or less concentric shells around a central nucleus, which often is an ice pellet (Fig. 5.10). This evidence suggests that hailstones are often picked up by successive updrafts strong enough to support the stone against the acceleration due to the force of gravity. The raindrops ascend rapidly compared with the stone, which may just hold a constant altitude. Many collisions between stone and raindrops may occur in perhaps just a few seconds. As the stone passes through successive updrafts, perhaps also downdrafts, and through large temperature changes, the water evidently does not freeze all at once. This may account for the ring shape of many large stones and the layers of water between shells of ice.

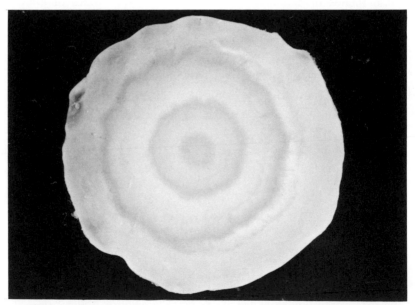

Fig. 5.10   Hailstone section showing growth in layers. Width of hailstone was nearly 3 in. (Courtesy R. A. Schleusener, Colorado State University.)

Hail is most frequent in spring and early summer, and in the afternoon (Figs. 5.11 and 5.12), when the temperature lapse rate of the air and the buoyancy of cumulus updrafts are largest. The regional distribution of hail is not readily explained. In the United States, hail days are most numerous about 100 miles (160 km) east of the continental divide of the Rocky Mountains. There, on the average, 6 to 8 days with hail occur per year at individual locations. Considering, however, a square with side of 50 to 75 miles (80 to 120 km) in northeastern Colorado, the number goes up to 20 to 30 days with hail, which causes anxiety to the farmers in the whole area. This is a semiarid region with mean annual precipitation near 15 in., mostly derived from spring and early summer rains. Precipitation and the number of days with hail are well correlated (Fig. 5.13). It is a mixed blessing when hail may accompany the urgently needed precipitation! In the Eastern and Southern United States, where heavy rain and thunderstorms occur more often, hail is much rarer.

Numerous attempts have been made to prevent hailstorms through silver iodide seeding. If enough freezing nuclei could be injected into cumuli in their early stages, it might be possible to prevent a huge mass of supercooled water from accumulating,

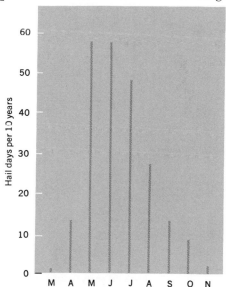

Fig. 5.11 Seasonal course of hailstorm frequency at Denver, Colorado, showing concentration in spring and early summer when temperature lapse rates are largest. (From W. B. Beckwith.)

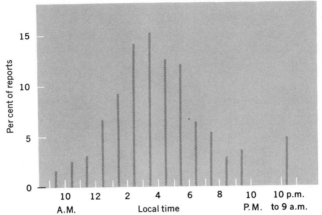

Fig. 5.12 Distribution of hail incidence over the hours of the day. (From W. B. Beckwith.)

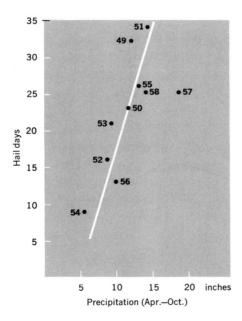

Fig. 5.13 Scatter diagram of precipitation from April to October against number of days with hail in these months for the indicated years at Denver, Colorado. (From W. B. Beckwith.)

thereby destroying a necessary condition for the growth of hail-stones. In Italy and other countries, rockets with loads of freezing nuclei have been fired into cumulonimbi. It has also been argued that shock waves generated by rocket detonation break up hail-stones, so that they reach the ground in fractured, mushy form, doing little damage. But the evidence in support of these claims is con-flicting. Chances for success of hail prevention will improve when the hail-forming processes are better understood.

TORNADOES

The most destructive storm in the atmosphere, the tornado, is a small funnel with winds up to several hundred mph revolving tightly around the core. Tornadoes travel along paths with lengths ranging from very short distances to 50 miles (80 km) and more (Fig. 5.14). The width of the area sustaining damage may be no more than a few city blocks. On most long paths the funnel strikes the ground several times, rising after impacts a few miles long; probably, a succession of new funnels forms.

Most information on tornadoes comes from inspection of the damage. No meteorological installation has been built which is able to withstand tornadoes; nor would it be worthwhile to build one that could, since the probability of a tornado's passing over it is vanishingly small. We are still awaiting the occasion when

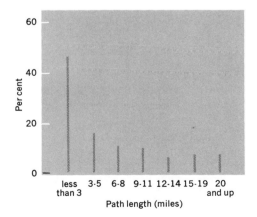

Fig. 5.14 Frequency distribution of the path length of tornadoes on the ground. (After L. J. Battan, University of Arizona.)

a tornado passes over a house with a barometer in the storm cellar. This barometer, from all estimates, must be capable of measuring pressure drops of $\frac{1}{10}$ to $\frac{3}{10}$ atm. Evidence from damage suggests that the destruction of buildings arises as much from explosion when the outside pressure drops suddenly as from violent wind. The wisest course, contrary to one's natural inclination, would be to open doors and windows wide if a tornado were imminent.

A mammatus sky—one with many dark bags hanging down from cloud base—often gives warning of impending tornado formation; it is therefore also known as a tornado sky. Typically, the funnel first appears near cloud base and then elongates downward (Fig. 5.15). Presumably it becomes visible when condensation begins in the air that is subject to sudden lowering of pressure and expansion cooling. After the funnel strikes the ground, it is blackened by soil and debris drawn into it and whirled upward. This movement of debris furnishes the only evidence of vertical motion in the tornado; it is, however, conclusive. Over water surfaces, dense spray is drawn upward in *water spouts.*

Tornadoes and water spouts need by no means be associated

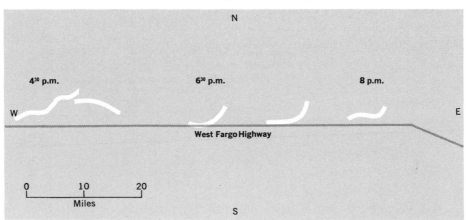

Fig. 5.15 *The Fargo, North Dakota, tornadoes of June 20, 1957. Above: path taken by five tornadoes on the ground between 4:30 and 8:05 P.M. on that day. The squall giving rise to the successive tornadoes traveled eastward at 17 mph. (From T. J. Fujita.) Opposite page: Five photos showing formation of tornado from low dark cloud inside 1 min. Lower right: another view of the tornado near Fargo; note the very low cloud base. (Courtesy T. J. Fujita and the North Dakota photographers Harry Jennings and Chet Gebert).*

only with the fiercest of cumulonimbus clouds. The author recalls one afternoon on the island of Guam in the tropical Pacific Ocean, when a tennis game was in progress on a court not far from shore. Three trade cumuli, with tops not higher than 12,000 ft (3,600 m), were on the ocean side of the shore, each with a water spout. The author missed a few balls while he kept an anxious eye on the three funnels. They persisted for about 10 min, stationary; then they gradually dissipated.

Tornado Warnings. Each year, a large number of tornadoes form over the United States. On the average, the number reported is about 200; undoubtedly, the actual number of funnels is much greater. The Midwestern and Western plains states are visited by more severe tornadoes than any other area on earth. They often occur along squall lines that precede cold fronts from the west or northwest. Through recognizing the general weather setting, and special temperature and moisture distributions in the upper air, the Weather Bureau is able to locate areas where the chance of tornado occurrence is highest and issue a forecast specifying the endangered areas and probable time of occurrence. Essentially this is an alert, often issued during the forenoon of the day when tornadoes are expected. Perhaps one-millionth of the warning area will actually experience a tornado.

The prediction is very useful in keeping people watching the sky and monitoring public warning broadcasts. Large radar sets, capable of tracking cumulonimbi as far as 200 miles (300 km) from the radar site, scan over most of the Midwest. The formation of a tornado can often be detected when a hook-shaped echo appears on the edge of a major storm cell (Fig. 5.16). As soon as this happens, very specific warnings can be broadcast. Tornadoes travel predominantly from the southwest or west with a speed of displacement of 20 to 30 mph; that is, they move with the upper winds in their vicinity. By knowing these winds, the most probable tornado path can be estimated. Random turnings, however, must also be expected, as the track of the tornado that crossed Fargo, North Dakota, in 1957 demonstrates (Fig. 5.15). Thus the immediate and urgent warning area is fan-shaped downwind from the spot where the tornado has been located.

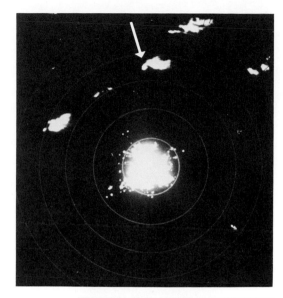

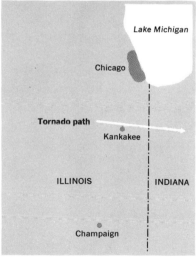

Fig. 5.16 Top: *Radar photo taken about 4 P.M. on April 17, 1963, looking northward toward tornado from Champaign, Illinois. Circles give distances at 20-mile intervals; arrow points to the hook of the echo where the tornado is thought to have been situated. (Courtesy Glenn E. Stout, Illinois State Water Survey.) Bottom: Map showing path of tornado; the distance between Champaign and tornado is 70 miles (After T. J. Fujita.)*

6

Large-scale Motion

SCALES OF MOTION

The height of the troposphere is about 6 miles (10 km), which is $\frac{1}{1,000}$ of the pole-to-equator distance. Horizontal motion must therefore predominate over vertical motion in wind systems on the scale of cyclones and the general circulation, which cover distances from 1,000 to 6,000 miles (1,600 to 10,000 km). For such systems the troposphere may be pictured as a very thin shell. The typical horizontal wind speed is 20 knots (10 m per sec), or a thousand times greater than the typical vertical speed of ½ mile per day (1 cm per sec) in cyclones.

Of course, not all air motion occurs on so large a scale that the picture of the atmosphere as a thin shell is useful. Thunderstorms are about as tall as they are wide or long; they resemble a cube, if anything. Vertical and horizontal speeds in thunderstorms differ by a factor of less than 10, which indicates considerable freedom for the air to move up or down. In these clouds, air may ascend from bottom to top of the troposphere in half an hour or an hour; an observer on the ground can watch this ascent as it takes place. Even in the tornado, with its exceptional speeds of rotation, the vertical motion, deduced from the speed of debris, attains at least $\frac{1}{10}$ of the rotational motion.

In large-scale motion, air may need days, even weeks, to cover several miles vertically while traveling horizontally across an ocean or around the whole hemisphere. As Chapters 1 and 4 showed, the condensation process, especially in tropical cumuli, largely shapes the vertical temperature structure of the atmosphere. The clouds may live for only half an hour, but the temperature lapse rate, which they create, remains. As soon as the cumuli die out, the temperature structure resists up and down motions. The atmosphere is then thermally *stable,* and this stability is one major factor that confines the air to nearly horizontal motion.

Because horizontal motion predominates in large-scale weather systems, we shall first examine the forces acting in the horizontal plane. Later the associated vertical motions will be included; though small, they are important for weather and for the energy of the winds.

FORCES IN HORIZONTAL MOTION

In principle, Newton's second law of motion holds: The acceleration of a given mass is equal to and in the same direction as the net force exerted on it. The two forces accelerating horizontal air motion are the pressure force and the frictional force. Above the lowest 2,000 ft (600 m), friction is normally small compared to the pressure force and, for the present discussion, may be omitted. The pressure force acts in the horizontal direction in the same way as shown in Fig. 3.1 for the vertical direction. A mass of air, subjected to higher pressure against it on one side than on the other, experiences a net pressure force accelerating it toward the lower pressure.[1]

The acceleration is that of the total air movement as it would be seen by an observer looking toward the earth from a distant point. This motion includes the wind—the travel of air across the face of the earth—and the movement of the earth itself. Only when this total, or absolute, motion is considered, can Newton's law be applied directly to the atmosphere. It is cumbersome and impractical, although possible, to take up this distant position. The earth's movement about its axis is huge compared to wind speed. At latitude 40° it is 770 mph. Adding a wind of 25 mph, the absolute speed is 795 mph. We are interested only in the small portion of this velocity—the wind.

A more satisfactory picture would be obtained if air motion could be analyzed from the viewpoint of a person standing still on the earth's surface. If that is done, however, Newton's law no longer holds without modification. It is necessary to take account of the fact that the observer is rotating with the earth.

Deflecting Force of the Earth's Rotation. Figure 6.1 shows the United States in relation to the earth's axis. As the hours of the day pass, the country travels eastward around the axis, rotating counterclockwise as seen from the north. Consider a particle of air well above the ground at 40°N, 90°W, which has a west wind speed of, perhaps, 100 mph. If we assume that no horizontal pressure force is acting (which there always is in reality), the particle will continue

---

[1] A chart on which pressures have been plotted and *isobars,* or lines of equal pressure, drawn shows the distribution of the pressure force (Figs. 6.13 and 7.8). The more closely the lines are spaced, the larger is the pressure differential over a given distance perpendicular to the isobars, and the stronger the pressure force. It is also possible to determine the pressure force from the slope of a surface on which pressure is constant. When this is done, the contours, or lines of constant height of this surface, take the place of the isobars. The pressure force is normal to the contours and increases as the slope of the surface increases, indicated by closer spacing of the contours. This method of representing pressure force—first instituted to meet aviation needs—has been adopted by all countries to depict flow in the upper air, and this book follows the established custom.

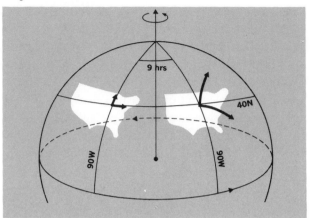

Fig. 6.1 Surface of the earth showing the rotation of the United States around the earth's axis during 9 hr. If no forces were acting, the air blowing from west or south initially at 40°N, 90°W will be moving 9 hr later from northwest or southwest as indicated, demonstrating the right deflection.

on a straight path in space, while the earth below it turns. The rotation of the country underneath is in no way communicated to it. However, an observer on the ground, unaware that it is *he* who is turning, thinks that the air has been deflected to the right from its starting direction—which it has, from *his* viewpoint on the rotating sphere. He will make the same "mistake" whatever the initial wind direction. The wind will always appear to have been deflected to the right of the initial direction (left in the Southern Hemisphere).

The observer may conclude that the deflection to the right has been brought about by a force acting to the right of the wind. In the nineteenth century the French physicist Coriolis formalized this concept of a force caused by the earth's rotation, later called the *Coriolis force*. This concept permits us to discuss the motions in atmosphere and ocean, as well as the path of projectiles and the meander of rivers, from the viewpoint of a fixed position on the earth's surface.

The magnitude of this "force" depends partly on the speed of the wind and partly on the inclination of the earth's surface with

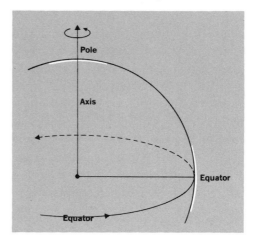

Fig. 6.2 *Surface of the earth showing change in inclination of the earth's surface with respect to the earth's axis from pole to equator. The surface is perpendicular to the axis at the pole and parallel at the equator. A person standing near the pole turns around on his heels once in 24 hr, while a person on the equator makes one somersault in space.*

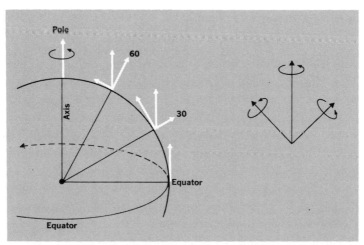

Fig. 6.3 *Rotation of the earth's axis and change in the perpendicular and parallel components of this rotation on the earth's surface with latitude. Insert diagram shows sense of rotation about arrows.*

respect to the earth's axis. An area of earth's surface close to the pole will rotate nearly *perpendicular* to the axis and therefore turn around completely once in 24 hr (Fig. 6.2). A surface area at the equator, however, is situated *parallel* to the axis. While this area *revolves* around the axis, it does not *rotate* in the plane perpendicular to the axis. The observer on the ground, viewing air motion from the west, will not have the impression that the direction of the wind movement is changing with time, because he himself is not turning. At the equator the deflecting force vanishes.

We can illustrate this difference further by dividing the earth's rotation into its parts or components which act parallel or perpendicular to the earth's surface (Fig. 6.3). The direction of rotation about the arrows (vectors) is depicted in the small diagram. At the pole, the entire rotation takes place in the plane parallel to the earth's surface. At latitude 60°, the earth's surface is turned away from the earth's axis only slightly, so that there is little change; at latitude 30° the component of rotation acting parallel to the earth's surface is only half as large as it is at the pole. At the equator, the whole rotation takes place in the plane perpendicular to the earth's surface.

GEOSTROPHIC MOTION

The outstanding fact about the large-scale upper-air flow in middle latitudes is that by and large it moves from west to east around the globe (Fig. 1.9). Balloons sent up over Japan to drift with the air currents at 30,000 to 40,000 ft (9 to 12 km) have arrived over North America and later over Europe. Therefore, the air carrying the balloons did move so that it essentially rotated about the earth's axis in the same direction as the earth's surface in middle latitudes does. This actual motion is quite different from that just described, where the air always keeps turning to the right of an observer on the ground, unaware of the turning of the earth underneath. Clearly, a link exists which constrains the air to take part in the rotation of the earth. The pressure force provides this link.

We shall examine the large-scale motion that is initiated after a north-south pressure difference has developed. This is not a very

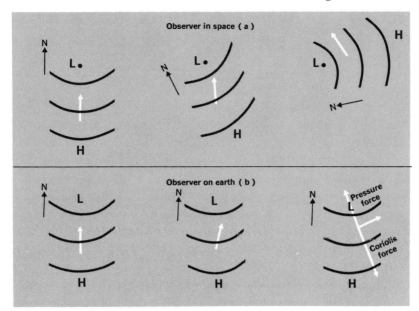

Fig. 6.4 Illustrating development of geostrophic wind. L and H denote low- and high-pressure areas. The solid curving lines are isobars; in this case they are drawn parallel to the latitude circles. The arrows give the position and direction of motion of the air particle followed as seen (a) by an observer looking to earth from a distant star and (b) as seen by an observer standing in a fixed position on earth. Local north denoted by N.

realistic case, but it illustrates the relation between the pressure and Coriolis forces.

In a non-rotating gas or fluid the mass would be accelerated directly from high to low pressure. On the rotating earth, the air also starts off toward low pressure; but it cannot get there directly because the pressure field rotates along with the earth. An observer at a distant point will see the events sketched in Fig. 6.4a. The air starts out along a straight path in space. However, as the pressure field rotates, the air is continuously accelerated toward the changing position where the low pressure is situated. The air path turns, seeking to maintain its direction toward low pressure, After some time, however, the air may no longer approach the low pressure, but move around it parallel to the isobars.

The observer on the ground sees the history of events quite

differently. From his viewpoint (Fig. 6.4*b*) the pressure field remains in the same position while the air, initially traveling toward north, is deflected to the east by the earth's rotation. The important result, of course, remains the same: the air may eventually travel from west parallel to the isobars. If this happens, the pressure force has exactly the strength needed to counteract fully the right deflection due to the Coriolis force. The direction of the wind in space will change so that its direction with respect to the earth becomes constant—for instance southerly. Since the air now turns as if it were part of the earth, its motion has been named *geostrophic,* or earth-turning, motion.

The observer on the ground feels, and justly so, that geostrophic motion represents a balance of forces in his reference frame, which rotates with the earth (right-hand diagram in Fig. 6.4*b*). The air travels instantaneously on a straight path on earth, and, since it no longer moves toward lower pressure, its speed is constant. We are interested in this rather curious earth-turning wind only because it approximates the actual wind very well indeed, except in the equatorial zone, where the Coriolis force vanishes. In Fig. 6.4*b,* the lower pressure is always to the left, and the higher pressure to the right, looking downwind; the reverse is true in the Southern Hemisphere. This rule is known as Buys-Ballot's law. In large-scale motion in the free atmosphere, higher pressure is never found to the left of the wind direction (in the Northern Hemisphere). However, as we shall see shortly, the pressure force is not always at exactly right angles to the wind; otherwise cyclones and rainy days could not occur.

Whenever an event occurring in large-scale motion unsettles the geostrophic balance, it does so only temporarily, and soon, usually within 1 or 2 days at most, approximate geostrophic flow is reestablished. This shows that there are constraints on the pressure as well as on the wind field. The only pressure distributions that are observed to persist are those that agree closely with the pressure distribution required for geostrophic flow. The proper conclusion is that pressure and wind fields adjust mutually. Figure 6.5, for instance, is a typical sample of wind observations in relation to the pressure field, or, more specifically, in relation to the height distribution of the 500-millibar surface. This, as the footnote earlier in this chapter explains, is an alternate way of depicting the pressure force. We see that over the Western United States, the winds are relatively weak and the contours widely spaced. In the east, the contours are closely spaced, denoting a large slope and a strong pressure force, and wind speed is much stronger than in the west. Everywhere, the wind direction nearly parallels the direction of the contours, so that the lesser height (or pressure) is to the left, the greater height (or pressure) to the right of the wind, looking downstream. To be sure, wind direction changes over the map. But the

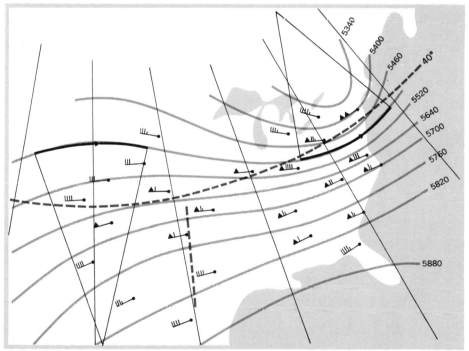

Fig. 6.5 Winds and contours of the height of the 500-millibar surface (meters) on April 23, 1963. For symbols see Appendix I; the contours indicate the pressure field (see text). Wind direction is nearly parallel to the contours everywhere; wind speed is high, where the contours are closely spaced. The distance from the trough at 75°W to the ridge at 110°W is 35° longitude; the whole wavelength therefore is 70° longitude. The curves drawn at trough and ridge show the vorticity of the air relative to the indicated centers of rotation.

turning is slow and smooth; we do not see many small eddies where wind direction changes drastically and reverses completely in very short distances.

Variation of Wind with Height. Figure 3.3 showed that the distance between two surfaces of constant pressure decreases as the mean temperature of the layer between them decreases. Since the troposphere is always colder in high than in low latitudes (Fig. 1.11), surfaces of constant pressure located in the high troposphere, such as the 300-millibar surface, slope downward more strongly from the tropics toward the polar regions than do surfaces of constant pressure at lower elevations, as drawn in Fig. 3.3. Consequently, the poleward-directed pressure force increases with height up to the altitude or the pressure at which the temperature becomes constant from equator to pole, 35,000 ft (10,500 m) at latitude 45° in Fig. 1.11. If the wind field is nearly geostrophic, the speed of the west wind must increase with height throughout the atmosphere up to 35,000 ft; then the Coriolis force will increase upward with the pressure force. The close correspondence of the west wind speeds of Fig. 1.10 to the temperature field of Fig. 1.11 shows that this is indeed the case. Further, above 35,000 ft, where the temperature field is reversed, the pressure force decreases upward, and so does the west wind speed.

Although the geostrophic wind closely approximates the observed large-scale flow, it is by no means exact, and cannot be so if there are to be any changes in wind and weather at all. In the remainder of this chapter we shall discuss how small departures from geostrophic balance bring about the weather we experience.

WAVE MOTION

The flow pattern in Fig. 6.5 is wavy; a ridge or crest of the wave overlies the Western United States, and a trough overlies the eastern part of the country. Wave motion is a preferred mode of air flow. For instance, the air situated at 300 millibars above the Russian test site at Novaya Zemlya at the time of large atomic tests in 1961 traveled on a trajectory with four waves around the globe

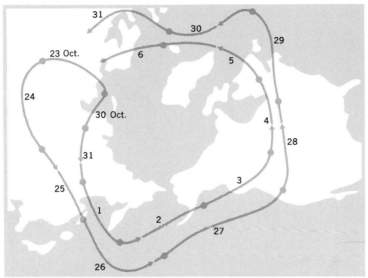

Fig. 6.6 The path of the air located at 300 millibars over Novaya Zemlya at the time of major Russian atomic tests on October 23 and 30, 1961. The trajectories described a circular path with waves; after one week the air was again entering eastern Europe.

(Fig. 6.6); this took a little over a week. Wave patterns, in large measure, govern weather events on time scales ranging from a day to weeks or months.

Our understanding of large-scale wave motion is due mainly to the late Carl-Gustav Rossby. In extended form, his theorems remain the core of our knowledge about such motion and provide a basis for weather prediction by large computers.

Vorticity. Figure 6.3 showed the rotation of the earth's surface about the earth's axis at different latitudes. In addition to this rotation, in which air columns take part when there is no wind, the air may also rotate with respect to the earth's surface. As Fig. 6.5 indicates, the air curves counterclockwise (cyclonic) in the eastern trough and clockwise (anticyclonic) in the western ridge. The sum of the two rotations—that of the surface of the earth about the earth's axis and that of the air flow relative to the earth—is what the observer looking toward earth from a distant star would see.

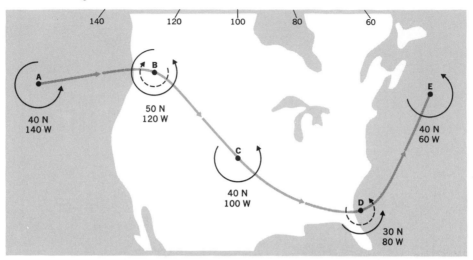

Fig. 6.7   Wave path under conservation of absolute vorticity. The solid arcs show the sense of the earth's rotation and its variation with latitude (qualitatively). The dashed interior arcs show the sense of rotation of the air relative to the earth (length exaggerated).

The combination is known as the absolute rotation or, more customarily, the *absolute vorticity*.[2]

   Conservation of Vorticity. Rossby's proposal is that the air in the upper westerlies conserves its absolute vorticity and that the persistence of waves with a long wavelength, such as shown in Fig. 6.5, can be explained in principle on that basis. The absolute vorticity hypothesis accounts for wavelength and motion of the waves quite well, when no major changes are occurring in the westerly belt.

   Consider Fig. 6.7. If the air moves on a straight path on earth at constant speed from southwest at point A, the motion is then geostrophic, and the air rotates about the earth's axis at the same rate as the earth's surface. This is the vorticity to be con-

   [2] It should be added that wind shear, change of wind speed in the direction perpendicular to the wind, also contributes to rotation, or vorticity. Along the dashed line in Fig. 6.5, wind speed increases from south to north. Air particles in the north overtake those in the south, and this imparts an anticyclonic vorticity to all of the air south of the maximum wind.

served in a broad current without strong shears. Advancing toward the northeast from A, the air current enters an area where the earth's rotation is higher than at A (from Fig. 6.3). In order to conserve the absolute vorticity it had at A, it must start to bend clockwise to offset the increasing vorticity of the earth itself. Ultimately, the southwest flow becomes westerly at point B; there the current no longer advances toward higher latitudes but is turned back toward south.

Now the reverse changes take place. The earth's rotation decreases toward the lower latitudes. Therefore, the clockwise curvature of flow must also decrease if the absolute vorticity is to be conserved. At point C the flow is straight, just as at point A. However, it is now directed from northwest, headed toward still lower latitudes, where the earth's vorticity is less. To compensate, it must acquire a counterclockwise curvature of flow. The decrease in the earth's rotation and the increase in counterclockwise flow keep the absolute vorticity constant.

Again the direction of the current becomes more westerly; at D it reaches its lowest latitude. From there the air turns northward, with decreasing counterclockwise flow curvature as the earth's rotation once more increases. Point E is identical with point A. Thus, a never-ending wave motion may encircle the globe.

Convergence and Divergence. In large measure the preceding discussion explains the existence of long waves in the westerlies, which link together the circulation around the entire Northern or Southern Hemisphere. The number of waves in a westerly belt usually ranges from three to six. On many occasions, however, the steady and coasting wave motion depicted in Fig. 6.7 is altered. For instance, a pattern of widely spaced waves with small north-south extent (or amplitude), as shown in Fig. 9.9, may change to the more closely spaced waves with large amplitude of Fig. 9.10. Such a transition happens when the vorticity of the wavy westerly current does not remain quite constant, but increases or decreases because of *horizontal convergence* or *divergence* of air. We speak of convergence of mass when the horizontal area occupied by a given mass of air decreases (Fig. 6.8); during divergence the area increases.

Since the gases constituting the atmosphere are permanent,

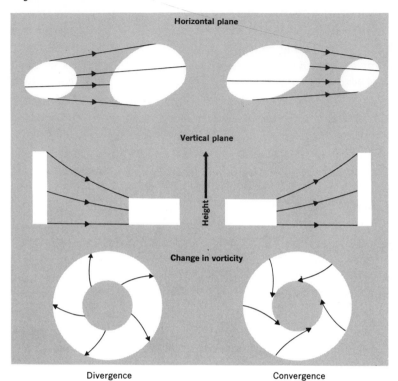

Fig. 6.8 Illustrating mass convergence and divergence in horizontal and vertical planes, and the change in vorticity of the air under the influence of convergence and divergence. In the center diagram, the base of the columns is assumed adjacent to the ground; therefore, the lowest streamlines are horizontal.

the mass of air remains constant. Air converging laterally must spread vertically (Fig. 6.8); with divergence, it expands horizontally and shrinks vertically. The vertical motion must be upward when the layer of convergence adjoins the ground; it must be downward when the flow near the surface diverges.

In large-scale motion, the area over which convergence or divergence takes place has a size of 50,000 to 500,000 sq miles (135,000 to 1,350,000 sq km). The magnitude of the convergence or divergence is such that the resulting vertical displacement has an average speed of about ½ mile per day (1 cm per sec). This, as we saw at the beginning of the chapter, is ¹⁄₁,₀₀₀ of the typical horizontal speed of 20 knots (10 m per sec). Nevertheless, it is these small up and down motions which produce the long-lasting bad weather periods connected with cyclones (Chapter 7).

Modified Vorticity Theorem. Rossby developed a modified form of his vorticity theorem, which takes into account changes of vorticity of an air column due to horizontal convergence or divergence, as depicted in Fig. 6.8. If a chain of particles contracts, its cyclonic circulation relative to the earth will increase, or the anticyclonic circulation decrease, at a constant latitude. During divergence, cyclonic circulation will decrease, or anticyclonic circulation increase (Fig. 6.8).[3] Thus the absolute vorticity of a mass of air increases during convergence and decreases during divergence.

Convergence and divergence can only either *concentrate* or *spread out* vorticity. Vorticity cannot be produced by convergence in a column of air having zero absolute vorticity. Therefore cyclones do not form on the equator; the rotation of the earth—the major part of the absolute vorticity—is zero there, and cyclonic large-scale circulation does not develop when the flow converges.

Suppose now that the air at point A in Fig. 6.7 starts to diverge horizontally. Its motion toward point B must change in such a way that it not only compensates for the increased vorticity of the earth underneath, but also decreases in absolute vorticity. This is accomplished when a column travels on a sharper clockwise bend than in Fig. 6.7. As a result, the column will never reach point B (Fig. 6.9). Turning sharply, it already attains its highest latitude at B' and then starts moving southward. Compared to the constant vorticity path A-B-C, the wavelength is shortened.

Next examine the column moving southeastward from point C in Fig. 6.7, where it may begin to converge. The flow must turn counterclockwise on a curve sufficiently sharp that the increase in cyclonic vorticity relative to the earth more than compensates for the decrease in the earth's vorticity on the path from C to D. The column will not reach point D (Fig. 6.9). Curving counterclockwise more quickly than on the path C-D, it will move from the west at

[3] The same effect can be obtained by rotating a ball on a string. If the string is shortened, the ball rotates faster; if it is lengthened, the rotation is slower.

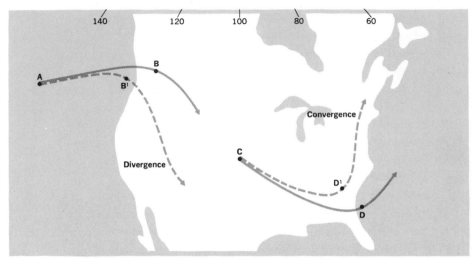

Fig. 6.9 Deflection of the paths of air from the constant vorticity trajectory of Fig. 6.7 because of horizontal divergence and convergence.

D' and then turn northward. Again the wavelength is shorter than it is on the path of constant vorticity.

Depending on the amount of horizontal contraction or spreading, the upper-air wave patterns assume varying wavelengths and north-south extents. This is why we find such a great number of flow configurations on daily weather charts, and so many different weather sequences. The pattern of Fig. 9.9 suggests that the wave motion takes place largely under conservation of vorticity, while convergence and divergence have been active long enough before November 2, 1963, for the pattern of Fig. 9.10 to develop.

STEADY VORTEX MOTION

Close to the surface, where the westerly winds are weak, horizontal convergence sustained for 12 to 24 hr normally leads to the formation of a vortex rotating counterclockwise (Northern Hemisphere); horizontal divergence will result in one rotating clockwise.

In the simplest case, the air circulates around a vortex at constant speed without moving inward or outward. Then the forces are arranged as shown in Fig. 6.10. In a cyclone, the pressure force accelerating the air toward the center is opposed by a weaker Coriolis force acting to the right of the wind, or outward. The difference between these two forces is the net acceleration toward the center—the *centripetal acceleration*. In response to this acceleration, the air curves counterclockwise; the rate of turning is such that it moves in a circle around the center.

In the case of an anticyclone, the pressure force acts outward. The pull to the right of the wind by the Coriolis force must exceed the outward acceleration due to the pressure force if the air is to experience a centripetal acceleration toward the center and move on a circular clockwise path.

Wind computations made from the pressure field on the basis of Fig. 6.10 approximate wind observations close to cyclone and anticyclone centers better than does the geostrophic wind, which does not allow for such curving paths of air on the earth's surface. Therefore we said, when discussing Fig. 6.5, that the flow is only approximately geostrophic. When air passes through troughs and ridges of a wave pattern, it must experience centripetal accelerations; otherwise the wave motion could not occur.

Close to the equator, and in cyclones with very rapid pressure drop toward the interior, the Coriolis force becomes small compared to the pressure force, although steady motion around the center is still possible. Wind speeds computed from the pressure field in

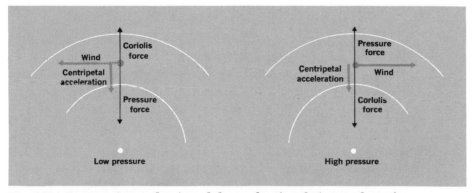

Fig. 6.10   Forces acting on the air, and the acceleration, during steady motion around low-pressure (cyclone) and high-pressure (anticyclone) centers in the Northern Hemisphere.

tropical hurricanes on this assumption agree with observed wind speeds within 10 per cent. However, a balanced anticyclone cannot persist on the equator. When the Coriolis force vanishes, the pressure force, acting alone, accelerates the air outward. High pressure at the earth's surface can be maintained on the equator only by compensating convergence of mass at high levels.[4]

CHANGING WIND SPEED

So far, we have discussed air currents that may curve in various ways while moving at constant speed. Now we shall consider two cases where the wind speed also changes. These cases illustrate the forces operating when important weather changes occur or are initiated. They do not cover all situations; understanding of unsteady motion and the origin and decay of weather systems remains a primary research task of meteorology.

Steady Jet Stream. The first example will be a westerly current with a velocity maximum, or jet-stream core, at its center (Fig. 6.11). The current itself may remain in a steady state; that is, the velocity profile of Fig. 6.11 may not change with time. Air moving toward the core, then, must successively assume the wind speeds shown in the figure. Otherwise, the observed wind distribution would change.

The trajectory in Fig. 6.11 points toward slightly lower pressure. Therefore, pressure and Coriolis forces do not act precisely opposite to each other as they do in the case of fully geostrophic wind. A component of the pressure force acts along the wind direction, and, not opposed by any other force, accelerates the air. When this happens, the Coriolis force increases, and this tends to deflect the air to the right of its direction. If the air is to be held along the direction toward the jet-stream core and higher velocities, the pres-

[4] On the equator the rotation around a low-pressure center can be clockwise or counterclockwise, just as in the well-known example of the bathtub drain. The latter is not affected by the earth's rotation, because the whole event takes place on much too small a time and distance scale. Experiments will show that the vortex revolves in the sense of the rotation which must first be applied to the water if there is to be a vortex at all.

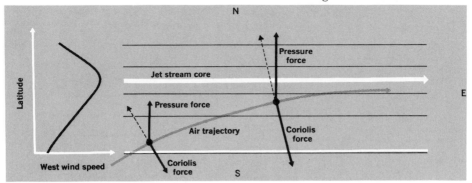

Fig. 6.11 Illustrating forces during acceleration of air into steady jet stream. Dashed: component of pressure force perpendicular to wind and balanced by Coriolis force. Straight black lines are isobars; pressure decreases from south to north across jet stream.

sure force must increase at least as rapidly as the Coriolis force. This is the situation depicted in Fig. 6.11.

Change of Wave Pattern. For the second case let us reexamine the wave pattern of Fig. 6.7, the western portion of which has been drawn again in Fig. 6.12. Frequently, a cyclone develops near point A. If this is a major storm, it may generate strong winds that move forward into the upper ridge, where wind speed increases suddenly. The path on which the air can travel without decelerating curves more gently than that followed previously by air in the ridge. The situation is analogous to that of the driver of an automobile who wishes to turn a corner. The higher the speed of the vehicle, the wider the bend which the driver must follow. If the turn of the road is sharp, the car, at high speed, may not be able to follow it.

This is exactly what happens to the fast air current in the ridge. Unable to make the bend of the isobars (or contours of a constant pressure surface), it advances on a trajectory with less curvature, hence begins to move toward lower pressure. At point *P* in Fig. 6.12 the component of the pressure force perpendicular to the wind is smaller than the Coriolis force; the trajectory is deflected to the right and the air turns clockwise with respect to the earth's surface. At the same time, the component of the pressure force acting *along* the wind accelerates the air; in consequence the wind speed increases even more.

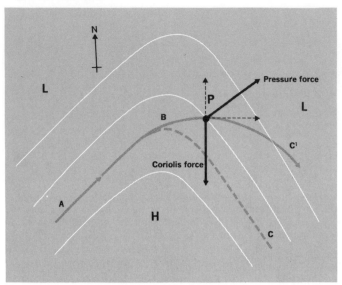

Fig. 6.12 Illustrating the mechanical origin of weather disturbances. Initially air moves on the path ABC parallel to the isobars or contours of a constant pressure surface (white lines). After strengthening of the wind along A–B from upstream, the air can no longer follow the clockwise bend and moves from B to P and C', accelerating. Dashed: components of pressure force parallel and perpendicular to wind at point P.

In the case of the jet stream we found it necessary that air moving into the core acquire the speed previously present at each point along its path. The current itself remained steady. In the case of the ridge, wind direction and speed have been changed, and this means the *onset of a change in weather*. The roots of many a severe storm traversing the United States can be traced back to just the event shown in Fig. 6.12, which may have happened near Alaska 3 days before the storm reached its full intensity.

WINDS NEAR THE EARTH'S SURFACE

In the lowest 2,000 to 3,000 ft (600 to 1,000 m) of the atmosphere, the frictional force produced by the stress of the wind upon the ground must be considered, along with the pressure and Coriolis forces. We shall examine the case when the frictional force acts in the opposite direction from the wind. In order for the air to continue moving at constant speed, a force must be applied against friction. Such a force is provided when the wind blows across the isobars from high to low pressure.

Surface weather maps nearly always show an angle between wind direction and orientation of the isobars (Fig. 6.13). A com-

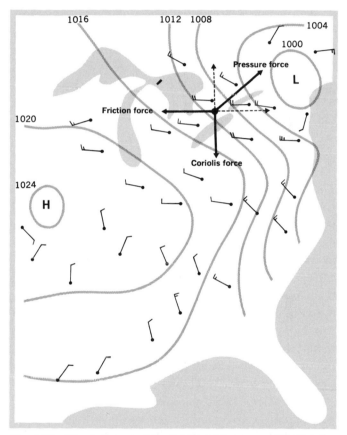

Fig. 6.13   The influence of the frictional force on wind direction in the surface layer. Chart for April 23, 1963. Isobars are drawn at intervals of 4 millibars, wind arrows as described in Appendix I. Variable crossing angle from high to low pressure is evident everywhere. Balanced motion is illustrated in the Great Lakes area. Dashed: components of pressure force parallel and perpendicular to wind.

ponent of the pressure force points along the wind as in Figs. 6.11 and 12. In this instance, however, it is opposed by the frictional force, so that the wind speed remains constant. Because of the frictional force a general outdraft of air takes place from high- to low-pressure centers near the surface, contributing to the weather patterns associated with these centers.

The angle at which the wind points across the isobars depends at least in part on the *roughness* of the ground, because the frictional drag at the surface increases with roughness. Over most types of land surfaces, except snow and sand deserts, the roughness exceeds that over the sea by 100 to 500 per cent and more, at least at low and moderate wind speeds when there are few breaking waves throwing up spray in the sea. On the average, the angle at which the wind crosses the isobars is near 10° over water and 30° over land, when the wind is measured at about 20 ft (6 m) above the surface.

SUPPLY OF ENERGY

The atmosphere must do work to maintain the wind systems against friction. Differences in heating and cooling between high and low latitudes and the effects of condensation ultimately supply the energy for generating and sustaining the winds. The precise way in which these heat supplies are made available for creating wind energy, however, is quite complex and not fully understood.

Consider a tank filled with water and containing a partition in the middle (Fig. 6.14 top). Half of the tank contains warm (light) water, the other half cold (heavy) water. When the partition is removed, energy of motion is created as the cold water sinks below the warm water because of its higher density. The center of gravity is lowered a little. Total energy thus remains constant in the tank.

By analogy, wind energy is created in the atmosphere mainly when cold air from high latitudes sinks below warm air from the tropics. But this is not so easily accomplished on the rotating globe or, for that matter, in the tank, when the latter is rotated with the lighter fluid overlying the heavier fluid without partition. If we accelerate the upper fluid relative to the lower one, the free surface at the top and the interface between the two fluids become shaped

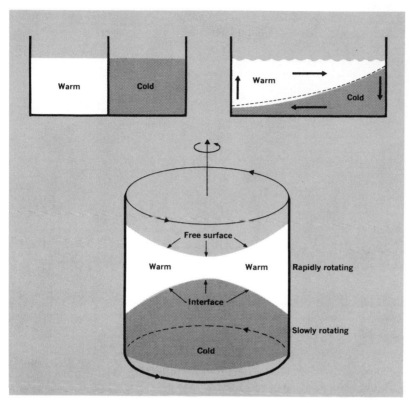

Fig. 6.14 Upper part: model of circulation developed in nonrotating tank when initial partition between cold and warm water is removed. Lower part: rotating tank with balanced flow of water around axis of rotation. The cold water dome is held in an elevated position and the free surface of the water lowers toward the axis resulting in a pressure force just as in Fig. 6.10 for the cyclone.

as depicted in the lower portion of Fig. 6.14; the cold dome at the bottom is raised. This is due to the action of the Coriolis force which takes the place of the partition in the nonrotating tank, and which cannot be arbitrarily removed. The whole arrangement can be stable for long periods.

In Fig. 6.15, the outline of a cold dome in the atmosphere has been drawn. This dome corresponds to the raised dome of cold water in the center of the rotating tank. The wind should be pic-

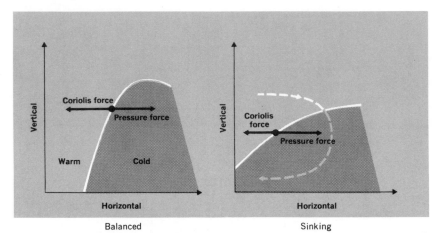

Fig. 6.15   Model of cold dome and of boundary between warm and cold air. Left: balanced geostrophic flow at edge of dome which is held up as in Fig. 6.14. Right: transverse motion and sinking of dome initiated after weakening of the Coriolis force.

tured as blowing from the page toward the reader. As long as the balance between pressure and Coriolis forces remains undisturbed, the wind continues to blow along the edge of the cold mass, and the dome retains its shape. In large-scale motion in the thin, curved shell, which is the troposphere, air mainly moves *around* heat and cold sources rather than *from* heat *to* cold source. Even the mean seasonal temperature cross section of Fig. 1.11 is determined in part by the earth's rotation. This is not a temperature field representing a state of radiation balance. If the earth's rotation were to stop suddenly, the polar air would sink at once and the temperature difference between high and low latitudes would be reduced. Similarly, it is not correct to speak of cold and warm air masses "coming together" and "forming" fronts. Without the effect of the winds the cold air would simply settle under the warm air and there would be no fronts. It is only when the winds blow with sufficient strength that the cold air can remain next to the warm air without sinking, and fronts can develop.

The adjustment between pressure and wind fields must be disrupted before a cold dome can sink. It is not an easy matter to specify the conditions which initiate such sinking in the atmosphere.

We shall consider here only one among many possible solutions. Clearly, the cold water in the rotating tank will subside if we slow down the rate of revolution of the lighter fluid. By analogy, if the cold dome in Fig. 6.15 travels from northwest toward southeast, toward latitudes where the earth's rotation becomes smaller, and the wind speed remains constant, balance of forces along the edge of the cold dome is no longer maintained. The Coriolis force decreases, and the air begins to accelerate in the direction in which the pressure force is acting. In this way a transverse flow is initiated, as indicated by the dashed curve on the right side of Fig. 6.15. The cold dome begins sinking, and the slope of the boundary between warm and cold air masses decreases. Energy released in this way can be converted to energy of motion in the air.

part two

Weather Disturbances

7

Weather Disturbances in Middle and High Latitudes

TRAVELING CYCLONES AND ANTICYCLONES

We were to have an eclipse of the moon at Philadelphia on a Friday evening [October 21, 1732] about nine o'clock. I intended to observe it, but was prevented by a northeast storm which came on about seven with thick clouds as usual, that quite obscured the whole hemisphere. Yet, when the post brought us the Boston newspapers, giving an account of the effects of the same storm in those parts, I found the beginning of the eclipse had been well observed there, though Boston lies north-east of Philadelphia about four hundred miles. This puzzles me, because the storm began with us so soon as to prevent any observation; and being a northeast storm, I imagined it must have begun rather sooner in places farther to the north-eastward than it did in Philadelphia. I therefore mentioned it in a letter to my brother who lives at Boston and he informed me that the storm did not begin with them till nearly eleven o'clock, so that they had a good observation of the eclipse. And comparing all other accounts I received from the several colonies, I found the beginning to be always later the farther north-eastward. . . .

These are comments by Benjamin Franklin. As one of his biographers, Carl Van Doren, notes: "This observation ranks him with the first and best meteorologists. He had not as Poor Richard forecast the weather for nothing."

Frànklin's inquiry perhaps gave the first hint on the travel of "weather." It came at a time when weather observing instruments were being installed in increasing numbers over Europe and North America in response to discoveries in natural science. A century later, the advent of telegraphy inaugurated the construction of weather charts on a daily basis. By that time it was known that areas of low and high barometric pressure, with counterclockwise and clockwise rotating wind systems, produce the changing daily weather. Low-pressure areas mainly travel toward northeast, carrying bad weather with them; this resolves Franklin's paradox.

Figure 7.1 shows the track of twelve major low-pressure centers during January, 1951, over the United States. This was a "normal" month. On the average, the cyclones traveled 700 miles per day, with a range from 200 to 1,100 miles per day, or from 8 to 47 mph. Motion of 60 mph would be extreme. Roughly, the storm paths followed the upper flow pattern of Fig. 1.9. Of the twelve cyclones, nine left the country at a latitude higher than the one at which they started. In all parts of the world, cyclones move mainly toward higher, and anticyclones toward lower, latitudes.

Most of the cyclones developed in the lee of the Rockies. One formed in the East Coast area near Cape Hatteras, where the ocean circulation produces a sharp change in temperature at a short distance offshore (Fig. 1.6). In some years many more cyclones form on the East Coast than in January, 1951 (Fig. 14.12).

Pressure at the center of cyclones is 1,000 millibars or somewhat higher for weak and average disturbances, 970 millibars for a very strong continental cyclone, and perhaps 920 millibars for an extreme oceanic storm. Because pressure change is closely related to wind

Fig. 7.1 Tracks of twelve major cyclones in the United States during January, 1951. Arrows show direction of motion; dots mark center positions at 24-hr intervals.

and occurrence of bad weather, the barometer has been valued for centuries as the key instrument for early detection of storms. A pressure drop of 2 millibars in 3 hr is a warning signal of an impending storm, a drop of 5 millibars is strong, and a drop of 10 millibars is extreme.

Changes in weather, often abrupt, accompany the traveling disturbances. Intense cyclones bring high winds and occasional weather catastrophes. The long Norwegian coast and much of Norway's population are exposed to violent weather arriving from the Atlantic. It is no wonder that Norwegians have taken a particularly active part in developing the science of meteorology. About 1920, Vilhelm Bjerknes and his son Jacob Bjerknes described the life cycle of cyclones in terms that convey a good idea of cyclone weather.

GROWTH AND DECAY OF CYCLONES

Initial Stages. In the classical Norwegian concept, cyclones are born along a *front* between warm and cold *air masses*, which may be blowing from opposite directions. A front is a zone of sharp changes in temperature, sometimes almost a discontinuity from warm to cold air. Except along fronts, temperature and humidity of the air near the surface change only slowly over great distances of 1,000 miles (1,600 km) or more, leading to the concept of broad, relatively uniform *air masses*. Temperature and moisture are their main distinguishing features. Basically, we differentiate between warm (tropical) and cold (polar) air masses, and between humid (maritime) and dry (continental) air masses. Combining these, the four principal air masses according to geographic origin are:

> Continental polar
> Maritime polar
> Continental tropical
> Maritime tropical

Classification of air masses has been carried much farther than presented in this simple scheme, but with little advantage in most circumstances.

The temperature contrast and opposing air motion along a front lead to wavy "perturbations." When these waves are about 1,000 miles apart, their amplitude may increase. The winds, assumed east-west at the outset, start blowing from south in the warm air ahead of the cyclone center and from north to its rear (Fig. 7.2*a*). Warm air replaces cold air at the ground in the area of south winds, so that we refer to the front in this area as a *warm front*. Cold air replaces warm air where north winds develop; here we speak of a *cold front*.

The northward-moving warm air must ascend over the *cold dome* in its path, which resists its advance. The cold air along the cold front will "underrun" the warm air ahead of it and force it upward. The weather pattern around a growing cyclone is a broad area of cloudiness and precipitation preceding the warm front and a band of precipitation, usually narrow, lying ahead of and along the cold front.

Mature Stage. During the initial phases the cyclone usually travels in a direction between east and north, "steered" by the upper winds over it (Fig. 7.4). Surface pressure at the center falls, say from 1,010 to 1,000 millibars, and the winds strengthen in response to the intensifying pressure field. This accelerates the cold front,

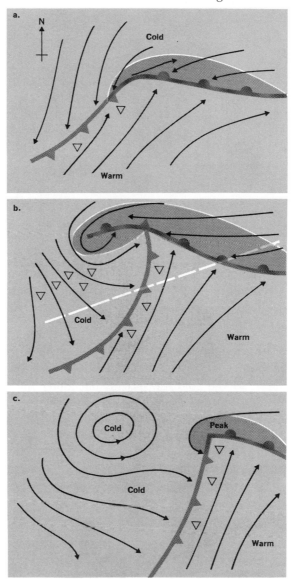

Fig. 7.2 *Three stages showing life history of cyclone according to Norwegian model. For symbols see Appendix I. See Fig. 7.3 for dashed line in center diagram. Shaded: precipitation area.*

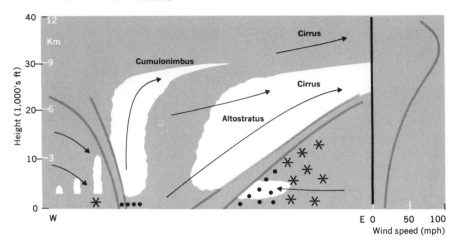

Fig. 7.3   *Sketch of weather distribution in vertical cross section along dashed line in Fig. 7.2b. Heavy lines mark warm and cold fronts. Right: variation of wind speed with height. For symbols see Appendix I.*

which, progressing from northwest, begins to overtake the surface center. When it approaches the warm front (Fig. 7.2*b*), the warm sector becomes *occluded*, i.e., closed or shut, from the cyclone center outward. The total area initially occupied by the warm air is reduced as the cold air spreads out along the ground and, because of mass continuity, undergoes sinking motion. Such sinking of cold air to the rear of cyclones, plus the ascent of warm air ahead of it, provides the main energy source for cyclone growth (Chapter 6).

In the mature stage the cloud system of the cyclone attains its greatest development (Fig. 7.3). The inclination or slope of the cold front with height—1 mile vertically to 50 or 100 miles along the ground—is much larger than that of the warm front, which may be as little as 1 mile vertically to 200 miles along the ground. At times the cloud tops are much higher than drawn in Fig. 7.3; on other occasions nearly all clouds lie below 20,000 ft (6,000 m) of altitude.

In the fast upper wind currents, clouds, especially cirrus, are often carried forward hundreds of miles from the place where they formed, another early warning signal of an impending storm.

Decaying Stage. Initially affecting perhaps no more than a few middle-sized states of the United States, a cyclone just starting to occlude may be the dominant weather influence over a fourth or more of the North American continent. The cyclone growth produces the setting for its own destruction. As the warm sector occludes, the energy release mechanism fails (Fig. 7.2c). The occluded center is filled with cold air entering from all sides. Gradually the cloud system weakens and surface pressure rises. Growing and decaying stages each normally last at least 1 to 2 days, so that the active life of a cyclone is 3 to 4 days or more.

After occlusion a new cyclone may originate at the remaining *peak of the warm sector* (Fig. 7.2c), where a strong air-mass contrast survives. Many severe winter storms striking the northeastern coast of the United States and Canada, and also the British Isles, form at such peaks of warm sectors.

WAVES IN THE WESTERLIES

We saw in Chapters 1 and 6 that the westerly winds of the middle and upper troposphere follow wavy paths. The distance between waves will be *long* (3,000 to 5,000 miles or 5,000 to 8,000 km) when air moves on a trajectory so that its absolute vorticity remains con-

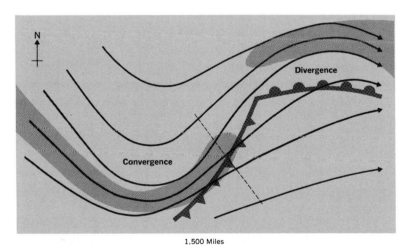

1,500 Miles

Fig. 7.4 Model of flow pattern in troposphere above developing cyclone. Surface fronts indicated. Shaded: band of highest wind speed, or jet stream. See Fig. 7.6 for dashed line.

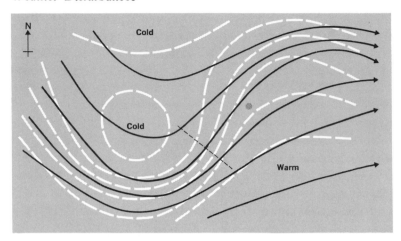

Fig. 7.5 Streamlines of upper flow pattern as in Fig. 7.4 and isotherms (dashed) during development stage of cyclone in middle troposphere (500 mb). Dot marks cyclone center.

stant (Fig. 6.7). Alternately, particles may follow wavy tracks with *shorter* wavelength (1,000 to 2,000 miles or 1,600 to 3,200 km) under the influence of horizontal mass convergence or divergence (Figs. 6.8 and 6.9). Such waves are associated with active cyclone development and generation of broad bad-weather areas.

Consider the model of Fig. 7.4, which holds for the layer from about 14,000 to above 40,000 ft (600 to 150 millibars). In this model the distance from trough to crest of the wave, or half wavelength, is 600 miles (1,000 km). Horizontal mass convergence brings about the counterclockwise bending of the streamlines in the west, horizontal divergence the ridge in the east. A developing cyclone is situated near the inflection point of the southwesterly flow. A little ahead of this point warm air has moved farthest northward from the tropics (Fig. 7.5). Streamlines and isotherms follow approximately the same course. Often a *cold dome* becomes isolated from the main cold pool at high latitudes; such a dome is sketched in Fig. 7.5 (see also Figs. 6.14 and 6.15).

The isotherms in Fig. 7.5 are not spaced evenly in the north-south direction. Rather there are two areas of concentration, around wave trough and wave crest. Here, the geostrophic wind increases most rapidly upward. A narrow belt with high wind speed is situ-

ated in the high troposphere, the jet stream (Fig. 7.6; for more details see Chapter 13). The current's core lies near 35,000 ft (10.5 km, 250 millibars). Underneath, temperature decreases from right to left across the current, looking downwind; above, the reverse holds. Thus the jet stream is centered at the height where the temperature pattern reverses with altitude, in accord with previous deductions about the relation between change of wind speed with height and horizontal temperature distribution. Left of the jet stream, the tropopause, or base of the stratosphere, is much lower than to the right. Close to the core a distinct tropopause often cannot be found. In this *tropopause gap* transfer of air from stratosphere to troposphere is thought to take place. Radioactive fallout from nuclear tests provides chief evidence for such transfer; the debris reaches the ground often along a narrow belt along the right edge of the jet stream.

The combination of short waves in the westerlies and a jet-

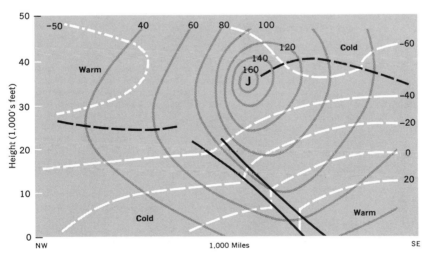

Fig. 7.6   Vertical cross section of wind speed (mph, solid) and temperature (°C, dashed), along the line normal to upper flow marked in Figs. 7.4 and 7.5. Black solid lines denote front, black dashed lines tropopauses. "J" indicates jet-stream center.

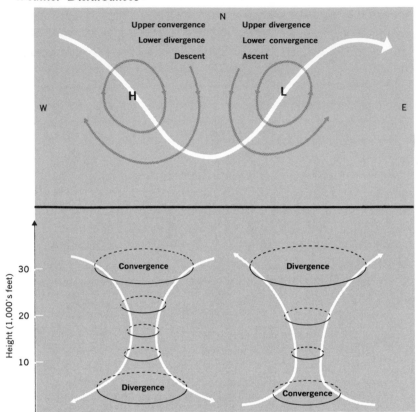

Fig. 7.7 Coupling between waves in upper westerlies and high- and low-pressure centers near surface. Top: horizontal view of upper jet-stream core in relation to surface systems. Bottom: vertical cross section showing the convergent and divergent parts of the motion in the horizontal plane, and the vertical motion.

stream core at the center of the westerly current provides the upper-air setting for the development of traveling surface cyclones and anticyclones (Fig. 7.7). Since surface barometric pressure varies by only a few per cent, mass convergence in one layer of the atmosphere must be nearly *compensated* by divergence in another layer, or surface pressure would rise or fall almost without limit.

Because mass is conserved, air must move vertically from the convergence to the divergence layers (Fig. 6.8). The sketches in the lower part of Fig. 7.7 show the convergent and divergent motion, and the vertical current in Highs and Lows. When air converges aloft, it moves downward bringing good weather. When it diverges aloft, upward movement leads to clouds and precipitation. Since the air flow becomes increasingly counterclockwise in a convergent layer and clockwise in a divergent layer, cyclonic and anticyclonic flow must alternate with height. The coupling results in clockwise surface flow where the upper air moves from ridge to trough and in counterclockwise flow where the upper air moves from trough to ridge. Vertical motion must be downward in the upper north-west flow and upward in the southwest flow (Fig. 7.7). Thus, *surface high-pressure areas have predominantly good weather and low-pressure areas bad weather.*

LIFE HISTORY OF A CYCLONE

Figures 7.2 to 7.7 are models; they serve to give a summary view of the salient facts about cyclone structure and development. Actual situations are always more complex. We shall examine the history of a cyclone which brought severe weather to eastern North America in January, 1962, and interfered there with the activities of man in many ways. While the southeastern part of the United States was treated to a brief and sudden spell of summer weather, very moist air with relative humidities near 100 per cent and much fog overlay the Northeast, slowing down most transportation. A danger-ous ice storm coated buildings, trees, and roads over a belt extend-ing eastward from Chicago to the Atlantic shore of southern Canada. Heavy snow covered much of the Great Lakes. The rare spectacle of January thunderstorms brought several inches of rain to a large area from Florida to Washington, D.C. and farther north, equaling or exceeding average precipitation for the whole month in many places.

Description of Events. We can explain these weather events, so different and yet related, by following the growth and motion of a cyclone that originated on January 4 in the lee of the southern Rocky Mountains (Fig. 7.8). On January 3, westerly flow, good weather, and mild temperatures prevailed over most of the United States. A trough at 500 millibars, weakly reflected at the surface,

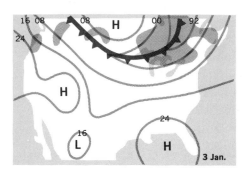

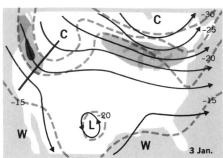

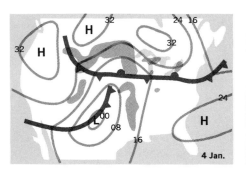

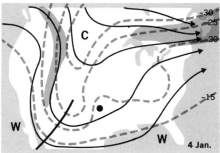

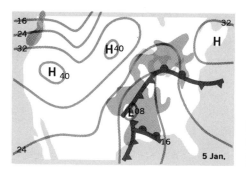

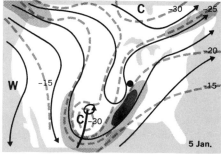

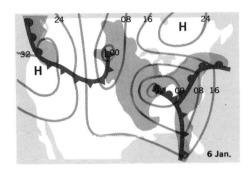
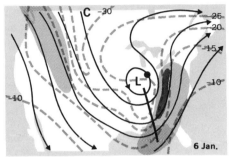
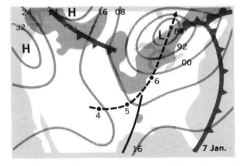
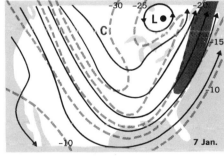

Fig. 7.8 *Surface and 500-millibar charts for North America, January 3 to 7, 1962. For symbols see Appendix I. At the surface, isobars are labeled by last two digits of whole millibars; precipitation areas shaded. At 500 millibars contours of the height of the pressure surface, marked with arrows, are drawn at 400-ft intervals (not labeled); isotherms (dashed) are in °C; areas with wind speed above 75 mph have light shading, above 100 mph, heavier shading; on January 7 only the region with 100-mph winds is shaded. The main surface center is indicated by a heavy dot; its track is shown on the January 7 surface chart.*

had entered the Rocky Mountain states from the Pacific Ocean, carrying cold air to lower latitudes. An upper cyclone, also containing cold air, was situated over western Texas. Chances for formation of a storm at the surface are greatest when these two disturbances of the upper air merge in the lee of the mountains. This mechanism is alternate to that of Fig. 7.2a in that the cyclone does not start from a small wave along a front but from preexisting large disturbances. A surface front may not exist at all, at least initially.

The merger occurred the following day. By January 4 a new surface cyclone had formed over Texas. The surface pressure distribution typical at the start of a major storm was evident—the cyclone was located in southerly latitudes, while a broad belt of high pressure overlay Canada in the wake of a cold outbreak there which penetrated into the Northern United States from the Rockies to the East Coast. The new cyclone was about to make contact with this cold air mass, *polar continental* in origin.

At 500 millibars the north-south amplitude of the flow increased from the preceding day. An elongated region of high speed marked the center of the current over the Rockies, the direction of which had become due north. Arrival of a jet-stream core upstream from a low-pressure center greatly enhances the chances for intensification.

By January 5 the surface storm had moved slowly out of the lee-of-the-mountains area toward the Mississippi on a course slightly north of east. The upper-air trough had acquired very large amplitude; jet-stream speeds exceeded 100 mph even at the relatively low altitude of the 500-millibar surface. A frontal arrangement resembling the wave structure of Fig. 7.2a had become established. However, the cyclone itself had formed the front. Its circulation imported cold air from north toward the center. At the same time, along the Gulf Coast, *tropical maritime* air with temperatures about 70°F at noon and high humidity was drawn onto the continent by the southerly winds east of the cyclone center. Arrival of this air mass close to the polar continental air west of the cyclone greatly strengthened the air-mass contrast, producing the surface setting favorable for major storm development.

The model of Figs. 7.4 and 7.5 was approximated on January 5. Strongest counterclockwise flow at 500 millibars overlay the cold air mass moving southward over the western plains, while the flow curved clockwise over the warm front. The cyclone center itself was situated near the inflection point of the southwesterly flow. Under the impact of the large amplitude of the upper flow, the strong jet stream, and the increasing surface air-mass contrast, a major weather development next occurred as the center intensified rapidly during the ensuing 24 hr. Central pressure fell by 20 millibars, the wind circulation strengthened, and the storm turned sharply northward.

On January 6 the cyclone extended far into the upper troposphere and became filled with cold air. Many times, under these circumstances, a center stagnates and weakens while a new storm forms at the peak of the warm sector (Fig. 7.2c). However, the primary Low was so vigorous that, despite several attempts, a new cyclone was not formed. The storm moved with increasing forward speed on a northeastward course into Canada on January 7. Its intensity continued to increase as seen by further lowering of the central pressure and expansion of the cyclonic circulation. Moreover, it suppressed a new disturbance which crossed the Rockies on January 5 and tried to develop in the lee of the mountains.

In summary, the upper-air flow held the key to starting this major event. Two disturbances at 500 millibars became connected and superimposed as they passed to the east of the Rocky Mountains. A surface low-pressure center, large in size from the outset, formed about this time, energized also by the arrival of a jet stream from northwest. In the initial phase the history differed from the model of Fig. 7.2. However, as the cyclone propagated slowly eastward, its converging wind system drew inward polar continental air from Canada and tropical maritime air from the Gulf of Mexico. After 24 hr of such converging flow a very strong air-mass contrast had accumulated near the center in low levels. It was about this time that the rapid intensification took place which also, in its turn, strengthened the upper jet stream. Thus a strong storm develops from an impulse in the upper flow when a temperature contrast between polar and tropical air at the ground also can be generated.

In many cases the upper trough is weak, or time does not suffice to bring the surface air masses together from great distances. Then a cyclone and its weather pattern develop only to feeble or moderate strength.

WEATHER DISTRIBUTION IN A CYCLONE

When the cyclone was approaching the Great Lakes on January 6, very lively weather accompanied it. On that day we could observe all the ingredients of the normal weather pattern as well as the unusually severe weather a winter storm may bring.

Surface Wind Field. Figure 7.9 shows streamlines, which indicate the field of wind direction. Taken as a whole, the circulation revolved around and converged toward the center near Chicago. The flow, however, was by no means symmetrical. Wind direction

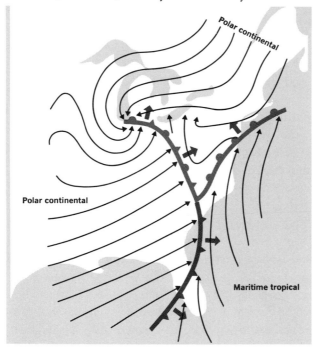

Fig. 7.9 Surface fronts and streamlines in the Eastern United States, January 6, 1962. Heavy arrows indicate the direction of motion of the fronts.

changed abruptly, almost discontinuously, across the fronts, from east to south at the warm front and from south to west-southwest along the cold front.

Wind speed is not shown because many local effects influence observation sites, making presentation of a reliable picture of wind strength difficult. Records of the more than 100 observing stations furnishing information for Fig. 7.9 indicate that winds were not exceptionally strong. Velocities of 10 to 20 mph prevailed. To the rear of the cold front, where strong and gusty winds are the rule, speeds of 30 to 40 mph were reported. Winds of 30 mph also were observed in the easterly flow along the shore of Lake Erie. Over the open water of the lakes, where ground roughness is small and friction retards wind speed only slightly, a gale was blowing.

Temperature Field. In Fig. 7.10 isotherms at intervals of 10°F (about 5°C) have been drawn. The arrows mark the points where the streamlines of Fig. 7.9 cross the isotherms. They indicate the direction in which warm and cold air is being transported.

If air were not subject to heating and cooling near the ground, isotherms would move with the wind. However, warm air traveling northward is cooled from below; cold air advancing over warmer ground is heated (Chapters 3 and 4). Therefore the isotherms move slower than the wind normal to them. Along a slowly moving warm front, they may be nearly stationary as the warm air is lifted over the top of the cold air mass in its path.

The temperature gradient was strongest along the Atlantic seaboard ahead of the warm front. As the front entered land, "summer" visited the coastal plain for a few hours. At and behind the cold front the temperature drop was weak compared to many storms of great intensity. The cold air was moving from south of west rather than from northwest or north on a direct path from the Canadian source of polar air. Its travel on a wide, curved sweep through the Central and Southern United States tempered the air by heating from below. A very strong cold front brings a temperature drop of 20 to 60°F (about 10 to 30°C).

January-type temperatures prevailed only in southern Canada. The air mass there, sometimes labeled *arctic* for emphasis, was warmed on its southbound travel despite snow-covered land. It was

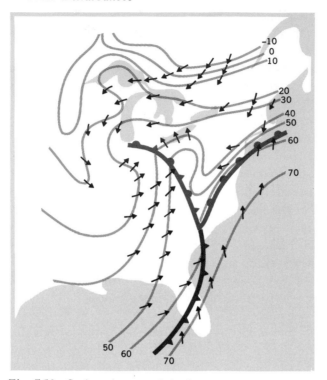

Fig. 7.10 Surface fronts and isotherms (°F), January 6, 1962. Arrows mark the places where the streamlines of Fig. 7.9 cross the isotherms indicating displacement of warm and cold air masses.

situated underneath the warm front, so that temperature increased with height at some distance above the ground, as in Fig. 7.12. Winds were strong enough to produce mechanical turbulence (Chapter 3), so that forced mixing led to downward transport of heat. Over the Great Lakes, under the influence of partly open water, strong heating from below set in, generating the large northward bulge of the isotherms over and near Lake Superior.

The Appalachian Mountains also affect the temperature field. Cold air pocketed in many valleys resists warm air advance, unless wind speed becomes strong. Thus, the 40 and 50°F isotherms bulged southwestward over and just east of the main chains of the Appalachian range.

Warm-front and Warm-sector Weather. The feature that really rendered January 6 a severe-weather day was the huge area in which precipitation in nearly all known forms occurred (Fig. 7.11).

Clear or partly cloudy skies were not reported except 600 to 700 miles north of the warm front and in the subsiding cold air in the Southern states. Going southward from Canada, typical warm-front weather was present. At the northern end of the front, where its altitude was highest and temperature lowest, clouds were thin and of cirrus type. A little farther south the cloud deck thickened to altostratus overcast. Still farther south, the overriding warm air formed precipitation-size crystals, leading to an elongated belt of snow. Where temperature rose well above freezing, the snow changed to rain.

The transition zone between snow and rain contains the danger

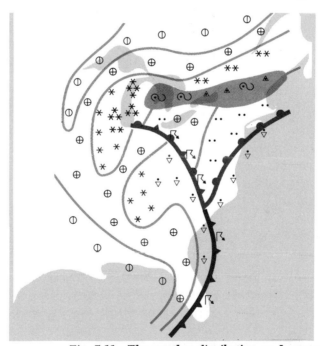

Fig. 7.11 The weather distribution on January 6, 1962. Open circles denote partly cloudy sky; circles with crosses denote overcast sky. For other symbols see Appendix I. Shaded: area with ice storm.

of ice storms (Chapter 5) and of truly severe weather. During warm-front advance it is always important whether a belt with sleet or freezing rain exists or will develop, where it is located, and how long it will persist. At Portland, Maine (Fig. 7.12), and at Albany, New York (Fig. 5.3), temperatures were above freezing through a deep layer in the tropical air above the warm front. Water falling from this layer through the polar air below arrived at the ground partly as sleet, partly as freezing rain.

The ice-storm belt was exceptionally large on January 6. It was about 150 miles (250 km) wide and over 1,000 miles (1,600 km) long, oriented east-west. Further, it persisted for several days and moved gradually northeastward with the cyclone.

Precipitation often stops near the surface position of the warm front. Skies may clear, at least above a deck of the low stratus clouds or fog that often persist in winter over land. However, with a warm sector of tropical maritime air and a deepening cyclone, thunderstorms may break out close to the surface warm front, and heavy showers may occur for 100 to 200 miles into the warm air mass. This happened on January 6. During the 24 hr ending at 1 A.M. EST on January 7, more than 1 in. of precipitation was recorded from Boston to Georgia. In the Middle Atlantic states the accumulation exceeded 3 to 4 in. in many places—well above average *January* precipitation.

Weather at and behind the Cold Front. Shower activity is expected along a cold front. The model of Fig. 7.3 certainly held on January 6 where we see the spectacle—rare for January—of an enormous line of thunderstorms reaching from the vicinity of the Great Lakes to Florida. In the South, shower activity died out quickly to the rear of the front.

Heating of cold air from below leads to cumulus formation. However, because cold air masses sink as they spread out, a strong lid counters the convection, and the cumuli remain small. A picturesque sky filled with many fair-weather cumuli and brisk winds in dry, clean air often marks the terminal stage of cyclone passage. Behind the occluded front the clearing, if any, persists only over a short distance. Then the upper trough with the coldest air aloft arrives. The low-level air is again subject to convergence; the

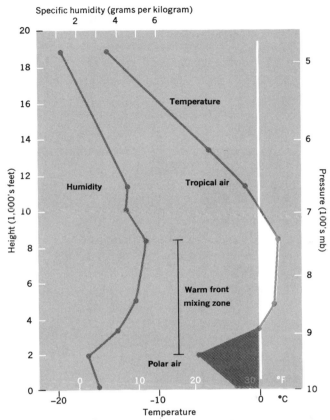

Fig. 7.12 *Distribution of temperature and specific humidity with height and pressure as measured by balloon ascent at Portland, Maine, during the evening of January 6, 1962. Warm front zone indicated. Outstanding is the layer with above-freezing temperatures above cold air near the ground, a combination producing sleet or freezing rain (see also Fig. 5.3).*

barometer, rising after front passage, may show a secondary fall. An overcast of strato-cumulus and higher clouds fills the area of the upper trough. Extensive light snow or snow showers occur, sometimes persisting for a day and more. All this happened on January 6.

HURRICANES OUTSIDE THE TROPICS

A "hurricane" often is understood to be a severe storm from the tropics. This definition is too limited. The threshold of hurricane-force winds is 75 mph (Appendix I). Winds of such strength occur at least a few times each cold season in cyclones outside the tropics.

Excepting local squalls associated with thunderstorms, hurricane winds are rare over land. When they occur, a weather disaster is at hand as, for instance, on November 11, 1940, in the Midwest and on November 25, 1950, in the East of the United States. Winds of 100 mph were recorded on these dates; distress and damage on account of snow, cold, and wind were widespread.

The Icelandic area of the North Atlantic and the Aleutian area of the North Pacific are favorite regions for the occasional development of hurricane winds which generate high ocean waves. Gale and hurricane winds may be blowing without appreciable change in wind direction for 1,000 miles or more, persisting for 24 hr or more. Over such a large area of *fetch* the highest waves are created. Coastal installations and homes are exposed to the dangerous force of these waves and exceptionally high tides.

On March 4, 1962, a weak low-pressure center moved eastward across the Atlantic Coast of the United States into the Atlantic. Then it intensified rapidly and, in contrast to that of January, 1962, stagnated. A broad belt of easterly to northeasterly winds developed parallel to the shore from New York to Nova Scotia. Hurricane winds appeared first on March 6; subsequently the high-wind core moved around the western boundary of the cyclone.

Figure 7.13 shows surface streamlines and the area with winds of or near hurricane force, as reported from ship and coastal observations around the time of peak intensity. The very large area with northeasterly winds is spectacular. Tides rose 2 to 5 ft above normal along the entire East Coast from Canada to Florida on March 6 and 7. All shore installations, as far as Miami Beach, were pounded by heavy surf causing extensive destruction especially to beaches, beachside homes, and piers. Exposed weather stations along the

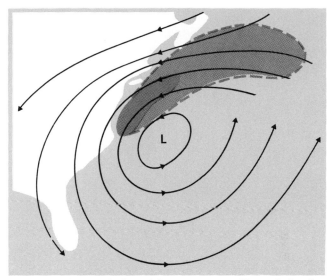

Fig. 7.13 Surface isobars (shown as streamlines of the flow paralleling the isobars), area of fetch for generation of ocean waves (light shading) and area with near-hurricane force winds (heavy shading), off the United States East Coast on March 7, 1962. The severe, slow-moving cyclone reached its peak intensity at that time.

shore and on offshore islands recorded at least brief periods with hurricane winds or gusts.

Here is an even more severe example of the havoc created by extreme winds (Fig. 7.14). On January 31, 1953, a low-pressure area situated north of Scotland took an unusual, but not unprecedented, course toward Holland, northern Germany, and Denmark while deepening to full hurricane intensity. To the rear of the center the direction of gale and hurricane winds was northwest to north with little curvature. In Scotland, about 4 million trees already had been blown down on January 31. Then, during the ensuing night and the early morning hours of Sunday, February 1, the surge of high waters arrived along the shores of southeastern England and the northwestern European coast, hitting Holland

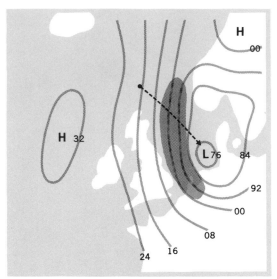

Fig. 7.14 Sea-level isobars in millibars (last two digits only) and area of hurricane-force winds (shaded) for western Europe during the catastrophic inundation of January 31–February 1, 1953. Track of low-pressure center marked with arrow.

most severely. Channeled by the configuration of the North Sea and intensified by the increasing cyclone strength and persistent fetch down the whole length of the North Sea and beyond, the high tides and waves broke through coastal dikes and other defenses and inundated land that had been gained from the sea over the years with hard labor and expense. In England, tides rose as much as 18 ft above normal in estuaries. This was a major disaster for the coast of northwest Europe, thought to be the greatest in centuries.

In assessing climate, weather catastrophes—such as ice storms or hurricane winds and waves—assume great importance, far more than is usually accorded to them in climatic description. Average conditions auspicious for human endeavor matter little if the catastrophes *recur* too frequently and destroy what man's effort has built. Before coastal protection works are constructed, an economic decision must be made about cyclone intensity and probability of recurrence against which safety is to be obtained. For instance, the chance of one disastrous cyclone per century must be weighed when deciding the height and solidity of dike and dam structures. Everlasting protection against weather can never be achieved. Hence man must decide against what cyclone intensity and what "return period" he wishes to guard, and beyond what limit he will take his chances.

8

Weather Disturbances
of the Tropics

Compared to the rapid, sometimes violent, weather changes along the path of middle-latitude cyclones, weather in the tropics follows a rather routine course most of the time. Missing is the frequent seesaw between north and south winds, accompanied by rising and falling temperatures. Instead, wind and temperature go through a daily cycle dictated by orographic, coastal, or other terrain features.

In some areas of the tropics, especially in the large trade-wind belts, this daily cycle so dominates weather that nothing unusual ever seems to occur, apart from occasional hurricanes. This view is exaggerated. Over most of the tropics a cycle of wet and dry seasons replaces the four seasons of middle latitudes, which are determined by temperature. There is a definite sequence of weather changes during the wet season, and sometimes also during the dry season. A period of heavy rain will follow dry weather when a disturbance passes. Disturbances produce more than 90 per cent of the rainfall in the tropics; a large fraction of the rain falls in a few intense spurts during the year. A typical record is that of the highlands of Kenya in East Africa. There, the months of April and November—at the height of the "long" and "short" rainy seasons (Chapter 10)—together average eighty disturbances lasting an average of nearly 4 days, in 10 years. Thirteen per cent of these storms, or ten in 10 years, deliver half of the precipitation in these months (Fig. 8.1).

Tropical disturbances vary widely in kind according to their location. Geographical differences are much larger in the tropics

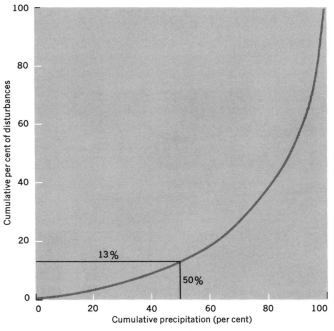

Fig. 8.1 *Per cent frequency of disturbances in the Kenya Highlands of East Africa during April and November against per cent of precipitation due to such storms in these months. Very few disturbances produce most rainfall. (Adapted from M. B. Oliver.)*

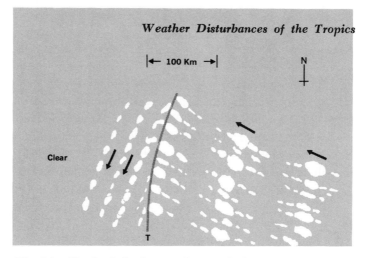

Fig. 8.2   Sketch of cloud rows photographed from aircraft passing through a wave in the easterlies on July 11, 1957, in the central Pacific Ocean. Arrows indicate direction of wind. Solid gray line: axis of wave. (J. S. Malkus and H. Riehl.)

than they are in higher latitudes, where the essentials of the cyclone model of Chapter 7 hold for all areas and seasons. Not all weather disturbances of the tropics have been studied and described satisfactorily, and we shall limit discussion here to a few well-known types.

WAVES IN THE EASTERLIES

The cloud arrays associated with tropical disturbances are best displayed over the open ocean, free from land influences. Figure 8.2 is a sketch of the cloud structure which aircraft carrying special photographic equipment encountered in the central Pacific Ocean northeast of the Mariana Islands on July 11, 1957. In that area, July is part of the rainy season. We see that the clouds were arranged in rows and that the orientation of these rows changed from northeast-southwest to southeast-northwest along a line extending nearly north-south. West of this line, small trade cumuli prevailed, dying out to the west, an unusual event for this location in July. There was heavy cloudiness with squalls east of the line, where the aircraft found showers from cumulus clouds that extended to 15,000 to 20,000 ft (4.5 to 6 km) height, and higher.

Because the clouds were cumuli, the disturbed area was not solidly overcast, in distinction to the stratus decks of higher-latitude storms.

The easterly flow in the lower 10,000 to 15,000 ft (3 to 4.5 km) above the ocean moved like a wave, turning northward and southward. At the outskirts of the disturbance, the flow curved clockwise, and near the center, counterclockwise. Where the cloud streets and the winds changed from southeast to northeast, the surface pressure was slightly reduced, by about 2 millibars, compared with the areas several hundred miles east and west of the solid line in Fig. 8.2.

We see a good example of such a wave in the western Atlantic Ocean in Fig. 8.3. There, the tropical east-wind belt frequently expands northward during summer to include the Florida peninsula and the Gulf Coast of the United States. At times, waves advance in these easterlies from the middle of the ocean across Florida into the Gulf of Mexico. These waves travel appreciably slower than middle-latitude cyclones, about 300 to 400 miles (500 to 650 km) per day, or 12 to 15 mph, compared to double this rate of cyclone displacement in the westerlies.

The positions of the wave trough one day before and one day after map time have been entered in Fig. 8.3. Between September 12 and 14 the wave traveled slowly at 11 mph. Therefore, the air crossed the wave trough from east to west at roughly 10 mph. A mass found less than 200 miles (300 km) west of the trough on September 13 was located on its eastern side one day earlier. This observation enables us to explain the observed weather distribution: fair to the west and rainy to the east of the trough line.

The absolute vorticity of the air that passes through the wave changes. At the trough, the counterclockwise flow curvature is greatest, and so is the air's vorticity relative to the earth. Further, the air moving through the wave from east to west reaches its highest latitude at the trough, where, from Fig. 6.3, the rotation of the earth's surface about its axis is largest along the path considered. Air columns in the low troposphere therefore gain absolute cyclonic vorticity while they move toward the trough line from the east; their vorticity decreases again as they move westward from the trough after passing it.

We found in Chapter 6 that the absolute vorticity increases when air converges horizontally and that it decreases when air di-

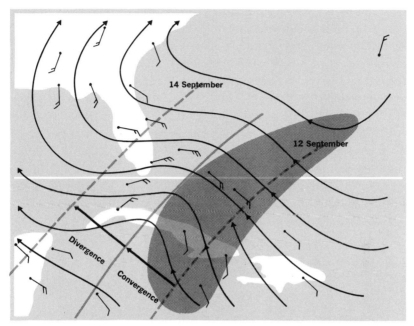

Fig. 8.3 *Streamlines for the layer 850 to 700 millibars (5,000 to 10,000 ft) for the western tropical Atlantic region on September 13, 1957. Solid gray line shows position of wave trough in the easterlies; dashed lines give positions one day earlier and later. Shaded: main precipitation area.*

verges. Therefore, convergence and divergence of mass must be distributed as shown in Fig. 8.3. Further, air must ascend in the low levels east of the wave trough and descend to its west. Large clouds yielding copious rain thus build up mainly on the eastern side, and they dissipate on the western side. Suppressed cumulus clouds, at times even clear sky, as in Fig. 8.2, often precede by one day the wind shift to southeast, followed by showers and, occasionally, thunderstorms.

EQUATORIAL TROUGH DISTURBANCES

A trough of low pressure at the surface extends around the equatorial belt (Chapter 1). Seasonally, this trough migrates from the winter into the summer hemisphere (Figs. 1.7 and 1.8), so the winter hemisphere controls a larger fraction of the oceanic tropics than does the summer hemisphere. The trough's mean latitude oscillates between 13°N and 4°S (Fig. 10.7).

The trade-wind streams from both hemispheres converge toward the equatorial trough, where the major buildup of tropical cumuli takes place. When the trough is at least about 5° latitude from the equator, the trade-wind streams may break up into small cyclones along the trough. Much of the ascent of air, which gives rise to the high equatorial rainfall, takes place in these cyclones. Although weather observations over northern South America are very sparse, we know that the flow along the equatorial trough there conforms to this model, illustrated for July 3–4, 1952 in Fig. 8.4. On those days, the trough extended from the Atlantic Ocean to the Andes of Venezuela and Colombia. A small cyclone was pin-

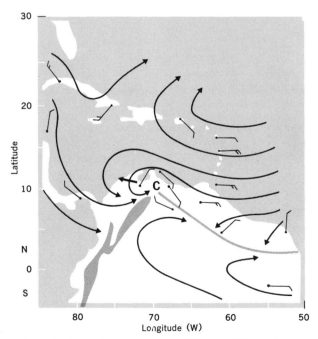

Fig. 8.4 *Streamlines at 850 millibars (5,000 ft) over northern South America and adjacent regions on July 3–4, 1952. Solid gray line is equatorial low-pressure trough. C denotes the center of a cyclone outlined by the winds; the heavy arrow shows its direction of displacement. Shaded: area above 2,000 m (6,600 ft).*

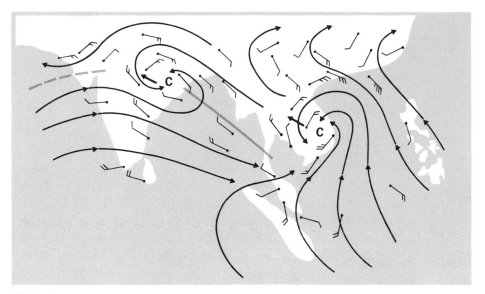

Fig. 8.5 Monsoon depressions. This chart shows streamlines at 700 millibars (10,000 ft) for southern Asia on September 23, 1961. Notation as in Fig. 8.4.

pointed by counterclockwise winds near the border between these two countries. Such cyclones yield 1 to 3 in. of rain, at times much more, during passage; the heaviest rain occurs just to the east of the center.

Surface temperatures are constant through the cyclone, except for a slight decrease in the area of most intense rain, where evaporation from falling drops cools the atmosphere. Pressure at the center may be 2 to 4 millibars lower than in the outskirts. Wind strength averages 10 to 20 mph but may rise to 30 mph close to the center on its northern side. Normally, these cyclones move toward west or west-northwest at 10 to 12 mph.

Monsoon Depressions. Weak cyclones, which broadly fit the above description, travel over many portions of oceanic and continental tropics. They are most prominent over southern Asia at the height of the summer monsoon season, when the equatorial trough is drawn on the Asiatic continent (Fig. 1.8). The cyclones, or "depressions," as they are called in India, move westward, steered by a strong easterly current above 25,000 to 30,000 ft (400 to 300 millibars). In Fig. 8.5 we see two such centers, one over northwestern India, the other over southeastern Asia. Except for strong topographic effects, much of the precipitation in these areas comes from such cyclones. Outside their vicinity shower activity often is suppressed.

TROPICAL HURRICANES: DESCRIPTION

Over the centuries, captains at sea and populations on shore have watched sky and ocean with anxiety for signs of an approaching hurricane. They feared to encounter the small central area of these cyclones with its extremely severe weather. Under the stress of winds that on rare occasions attain 200 mph, huge waves are generated in the ocean. Along concavely curving coasts such as that of the Gulf of Mexico, and in estuaries, the storm surge—the rise of the water above the tide otherwise expected—may exceed 10 ft, threatening coastal protection works and settlements just as the North Sea storm of February 1, 1953, did.

Winds of 200 mph have never been recorded in hurricanes at the ground; most wind-measuring equipment is destroyed at much lower velocities. Extreme winds are estimated from the structural damage they produce. In the Atlantic hurricane area, a storm of extreme violence strikes land perhaps ten times per century at irregular intervals. Action of the ocean then brings about a disaster along the shore. In addition, wind damage can become appreciable because the pressure of wind on buildings increases with the square of the wind speed.

During the night of June 26–27, 1957, a hurricane moving northward in the Gulf of Mexico intensified greatly before its landfall near the Texas-Louisiana border. Inundation was confined, as is normal, to the area situated to the right of the direction of storm motion, where the winds blow onshore (Fig. 8.6). There, the ocean invaded the lowlands to a distance of 30 to 60 miles (50 to 100 km); many places reported extreme water heights of 10 to 15 ft (3 to 4.5 m) in estuaries.

In spite of the disasters, hurricanes are by no means entirely destructive. Many areas, for instance southeastern Asia and the west coast of Mexico, rely on tropical storms for much of their water

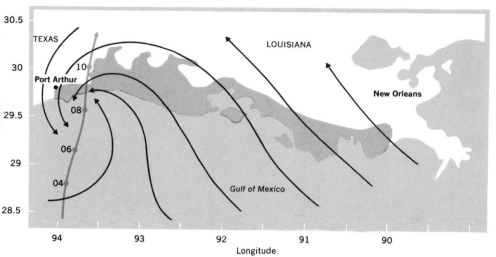

Fig. 8.6 Inundation due to hurricane striking Gulf Coast of the United States near Louisiana-Texas border during morning of June 27, 1957. Path of hurricane marked in 2-hr time steps. Surface streamlines for time of landfall. Shaded: the inundated area; all elevations are very close to sea level. (Source: U.S. Weather Bureau.)

supply. Hurricanes have relieved drought throughout the Southern United States from the East Coast to western Texas.

Hurricane Winds. Since the early 1940s, surveillance of hurricanes by air to aid in warning shore areas and ships has been a regular task of the United States military forces. Many research aircraft missions have also been conducted, principally by the U.S. Weather Bureau. During early September of 1960 a large hurricane gradually approached the American mainland from the tropical Atlantic, moving toward west-northwest at 9 to 10 mph (Fig. 8.17). Research aircraft flew many missions in this storm. On September 7, they obtained an excellent record of the fields of wind direction and wind speed (Fig. 8.7), flying at 7,000 to 8,000 ft pressure altitude (750 millibars); this wind field approximates conditions near the ocean surface. Wind speeds of hurricane force (greater than 75 mph or 65 knots) covered most of the area within 50 to 70 miles (80 to 110 km) from the core. They were strongest north of the center, or to the right of the direction of hurricane displacement. In this sector wind strength attained 150 knots (165 mph).

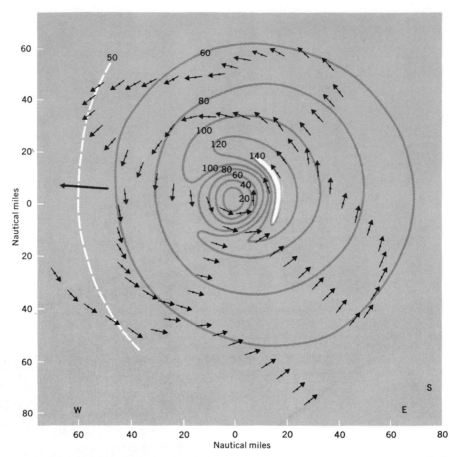

Fig. 8.7 Wind direction (arrows) and wind speed (knots, extreme wind belt white) in hurricane north of Greater Antilles on September 7, 1960. Heavy arrow on left shows the direction of hurricane displacement. Measurement by U.S. Weather Bureau research aircraft flying near 750 millibars. North-south and east-west distances are counted from center.

Above 15,000 to 20,000 ft (4.5 to 6 km) the hurricane circulation weakens. At 30,000 ft (9 km) and higher, a broad ring of winds rotating clockwise overlies the low-level counterclockwise circulation (Fig. 8.8). The upper limit of most hurricanes is found between 40,000 and 50,000 ft (12 to 15 km), rising as a storm intensifies.

Mass Flow, Clouds, and Precipitation. Air flows toward the center of the hurricane at low levels, where moisture is high; compensatory outflow occurs in the upper troposphere (Fig. 8.9). To provide continuity of mass, the inflowing air must ascend near the

0   60   120   180
Nautical miles

Fig. 8.8 Streamlines at 200 millibars (40,000 ft) for the hurricane shown in Fig. 8.7, based on balloon observations in the area through which the hurricane passed. At this level the flow is outward, turning clockwise with increasing distance from the center. (From Science, vol. 141, p. 1006, 1963.)

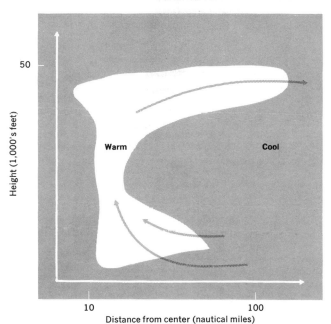

Fig. 8.9 Model showing vertical cross section through hurricanes with inflow and outflow layers, main cloud structure and temperature field. (From Science, vol. 141, p. 1006, 1963.)

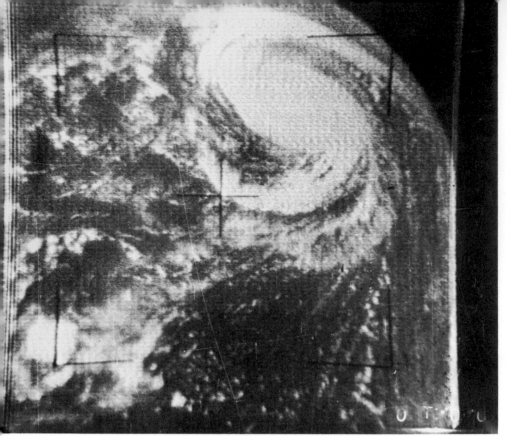

Fig. 8.10   TIROS III photograph of hurricane near 36°N, 59°W, on September 8, 1961. Notice very large spiral arms converging into solidly overcast core. (Courtesy U.S. Weather Bureau.)

core, which contains a thick mass of clouds and heavy rainfall. At the outer limit of the hurricane cloud deck only a sheet of cirrus remains. Frequently, this sheet has a sharp edge, seen beautifully in satellite photography (Fig. 8.10). Along this edge the ascent ends and gives way to subsidence in the hurricane's outskirts. Very fine weather, with hardly a cloud in the sky, often precedes arrival of a hurricane by one day, when the storm is moving westward in the tropics.

Satellite photos have great operational value. Spotting hurricanes over vast ocean areas with few or no weather data, they serve to warn ships and to alert weather services to the threat of an impending storm. The hurricane cloud bands, and also the cloud array of cyclones outside the tropics (see frontispiece), resemble spiraling stellar nebulae to a remarkable degree (Fig. 8.11).

Fig. 8.11   The Whirlpool Galaxy in the constellation Canes Venatici (Hunting Dogs, near the Big Bear). The resemblance to Fig. 8.10 is striking. NGC 5195. (Photograph from the Mount Wilson and Palomar Observatories, 200-in. telescope.)

Radar observations have revealed that the major hurricane clouds form spiraling bands (Fig. 8.12). The spirals, sometimes hundreds of miles long, are at most a few miles wide. The distance between spirals is 30 to 50 miles (50 to 80 km), decreasing toward the center. Since radar waves are reflected mainly from clouds with high liquid water or ice content, only a small fraction of a hurricane's area, not more than 10 per cent, often contains the ascent giving rise to most condensation and precipitation. This is a surprising, yet indisputable, fact which was not suspected before radar became a tool for weather measurements.

Close to the center, the clouds form a ring around the hurricane eye, creating the famous eye wall beautifully depicted in Fig. 8.12. Here strongest wind and heaviest precipitation combine, producing the extreme of a hurricane's fury. Rainfall, like wind

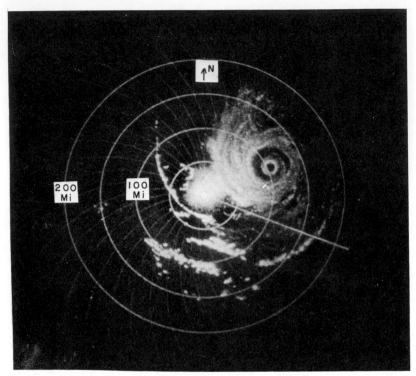

Fig. 8.12   Radar photo of cloud bands in hurricane off the Florida coast on August 27, 1958. Circles at 50-mile intervals from U.S. Navy plane monitoring storm. (U.S. Navy photograph. Courtesy Chas. L. Jordan, Florida State University.)

strength, is most intense and widespread to the right of the direction of hurricane displacement. To the left, large breaks appear in the low clouds between narrow spiraling bands at points as little as 30 to 50 miles (50 to 80 km) from the core.

How precipitation varies outward from a hurricane center is best seen from computations made for storms at sea, because rain gauge measurements are unreliable under extreme wind conditions. In the September, 1960, hurricane, precipitation rose to a rate of not less than 20 in. (50 cm) per day in the core (Fig. 8.13). Of course, any given site normally does not remain in the zone of extreme rain for more than a few hours. The 1960 hurricane traveled at about 10 mph, when it was approaching Florida. Locations directly in its path should have measured 8 in. (20 cm) in 24 hr and 11 in. (27 cm) in 48 hr. These values are by no means extreme; they are almost identical with the average precipitation computed for tropical storms in the Pacific Ocean. Amounts much higher and lower have been measured, depending on the position of a recording site with respect to the center, on the rate of hurricane travel, and on local topography. When a hurricane becomes stationary for a day or more; disastrous flooding will develop. Then, indeed, 20 in. of rain and more will accumulate on the ground while the storm lingers; this is a substantial fraction of average annual rainfall in

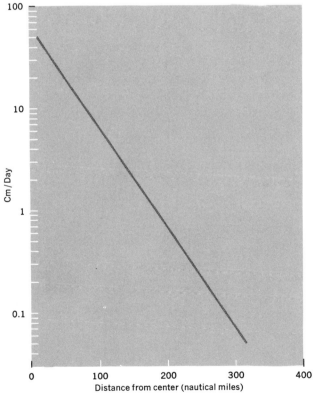

Fig. 8.13 Distribution of precipitation rate with distance from hurricane center shown in Fig. 8.7.

most parts of the hurricane belt. During early October, 1963, such a disaster overtook eastern Cuba when a hurricane, of intensity comparable to the hurricane of September, 1960, executed a slow loop there during 4 days (Fig. 8.17).

The Hurricane Eye. The ring of strongest wind and rain, or edge of the eye, is 5 to 30 miles from the hurricane center, most frequently about 15 miles. Inside this eye wall, winds decrease quickly, and the heavy rains cease. Here is the celebrated hurricane *eye*—a term coined long before the age of suggestive radar and satellite pictures. The eye offers a brief and deceptive respite from the extreme weather around the eye wall. Many descriptions, exaggerated through the great contrast, speak of calm air and sunshine inside the eye. Actually, the winds decrease at a more or less uniform rate from eye wall to center, and the eye often is filled with clouds at middle and high levels, at times even low clouds forming miniature spirals.

Temperature and Pressure Distribution. It was long suspected, and proved in the years after 1940, that the atmosphere in the interior of hurricanes is warm compared with that outside. In Fig. 8.14 the curve on the left represents the temperature structure typical for the air surrounding the hurricane; the curve on the right is based on aircraft measurements made in the wall cloud shown in Fig. 8.12. The temperature difference is substantial. It can be explained only by assuming that air drawn into the hurricane circulation absorbs heat and moisture from the ocean along its path. Because of its high wind and turbulence, the inner area of hurricanes offers a very fine setting for rapid heat and moisture flow from ocean to atmosphere.[1]

In the eye wall the warm layer extends from the ocean to the top of the hurricane. From there its thickness decreases outward to the terminal point at the edge of the cloud shield (Fig. 8.9). We saw in Chapter 3 that the vertical thickness of the layer between two pressures increases when its temperature increases. In a hurricane,

---

[1] Still warmer temperatures occur in the eye itself. But these are derived from subsiding motion and do not contribute to the storm's energy; this is discussed in advanced texts.

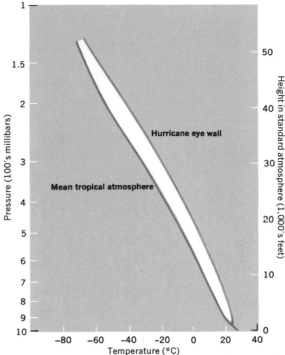

Fig. 8.14 The interior warning in hurricanes. Diagram of temperature against pressure and height showing mean tropical atmosphere and temperatures measured by research aircraft in eye wall of hurricane seen in Fig. 8.12. Curve above 250 millibars extrapolated.

pressure is nearly constant horizontally above the top of the storm. Therefore, as the depth of the warm layer increases inward, surface pressure must drop. In the outer parts, where the warm layer is shallow, this decrease will be gradual. Close to the core, where the warm column occupies most or all of the troposphere, surface pressure must fall rapidly inward. This has, in fact, been observed (Fig. 8.15). Very low pressures have been recorded on occasion; in extreme situations the pressure reduction approaches $\frac{1}{10}$ atm.

A pressure profile shaped as in Fig. 8.15 is necessary to produce the high wind speeds and maintain them against friction. Thus the heat source at the ocean surface, the pressure difference between

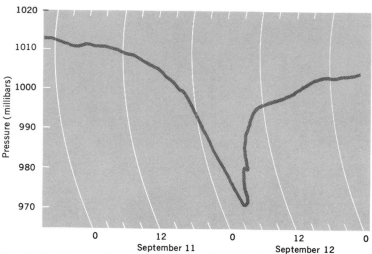

Fig. 8.15 *Barograph trace recorded at U.S. Naval Air Station, Norfolk, Va., as the hurricane seen in Fig. 8.7 passed there on September 11–12, 1960.*

inside and outside, and the maximum wind speed are correlated. The stronger the wind, the lower must be the pressure on the inside, and the more intense the heat and moisture transfer from ocean to air inside the storm.

TROPICAL HURRICANES: ORIGIN

Severe tropical storms occur in all oceans except the South Atlantic. Hurricane is their name in the North Atlantic; it means "big wind" in the Carib language. Tropical storms are known as *typhoons* in the western North Pacific Ocean, elsewhere as tropical cyclones.

In order for cyclonic circulation to develop, converging air currents must be able to concentrate the vorticity they possess by virtue of their participation in the earth's rotation at any altitude (Chapter 6). This vorticity is very small close to the equator (Fig. 6.3), so that hurricanes rarely form within latitudes 5° North and South. Further, the uptake of heat from the ocean will be greatest when a storm develops in the areas and seasons with highest ocean surface temperature—over the western parts of the oceans during August to October in the Northern Hemisphere, and during January to March in the Southern Hemisphere. Exceptions are the waters around India and the western Caribbean, where hurricanes occur in May–June and in late September–October, controlled by north-south movements of the equatorial low-pressure trough. Further, hurricanes form on the Pacific as well as on the Atlantic side of Central America.

It is quite uncertain how many storms form in each area. Table 8.1 contains a rough estimate. Although storms of somewhat less than hurricane intensity are included in the table, hurricanes evidently do not occur very often. Even in an active year, only rarely will the total number of cyclones of hurricane intensity in the Northern Hemisphere exceed fifty. In contrast, about twenty cyclones occur almost every day outside the tropics in winter.

A tropical disturbance cannot intensify without special dynamic conditions in the air flow near 40,000 ft ((200 millibars). These are partly controlled by the westerly wind belt of higher latitudes. Further, the 200-millibar flow pattern inside the tropics varies greatly from one hurricane season to the next. As a result, a situation favorable for a hurricane to form in a wave in the easterlies, for instance, arises only rarely. Only 10 per cent or even less of the rain-bearing disturbances in the tropics intensifies. The number of opportunities not only is low on the average; it also fluctuates greatly from year to year. In the Atlantic area, the number of hurricanes has ranged from one to eleven per season between 1886 and 1963. Long-term trends also occur. Many storms formed before 1895, few in the first 30 years of the twentieth century, many from

Table 8.1   Frequency of Tropical Cyclones per 10 Years

North Atlantic Ocean	73
North Pacific—off west of Mexico	57
North Pacific Ocean, west of 170°E	211
North Indian Ocean, Bay of Bengal	60
North Indian Ocean, Arabian Sea	15
South Indian Ocean, west of 90°E	61
South Indian Ocean, northwestern Australia	9

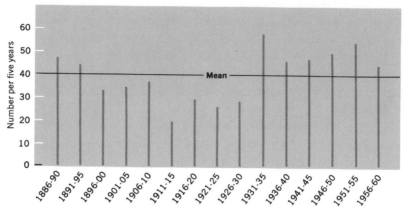

Fig. 8.16   Number of hurricanes and tropical storms of less than hurricane intensity in Atlantic hurricane region in five-season totals. (Data from U.S. Weather Bureau.)

1930 to 1955, and fewer again thereafter (Fig. 8.16). The long-term trend is weakly correlated with temperature changes at the ocean surface, though not enough to prove a close relation. In 1962, in spite of high ocean temperatures, it was almost impossible for a hurricane to get started; September was without a hurricane, a rare record. But in 1950 almost every weak tropical disturbance grew into a hurricane. Indications are that long-period changes in the atmospheric general circulation control the number of hurricanes.

TROPICAL HURRICANES: TRACKS

The hurricane of September, 1960, followed a typical track (Fig. 8.17). After forming in mid-Atlantic, it moved west to west-northwest for a week, guided or steered by the tropical east winds. On September 9–10 it approached, near latitude 25°, the boundary between tropical easterlies and middle-latitude westerlies. It then recurved from the easterlies into the westerlies and moved out of the tropics with increasing forward speed. In contrast, the 1963 hurricane which devastated Cuba literally became suspended in the boundary zone between tropical and middle-latitude wind currents of the upper troposphere. Subject to no steering influence, it drifted for 4 days, until at last the westerlies dipped southward and picked it up.

These two tracks make it rather clear that hurricanes follow diversified and sometimes very erratic paths. Glancing merely at the history of several intense hurricanes between 1954 and 1963 (Fig. 8.17), we find all kinds of odd turns. Generally, when the westerlies are farthest north in midsummer, hurricanes penetrate farthest west and often do not recurve into the westerlies. But, as Fig. 8.17 clearly shows, nothing can be taken for granted.

The September, 1960, hurricane had the unusual distinction of striking, with considerable force, all three areas of the United States East Coast mainly exposed to such storms. Because of the shape of

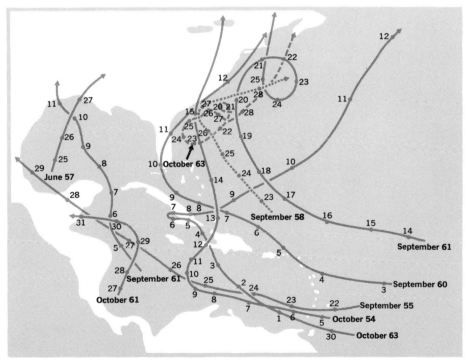

Fig. 8.17   Tracks of ten major hurricanes in Atlantic between 1954 and 1963. Positions shown at 24-hr intervals.

the coast line, which is the same as that of Asia, recurring hurricanes at times enter land far to the north without ever coming close to the southern part of the continent. The decision about warnings is very difficult in these cases, because the hurricanes often accelerate to

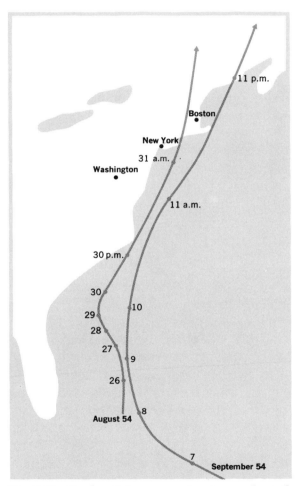

Fig. 8.18 *Tracks of two severe hurricanes along the U.S. East Coast in 1954. Position for 7* A.M. *EST except where marked* P.M. *Very slight turning of the second hurricane on September 11 kept it from following exactly on the path taken by its predecessor.*

forward speeds of no less than 40 to 60 mph, covering 500 miles (800 km) in just 12 hr (Fig. 8.18). Very slight differences in direction of motion will lead to enormous differences in weather over New England. If the hurricane of September, 1954, had moved only a few degrees of arc to the left of its actual track, it would have struck the very same area as its predecessor did 12 days earlier (Fig. 8.18). As it happened, the severe eastern part of the hurricane bypassed most of New England; however, it struck parts of Maine and eastern Canada.

THE U.S. HURRICANE WARNING SERVICE

From humble beginnings the U.S. Weather Bureau has evolved a very effective surveillance of the hurricane area comprising the western Atlantic, the Caribbean, and the Gulf of Mexico. Land station and ship reports, satellite overpasses, radar screening, and reconnaissance flights by the military services combine to permit pinpointing the position of a hurricane center usually within 50 miles. International cooperation for the most part is excellent. The eastern Pacific is also watched to protect shipping and to detect the rare storm that comes to Southern California, bringing damage to the shore but also much needed rain at the height of the drought season (Chapter 10).

When a hurricane reaches a position from which it can become a danger to the coast within 36 hr, a "hurricane watch" is announced. People are alerted that a possible threat exists, and they are urged to keep in close touch with the weather bulletins transmitted by the news media.

When winds of hurricane or near-hurricane force are likely to reach the coast within 24 hr, a "hurricane warning" is issued. This is the major announcement notifying everyone to take all emergency precautions, secure property, and abandon sites likely to be inundated or cut off by rising waters. Electric power, gas, and water supply failure can be the most serious results of wind action. Streets become impassable due to fallen trees and debris, so that ambulances and fire equipment cannot answer emergency calls. But the greatest danger occurs along beaches and inlets; these sustain the combined effect of rising water and high waves.

Over the years, the Weather Bureau has made spectacular progress in the effectiveness of its warning service. Many cities have adopted building codes that protect against all but the most extreme occasions. Through excellent cooperation of local officials and news media loss of life from hurricanes has dropped to very low numbers compared with former years. Property damage, of course, continues to rise—due to the fact that population increases rapidly and that coastal areas are undergoing development everywhere.

Occasional disasters still occur. Over 500 people lost their lives during the hurricane inundation shown in Fig. 8.6. The warnings of the Weather Bureau were excellent, and they were widely disseminated. Nevertheless, a part of the population—by no means all of it—failed to evacuate exposed locations near the Gulf Coast. A claim has been made that the warnings were not understood. The author, who has been in situations where he was exposed to the incessant din of the hurricane publicity, can hardly accept this statement. Shore residents should not assume that their area is immune to hurricane threat, even though it may have escaped damage within man's memory. Hurricanes strike rarely; the location of their precise paths is sufficiently random that in time all areas along the coast might expect a visitation. Further, emergency preparations and evacuation must begin at once upon announcement of the hurricane warning. Sometimes these measures will be taken in vain, when the course of the storm changes a little by good fortune. But no responsible person should delay his action until the hurricane has become a certainty; by that time it is often too late.

The Weather Bureau issues detailed and dramatic hurricane warnings in order to arouse all segments of the public to their impending fate. Following is an example of an excellent prediction issued by the Miami Weather Bureau in the face of very complicated meteorological conditions on August 26, 1964:

Hoist hurricane warnings 2 pm along the lower east coast of Florida from West Palm Beach to Key Largo.

A hurricane watch is in effect north of West Palm Beach to Cape Kennedy.

Dangerous hurricane Cleo continues to move toward the southeast Florida coast and safety precautions against hurricane winds, heavy rain and above normal tides should begin immediately and be rushed to completion with all possible urgency in the area of hurricane warning display from West Palm Beach to Key Largo.

At 2 pm the center of the well organized and intensifying hurricane Cleo was centered by land based radar and air reconnaissance near latitude 24.0 North, longitude 79.7 West, or about 125 miles south-southeast of Miami. Cleo is moving on a course toward the northwest at 17 mph and is expected to be just a very short distance south-southeast of Miami early this evening. The projected track would take the hurricane very near the southeastern Florida coast later this evening with a turn more to the north and no important change in forward speed late tonight and early Thursday.

Highest winds are estimated to 110 to 125 mph near the center. Hurricane force winds will extend 50 miles from the center and gales around 100 miles in all directions.

Small craft along the southeast Florida coast should seek safe harbor immediately and small craft elsewhere along the east Florida coast should remain in port.

Gales and possible hurricane force winds are expected in the extreme western Bahamas, especially around Bimini, by early evening.

Hurricane Cleo is expected to skirt the southeast Florida coast tonight. However, a slightly more northwesterly course would mean a direct hit on the coast. This would mean that storm tides of possibly 8 feet would develop near and just north of the center.

part three

Climate Controls. Climates

9

Mechanisms
of the
General Circulation

The world-wide features of the atmospheric circulation were described at the beginning of this book. Subsequent chapters showed the physical processes in the atmosphere and the motions which, on large and small scales, together produce the world-wide circulation. With this information, we can analyze the way in which the general circulation is maintained, at least within certain limits. If, subsequently, we include the effects of oceans, continents, and large mountain ranges, a picture of the major climates will develop.

HEAT BALANCE

The atmosphere in its entirety absorbs less heat from the sun than it radiates to space (Chapter 2). Yet, the mean temperature remains constant from year to year. Warming of the air in contact with the ground and, more important, the evaporation-condensation-precipitation cycle establish heat balance. Such balance is not achieved locally at every point on earth, nor in every latitude belt. Rather, earth and atmosphere absorb more heat in the tropics than they send to space, while the reverse is true in high latitudes. Flow of heat from the tropics poleward cools the low latitudes and heats the high latitudes (Fig. 1.1); it moderates the climate everywhere.

In a broad sense, the different parts of the earth do experience a solar climate. Temperature rises as the sun's altitude increases and the day lengthens. These two factors combine to produce very large seasonal differences in solar radiation received at the outer limit of the atmosphere (Fig. 9.1). During winter, the radiation decreases steadily toward the pole and vanishes near the polar circle. During summer, it is almost uniform over the whole hemisphere. The sun's altitude in the sky, and with it the amount of radiation received per unit area and time, decreases from latitude 20 to 25° poleward. But the length of day increases, and the long daylight hours compensate for the low solar altitudes.

Earth and atmosphere absorb only a portion of the incoming sunlight. In the tropics and subtropics about 30 per cent of the incident radiation is reflected back to space (Fig. 9.1). From there, the albedo increases to well over 50 per cent in the polar belt, especially in summer. This increase is due partly to the long path the solar rays take through the atmosphere at high latitudes, partly to heavy cloud cover over the polar cap during summer. The atmospheric circulation itself lays down the cloud cover; thus, it controls to a considerable extent the amount of heat made available to earth and atmosphere.

Absorption of radiation during summer is highest in the belt from 30 to 40°, where a large part of the United States lies. Extreme summer temperatures of 100 to 115°F (38 to 46°C) do not result

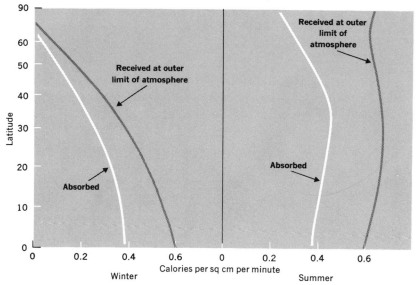

Fig. 9.1 Solar radiation received at outer limit of the atmosphere, and solar radiation absorbed by earth and troposphere, for winter (December to January) and summer (June to August) in the Northern Hemisphere. Latitude scale proportional to area on the globe. (Adapted from J. London.)

through importation of hot air from the south, but by direct broiling of the continent itself!

Radiation emitted to space from earth and atmosphere below the tropopause varies within narrow limits, both seasonally and from pole to equator (Fig. 9.2), compared with the changes in incoming radiation. Over the tropics as a whole, temperature and cloudiness, and thereby infrared radiation, are almost constant through the year. In high latitudes, where temperature changes seasonally, the outgoing radiation increases from winter to summer. It moderates the seasonal temperature changes and acts to limit temperature extremes. When temperatures are low, the radiation is small, which slows cooling; at high temperatures it becomes large, and this counteracts further warming.

Almost the whole hemisphere experiences net radiation cooling in winter, while in summer net heating takes place at all latitudes (Fig. 9.3). Most of this heat is stored in the surface layer of the earth, mainly in the oceans. Heat transport from the tropics pole-

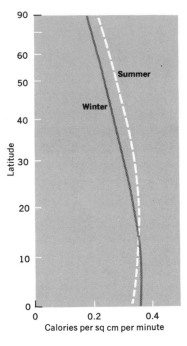

Fig. 9.2 Infrared radiation emitted to
space from earth and troposphere in the
Northern Hemisphere during summer
and winter. (Adapted from J. London.)

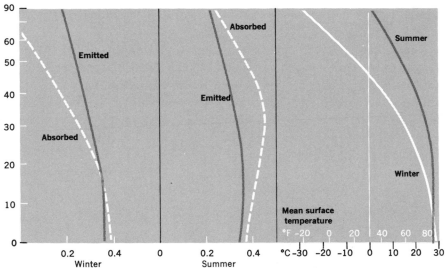

Fig. 9.3 Comparison of solar radiation absorbed and of infrared radiation
emitted by earth and troposphere during winter and summer. Right: mean
temperature of atmosphere at 5-ft height in the Northern Hemisphere.

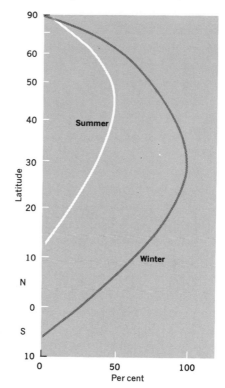

Fig. 9.4 Transport of heat from the tropics toward North Pole in winter and summer. Expressed in percentages of largest transport at latitude 30° in winter.

ward still takes place in summer, though at a much lower rate than in winter (Fig. 9.4). Both the temperature difference between low and high latitudes (Fig. 9.3) and the heat transport are about half as large in summer as they are in winter in the Northern Hemisphere. Heat transport is strongest near latitude 30° in winter and near latitude 45° in summer.

MECHANISMS OF HEAT TRANSPORT [1]

Poleward heat transport, mitigating the climates, should be expected from the general principle that heat flows from a warmer to a colder body. It is not obvious, however, why the transfer takes place at the observed rate. If the heat exchange were a little more

[1] A parallel discussion of momentum exchange is given in advanced texts on meteorology.

rapid, the tropics would become slightly cooler and the polar belt, with its relatively small area, might be warmed enough so that all ice in the Arctic would melt. With slower heat transport a new ice age could develop. Lacking knowledge about the factors controlling the actual heat transport, we can still search for the mechanisms which produce it.

One such mechanism is within the everyday experience of all who have spent a winter in the United States, Europe, or another middle-latitude area (Fig. 1.3). With winds from south the air becomes warmer; with winds from north the temperature falls. The movement of warm air masses into the polar regions and of cold air masses into the tropics opposes the warming and cooling trends that would result from radiation alone.

The oceans also play a role in heat exchange. As we saw in Fig. 1.6, warm water flows poleward along the western side and cold water equatorward on the eastern side of an ocean basin in the subtropics. At higher latitudes the east-west position of warm and cold currents in the ocean reverses, but still the warm water moves to higher and the cold water to lower latitudes. Thus the oceans contribute to poleward heat transport, accounting for about 25 per cent of the total transport in the subtropics and middle latitudes.

Figure 9.5 depicts a different means for heat exchange, the simple heat engine. This diagram has coordinates of latitude and height (or pressure) showing the *vertical* plane, while the motion in Fig. 1.3 is *horizontal*. The simple heat engine rests on the principle that warm fluid moves from heat to cold source at low pressure, while cold fluid moves from cold to heat source at high pressure. At the cold source the warm mass loses heat, increases in density, and sinks; the reverse takes place at the heat source.

In principle, the concept of the simple heat engine applies to land and sea breezes (Chapter 11) and to the monsoon circulations. For those wind systems, and even more so for the general circulation, condensation heating from cumulus and cumulonimbus clouds becomes the strongest heat source, after the motion sketched in Fig. 9.5 has started. The right-hand edge of this diagram resembles the equatorial low-pressure trough with its narrow zone of

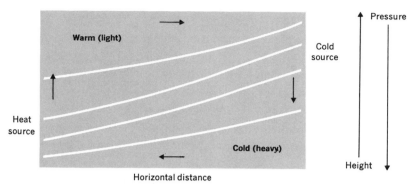

Fig. 9.5   Model of simple heat engine.

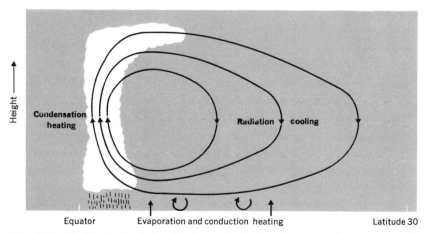

Fig. 9.6   Model of circulation in the vertical plane between the equator and latitude 30°.

heavy precipitation. However, the atmosphere does not cool in so confined a region. It is a cold source over nearly the entire volume it occupies, so sinking motion must also be spread throughout this volume. The model of Fig. 9.6 shows a narrow rainfall belt and a broad zone of descent—realistic, at least, for the low latitudes with their narrow equatorial rainfall belt and the broad area of descent, coupled with dryness, in the subtropics.

Because the analogy is realistic in low latitudes, the whole general circulation was once thought to act as a simple heat engine. Then computations which were begun in Austria about 1920 and pursued widely from the 1940s onward demonstrated that the cyclones and anticyclones outside the tropics, and the waves in the upper westerlies, provided an important means for exchanging heat between tropics and polar zone. Fortunately, light has been thrown on the importance of the disturbances in the westerlies compared to the simple heat engine, through laboratory experiments conducted by Dave Fultz (University of Chicago) since the late 1940s.

GENERAL CIRCULATION IN MODEL EXPERIMENTS

In the 1940s the late Carl-Gustav Rossby discovered that general circulations on rotating bodies of widely different sizes—ranging from small experimental basins to huge balls like the sun—could be made comparable by reducing their scale in the following way. He proposed to express the characteristic velocity of a rotating gas or fluid—in the atmosphere, wind speed—as a percentage of the speed of the body around its axis at the equator. The surface of the earth revolves at 1,000 mph about the earth's axis at the equator; the typical speed in middle-latitude jet streams is 100 mph and Rossby's ratio, therefore, is 1:10.

Following this discovery, Fultz began to study the motion of water in small rotating basins, initially using dishpans, with heat and cold sources. Varying the rates of rotation and heating, he found that he could produce different types of general circulations. Rotating the basin slowly he observed that the "winds" around the cold source attained the speed of the basin at its outer rim, or equator, so that Rossby's number became unity (Fig. 9.7). In this general circulation, heat transfer takes place according to the simple heat engine model; the flow field is symmetrical around the cold source and constant in time. At faster rotation of the basin, the ratio of highest water speed to rim speed of the basin dropped to 1:10, so that the flow corresponded to wind speeds of 100 mph in the atmosphere. Wave trains developed that kept changing shape with time (Fig. 9.8). They resemble the waves in the upper wester-lies to a remarkable degree (Figs. 9.9 and 9.10).

The basin in which these experiments were conducted was flat, so that its whole area rotated solidly about the center. The earth's surface, however, becomes more and more tilted with re-spect to the earth's axis as latitude increases, and it therefore rotates at an increasing rate about the axis (Fig. 6.3). Thus the tropical general circulation should be compared with the basin experiment at low rotation rates, while the fast rotation experiments are more applicable to the higher latitudes.

These analogies succeed remarkably well. In the tropics we encounter the trade winds, which are the steadiest low-level air current of the world. Although the high-tropospheric flow is vari-able, heat transport from the tropics to their poleward limit takes place largely according to the simple heat engine model. Outside the tropics the flow field is unsteady at all heights; cold outbreaks toward the tropics and warm air incursions toward high latitudes accomplish the heat transfer. It follows that the *difference in the component of rotation about the earth's axis is a most important factor in producing different types of general circulations and climates inside and outside the tropics.*

The rate at which the earth rotates in large measure deter-mines the latitude separating low- and high-latitude types of general circulation and climate. If the length of a day were 48 or 96 hr in-stead of 24, the low-latitude general circulation might reach as far as latitude 60° because of the decrease in rotation rate. Then the daily weather in middle latitudes would be vastly different from that which we know.

The knowledge that general circulations differ according to the rotation rate of a star or planet is exciting, because man is on

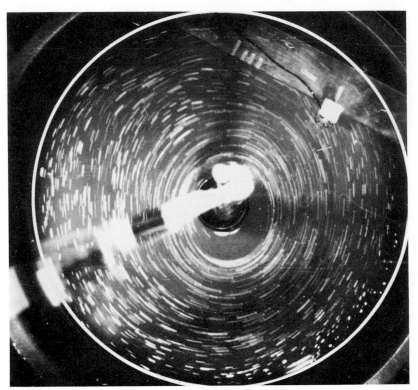

Fig. 9.7   Flow at the top of the water in model experiment with slow rotation of basin. Motion made visible by time exposure photographs of aluminum filings floating on the top. The longer the streaks, the faster the motion. This experiment shows a symmetrical circulation with strongest speeds near the inner cold source (ring), where the streaks are longest. (From Dave Fultz, in American Meteorological Society Monograph No. 21, vol. 4.)

the threshold of observing the atmospheres of other celestial bodies in some detail. Since the length of day on Jupiter is about 10 earth hr, while Venus hardly rotates at all, we should expect very different general circulations on these two planets. Obviously, factors such as the composition of atmospheres, the nature of surfaces, and internal heat sources also play their role. It is interesting, however, that the model experiments have produced great similarities with the general atmospheric circulation, although heat and cold sources are quite different in the two systems. General circulations may well

Fig. 9.8 Surface flow in fast rotation model experiment showing five long waves. Long streaks along narrow band outline jet-stream type current. (From Dave Fultz.)

be independent, at least to some degree, of the precise way in which heat is made available to them.

VARIATIONS OF THE GENERAL CIRCULATION

The troughs and ridges of the basin experiment in Fig. 9.8 march eastward without interruption. The troughs and ridges in the atmosphere persist in preferred positions (Figs. 1.9 and 1.12), because the surface of the earth is not uniform. Sometimes, however, the

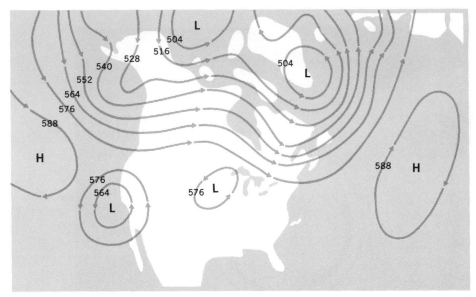

Fig. 9.9   *Flow at 500 millibars on October 17, 1963 (contours of the 500-millibar surface in ten-meter units). The waves are widely spaced and have little north-south extent.*

location of the long waves departs widely from the normal over long periods—a month or even a season. This is discussed in Chapter 14. In addition, the westerly circulation changes greatly over periods of 1 to 3 weeks' duration, accompanied by large weather changes. This oscillation also occurs in certain basin experiments. Although not fully understood, it is probably part of the means by which the general circulation maintains its heat balance.

For a week the waves may be very weak and hardly recognizable. Then a change occurs, often suddenly; the waves become prominent and intense, again for about a week. When the waves are flat, the belt of westerlies contracts toward the pole. We see this in Fig. 9.9, where the entire belt of westerlies lies north of 40°. Little north-south motion of air takes place, and over most of the area along the southern margin of the westerlies the mild and pleasant weather of Indian summer prevails. In contrast, the westerlies acquired large amplitude by November 2, 1963, two weeks later (Fig. 9.10). Some of the streamlines on that day wander all the way be-

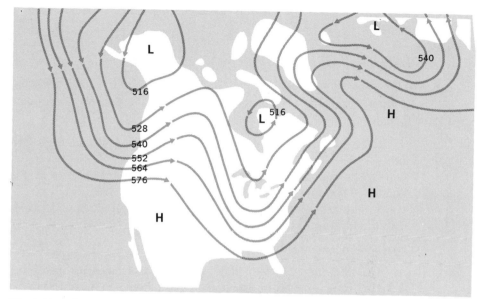

Fig. 9.10   Flow at 500 millibars on November 2, 1963. Spacing between waves is much shorter than on October 17, 1963, and their north-south extent is much greater.

tween latitudes 30° and 60°. Wavelengths are much shorter than in Fig. 9.9; three waves overlie the western part of the hemisphere compared to two on October 17. Wide incursions of cold air toward the equator occur in the troughs over the eastern Pacific, eastern North America, and the eastern Atlantic. Warm air moves far northward over northwestern Canada and Greenland. So the pattern of Fig. 9.10 suggests strong heat exchange between high and low latitudes, which reduces temperature contrasts, while such exchange is very weak on October 17.

Vigorous cyclones at the surface, widespread bad weather, and alternating warm spells and cold outbreaks accompany the large-amplitude flow. Such cyclones move northeastward, even northward, under the influence of the upper winds, while, during small-amplitude flow aloft, they travel mainly from west to east. Fig. 9.10 shows a climax of weather activity. A relatively quiet period normally follows such a peak until the north-south temperature difference, weakened by the intense air-mass exchange across latitudes, once again attains average, and then above average, values.

LARGE–SCALE CONTROLS OF CLIMATE

The discussion in this chapter has brought out three factors controlling the general circulation and, ultimately, the large-scale climates:

1. The relative strength of heat sources in low and high latitudes;

2. The rate at which the earth revolves about its axis at the equator—1,000 mph;

3. The rate at which the earth's surface rotates about the axis at different latitudes.

To these factors must be added:

4. Differences between land and water surfaces in absorbing, radiating, and exchanging heat by conduction and evaporation;

5. Barrier effects of the large mountain ranges.

Differences between Land and Water Surfaces. The temperature of the surface of the oceans remains almost constant through the 24 hr of the day, and it changes very little with season compared to the temperature of the land. Water warmed at the surface can be mixed downward by the winds, and this mixing may extend over a layer 300 ft (100 m) and more in depth. Since the heat capacity of water is very high, its temperature rises only slowly in response to heating. Thus the outgoing radiation remains nearly constant during the season when the water is heated, and the heat is stored in the ocean. During the cooling period, the top layer in the water becomes denser than the layers underneath and begins to overturn; this transports warmer water to the surface. Thus, turbulence keeps ocean temperatures relatively constant throughout the year.

The warm and cold ocean currents also act to keep ocean temperature changes down by moving warm water away from the regions with heating, and cold water from the regions with cooling. Finally, evaporation from the ocean into the atmosphere reduces the oceanic heat storage, mainly in the tropics and subtropics.

Over land, in contrast, very little heat penetrates into the ground and then to a shallow depth (Fig. 11.19). The topsoil, which usually has a low heat capacity, warms strongly during the day and during summer. Back radiation from the ground at high temperatures is large, so the ground stores little heat. When nighttime and winter come, the land surface cools strongly; there is little or no upward flow of heat from deeper layers in the soil that could keep the surface temperature constant.

Adjacent to the ground, the air becomes warmer and colder mainly through contact with the earth, as we found in Chapters 2 and 3. Thus, the daily and annual ranges of temperature are much larger over land than over sea: a *marine* climate is always temperate, a *continental* climate filled with extremes.

The Effect of Large Mountain Ranges. The protrusion of large mountain ranges into the atmosphere affects large-scale climate in several ways, even in regions remote from the mountains. Barriers such as the Rocky Mountains channel cold air outbreaks; they effectively protect the West Coast of the United States from most cold air invasions from Canada. The Rockies also prevent marine air from penetrating inland, so that the Central United States is colder and drier than the region would be if the westerly flow could continue unhindered across the width of the North American continent.

In mountainous regions, the surface heat source for the atmosphere is raised above the surrounding plains and ocean areas. The consequences of this difference in altitude are not fully understood, although it is known to play an important role in establishing and maintaining the Asiatic summer monsoon. Probably the strongest impact on the general circulation comes from mountain ranges, especially the Rockies and the Andes, that extend perpendicular to the westerly flow in the upper air, over thousands of miles. Because of this very great length, the major portion of the westerly current cannot go around these ranges; it must cross them. Air columns shrink vertically as they approach the mountains in order to get across; on the lee side they expand vertically (Fig. 9.11). This pattern of vertical displacements agrees with observed precipitation: much on the windward and very little on the leeward side (Fig. 11.1).

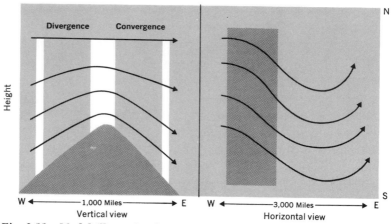

Fig. 9.11   Model illustrating large-scale airflow over a mountain range in vertical view (left) and in the horizontal plane above the mountains (right). Changes in vertical and horizontal extent of the air columns crossing the mountains indicated by shading on left.

On-the windward side the contracting columns must expand horizontally, or diverge; the reverse happens on the lee side. As discussed in Chapter 6, the absolute vorticity of the columns decreases when they diverge horizontally and increases when they converge horizontally. A broad westerly current will therefore move on the wavy path shown in Fig. 9.11. (See also Fig. 6.9.) This wave is forced by the mountains; it will be stationary or, at least, recur in the same location. Climatic upper-air charts (Fig. 1.9) do, in fact, show the wave.

When the wave pattern is established, the northwest flow east of the mountains will act to draw cold outbreaks southward and thus to intensify the continental climate west of the Mississippi. Further, the wave motion, once initiated, should continue downstream from the United States. In Fig. 1.9, we observe a climatic ridge over the Atlantic and a trough over eastern Europe. The speculation has been advanced that this trough is part of the wave motion of the westerlies begun over the Rockies. If this is true, a single large mountain chain would indeed influence climate around a very large portion of the latitude belt in which it is situated. Whether the speculation is valid, however, is still unknown.

10

Large-scale Climate

By creating belts with little cloud and much sunshine and belts with large cloud cover and much precipitation, the general circulation lays down preferred states of weather and weather sequences over large areas, setting the conditions and limits for many manifestations of life. In part, we can summarize this impact of the general circulation with a global view of the weather elements; in part we must turn to a closer inspection in smaller areas because of the large role played by geographical features.

Average winds near the surface and aloft, the variability of wind, and the paths which disturbances follow have already been described. Further, we have seen how important occasional destructive winds and weather extremes in general are for climate. We now turn to large-scale temperature and precipitation fields.

SURFACE TEMPERATURE

The right-hand diagram of Fig. 9.3 shows that the temperature difference between tropical and polar zones of the Northern Hemisphere averages about 110°F (60°C) in winter, and half this amount in summer. Seasonally, temperature is almost constant at low latitudes; from there the range increases northward to attain 55°F (30°C) in the polar belt.

Continents and oceans modify this picture profoundly, as we see by comparing temperatures at 50°N and 50°S for January and July (Figs. 10.1 and 10.2). Latitude 50°S is situated entirely over the Southern Ocean, except for an intercept by the southern tip of South America near 60°W. Temperature varies little around the globe in both seasons. The average seasonal temperature difference (10°F or 6°C) would be slightly larger if we compared February and August. Because water is permeable and has a high heat-storage capacity, the highest and lowest temperatures of the ocean surface, and of the air over the oceans, lag behind the solstices by 2 months. Over land, the lag is only 1 month.

At 50°N the seasonal temperature range is 47°F (25°C). This latitude circle passes through the bulk of the North American and Eurasian continents. Over the oceans, especially their eastern parts, temperature and temperature range approach that at 50°S. But the continents are much colder than the oceans in winter and warmer in summer; the contrast between summer and winter temperatures is largest a little inland from the eastern shore of the continents.

The east coasts are about as warm in summer and colder in winter than the west coasts at latitude 50°. At lower latitudes west coasts are much colder in summer than east coasts. The influence of the prevailing westerly winds is evident: oceanic air is carried inland across the west coasts, producing a marine climate; along east coasts this influence is felt only rarely, when the wind blows from

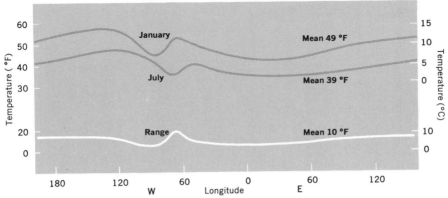

Fig. 10.1 *Mean surface air temperature for January and July, and seasonal temperature range, around the globe at 50°S. Heavy bars at top of diagram denote land.*

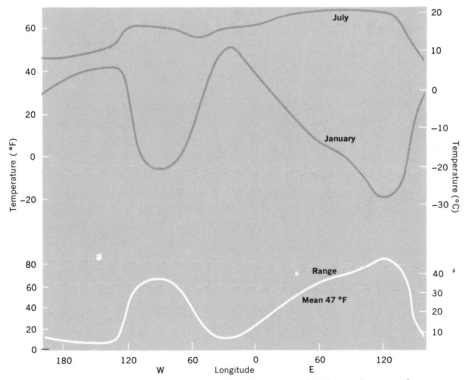

Fig. 10.2 *Mean surface air temperature for January and July, and seasonal temperature range, around the globe at 50°N. Note abrupt transition at American West Coast compared to gradual change across Europe.*

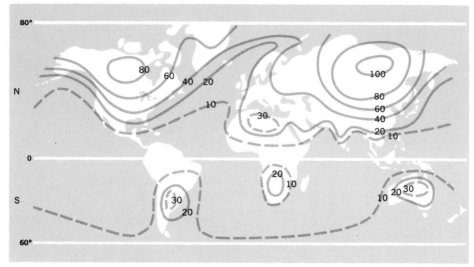

Fig. 10.3   Seasonal range of surface air temperature (°F).

east against the prevailing drift. The marine climate extends much farther inland over Europe than over North America, because the westerly flow is not blocked by a mountain range.

Globally, the seasonal change of mean temperature is largest, above 100°F (55°C), at high latitudes of the largest continent, Eurasia (Fig. 10.3). The next highest variation is in Canada (80°F or 45°C). In the Southern Hemisphere, Australia has the greatest range, comparable to that over North Africa, at about the same latitude. Across the oceans, the temperature range decreases from west to east, as air moving offshore from the continents gradually assumes the temperature of the ocean surface.

WORLD PRECIPITATION

Two factors that control temperature to a high degree, latitude and distribution of continents and oceans, exercise relatively little influence on precipitation. For instance, we cannot state that it rains more over oceans than over continents. Large ocean areas are completely deficient in precipitation, including such areas as the Arabian Sea during the southwest monsoon season, when thick dust is carried all the way from Africa and Arabia to the vicinity of the Indian coast.

Averaging rainfall around the globe at different latitudes (Fig. 10.4), we find a peak near 5°N, the mean latitude of the equatorial low-pressure trough. Minima in the subtropics reflect the descending branch of the general circulation cell of Fig. 9.6. Farther poleward, in the regime of unsteady westerly flow with traveling cyclones, there is a second maximum of precipitation.

Figure 10.4 smooths out many sharp regional contrasts. For instance, equatorial trough rainfall is confined to a very narrow belt over the ocean areas where the trough position remains almost constant through the year. Large groups of islands in the equatorial Pacific are arid. Just once in a while disturbances along the equa-

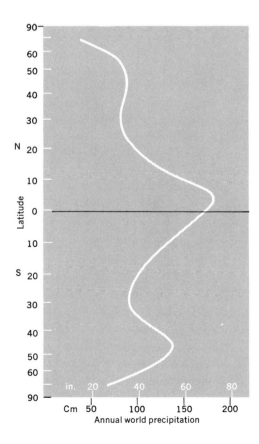

Fig. 10.4 Estimated distribution of annual precipitation with latitude. The latitude scale represents equal areas on earth.

torial trough move several hundred miles north or south from their normal track. Then these islands receive a deluge, followed perhaps by 10 years with almost no rain. Obviously, the term "average precipitation" means nothing under these circumstances.

The trade-wind areas appear in Fig. 10.5 as westward extensions of the continental deserts. Here is the center of subsiding motion of the general circulation, mainly over the eastern and central parts of the oceans. Under the influence of compression heating a semi-permanent temperature inversion forms, the *trade-wind inversion*. It puts a lid on cumulus cloud development; stratocumulus overcast without rain covers very large areas. The inversion gradually weakens and rises in altitude along the trade-wind flow as heating and absorption of moisture from the ocean take place. Over the western parts of the oceans the inversion disappears in summer. Cumulus clouds can break through to great heights; the trade-wind flow becomes wavy and the disturbances described in Chapter 8 make their appearance.

In middle latitudes, the large mountain ranges superimpose strong east-west variations on the broad belt of precipitation along the main storm tracks. Wherever the mountains block the westerly flow, precipitation is very high on the western slopes, while the lee side is arid. The mountain effect is largest over North and South America, but smaller ranges, such as those of Scandinavia and New Zealand, also produce precipitation discontinuities. There are no mountains to oppose the entry of cyclones and marine air into Europe, and there precipitation decreases only slowly toward the east. Mild temperatures and ample rain provide a favorable setting for human development.

Distance from the oceans controls precipitation only weakly compared to the influence of mountain ranges, subsidence regions, and cyclone tracks. In the higher latitudes of North America and Asia, precipitation decreases on the poleward side of the main storm track. This decrease does not produce aridity. As discussed in Chapter 4, evaporation increases strongly as temperature increases. Therefore, the water needs of vegetation are much greater in warm than in cold climates. In the trade-wind zone, where strong winds augment the evaporation rate, an annual rainfall of 60 in. may not be

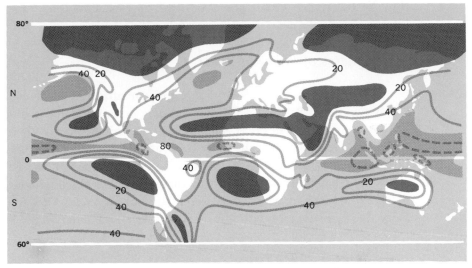

Fig. 10.5   World distribution of annual precipitation (in.), simplified to show only major regimes; oceanic rainfall estimated. Lines are for 20 and 40 in. Areas with precipitation below 10 in. and above 80 in. shaded; dashed lines: 120 in.

enough to support forest growth, while in high latitudes forests can thrive on 20 in.

Figure 10.5 contains many uncertainties. Over sparsely settled land areas, knowledge of annual precipitation is poor. Instruments to measure rain over the oceans have not been perfected (Chapter 1); all oceanic precipitation values are based on estimates. Nevertheless, Figs. 10.4 and 10.5 are regarded as giving world precipitation within 25 to 33 per cent accuracy. Since the height of the ocean surfaces remains essentially unchanged from year to year, evaporation from the oceans must equal the rainfall into the oceans plus runoff from rivers—the *hydrologic cycle*. According to one estimate, the evaporation per unit area averages 20 in. per year over land and 33 in. over the oceans; the precipitation, 29 in. over land and ocean alike. The land therefore has a water surplus of 9 in. and the oceans a deficit of 4 in. Since the territory of the oceans is roughly 2½ times larger than that of the continents, the surplus over land equals the deficit over the oceans. Balance must be provided by water return through the rivers. Observations of river flow confirm that these water balance estimates are approximately valid.

Climates of Selected Areas

If the globe were covered with a uniform surface, the climate at any point would, presumably, depend only on latitude and could be looked up in a small table. All complications arise from the great variety of geographical features—from location and size of the continents,- to hills, streambeds, and soils. Local climate will be the subject of Chapter 11. Here we shall examine briefly a small number of climates, each of which is representative of large areas on the globe, located similarly with respect to the general circulation.

EQUATORIAL TROUGH

In the heart of the equatorial zone, temperature varies so little through the year that one speaks of dry and wet seasons rather than summer and winter. The daily temperature range (10 to 20°F) greatly exceeds the seasonal range. Man grows sensitive even to small temperature changes in the tropics; a move to just a 2,000-ft (600-m) elevation means considerable relief (Fig. 10.6). Capital cities of several countries, or at least "summer capitals," are located several thousand feet above sea level rather than along the shore.

The perpetual fear in many parts of the tropics is that the water supply will fail, even though much of the world's heaviest rainfall occurs there. Drought for one or more years contains the real ingredients for catastrophe in a world in which the demand for water is rising rapidly. Compared to drought, the problem of flood control appears to be receding as the scope of engineering work widens. Dams can be built to contain most floods, but constructing huge reservoirs for storage does not assure that they can be filled and maintained.

The equatorial trough zone, migrating north and south in the course of the year, passes the latitudes between its extreme positions twice, lagging behind the sun by about 2 months (Fig. 10.7). Therefore, many parts of the equatorial belt, but by no means all, have

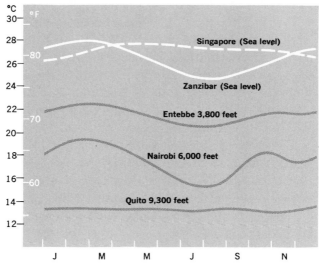

Fig. 10.6 *Seasonal course of surface air temperature at equatorial locations showing small seasonal range but large decrease of temperature with altitude. Singapore, Malaya, 1°N, 104°E; Zanzibar, off eastern Africa, 6°S, 39°E; Entebbe, eastern Africa, 0°, 32°E; Nairobi, eastern Africa, 1°S, 37°E; Quito, Ecuador, 0°, 78°W.*

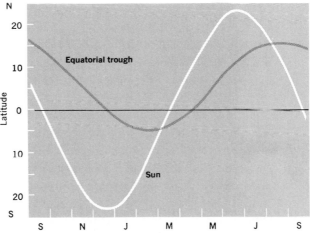

Fig. 10.7 *Seasonal course of mean latitude of the equatorial trough of low pressure compared to overhead position of the sun.*

two rainy and two dry seasons. Where the trough moves as it does in Fig. 10.7, the peaks of the rainy seasons occur in December and April on the equator, in May and November at latitude 5°N, and in June and October at latitude 10°N. At latitudes 15°N and 5°S, the two rainy seasons merge into a single broad peak. Where the trough migration differs from Fig. 10.7, this scheme must be adjusted. Over East Africa, for instance, the trough moves as far as 15°S in the southern summer, January to March. There a double rainfall peak occurs well south of 5°S. At the island of Zanzibar, just off the East African coast at 6°S, the "long" rainy season is centered in April–May, the "short" season in November–December. Between them, a short dry season falls in January–February, a long dry season in July–October. Mean annual rainfall is moderate, almost identical with the precipitation averaged around the globe at 5°S (Fig. 10.8).

In many years the seasonal course of rainfall deviates widely from the average. In 1939, half of the annual total, fully 26 in., fell in May. Although the short rainy season failed, this was enough to bring the total for the year close to average. In 1925, the long rainy season was deficient, but heavy water delivery in the short season—not so short in that year—compensated. Wherever there are two chances for rainfall during the year, rather than just one, the probability of ample rain is, of course, enhanced.

How often does total yearly precipitation fall substantially above or below the long-term mean? We shall consider departures in three classes: 20 to 30 per cent, 30 to 50 per cent, and greater than 50 per cent of mean rainfall. Deficiencies of 50 per cent and greater create serious difficulties. Above-average rain may relieve drought; when the soil is saturated, however, it will lead to floods.

At Zanzibar, two-thirds of the years in the 60-year record had precipitation within 20 per cent of average, and 8 per cent (5 years) had a deficiency greater than 30 per cent, severe drought. If these numbers were stable, serious rainfall failure would be expected six times, and disastrous drought twice, per century. The actual situation is likely to be more extreme. Only 60 years of record were available for constructing Fig. 10.8. Even with 100 years it is unlikely that the true probability for extreme drought could have been

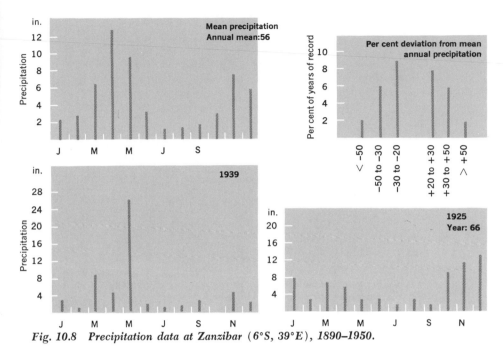

Fig. 10.8   Precipitation data at Zanzibar (6°S, 39°E), 1890–1950.

determined. A much longer record is needed for this purpose, even in the absence of long-period (secular) climatic changes.

MONSOON

The continental areas 5 to 10° latitude and more from the equator, which the equatorial trough enters during summer, experience a tendency toward seasonally reversing wind, or monsoon. In the Northern Hemisphere, wind direction reverses from northeast to southwest, and in the Southern Hemisphere from southeast to northwest.

Two or three weeks of light wind normally precede the wind change. Over southeastern Asia, the summer, or southwest, monsoon usually begins in May and retreats in October, variable by 2 to 3 weeks from year to year. Over India, the summer monsoon is retarded until the middle or late June by the westerly winds aloft, which flow around the southern periphery of the Himalayan Moun-

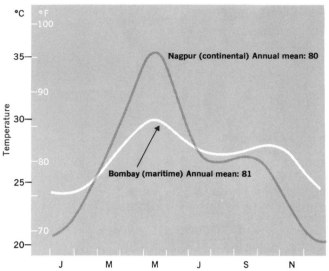

Fig. 10.9   Seasonal course of surface air temperature at Bombay (19°N, 73°E) on the west coast of India, and at Nagpur (21°N, 79°E) in the middle of the subcontinent.

tain barrier. The advance, or "burst," of the monsoon is always awaited with anxiety since it brings much-needed rain after long dryness and heat.

During both monsoon advance and retreat, tropical storms of hurricane intensity may form in both oceans flanking India—the Bay of Bengal and the Arabian Sea. Occasionally, these storms move onshore, mainly along the east coast from Madras to Calcutta. They have produced some great disasters through inundation from storm surges (Chapter 8) costing thousands of lives.

Temperature. In India and Pakistan, we are concerned with latitudes where over the largest part of the subcontinent the sun essentially makes one overhead appearance and then recedes to a minimum altitude from the zenith of 40 to 50° during December–January. Seasonal temperature changes should be much greater than they are on the equator. At Bombay (Fig. 10.9) the mean annual temperature is 80.6°F (27°C), almost the same as it is at Singapore (Fig. 10.6), but the seasonal range is 9°F (5°C). Even so, this is still a low value due to Bombay's coastal location. At inland cities like Nagpur, the mean May temperature of 96 to 97°F—with all daily maxima far above 100°F—equals the best (or worst!) that the Sahara and Arizona have to offer.

Both at Bombay and Nagpur the temperature rises from comfortable values in midwinter to the premonsoon extreme in May. Then temperature falls under the influence of cloudiness and rain—typical for all monsoon regimes. A second minor, but humid and unwelcome, temperature rise follows retreat of the summer monsoon, before winter brings several months of relief.

Bombay and Nagpur illustrate the difference between continental and coastal location. Though the mean annual temperature of both cities is identical, Nagpur's winter is markedly colder and its spring hotter than Bombay's; the annual temperature range is 27°F (13°C), three times the range at Bombay.

Precipitation. Virtually all rain falls in the brief summer monsoon season (Fig. 10.10). The water yield during the few rainy season months is absolutely vital for the huge population of the sub-

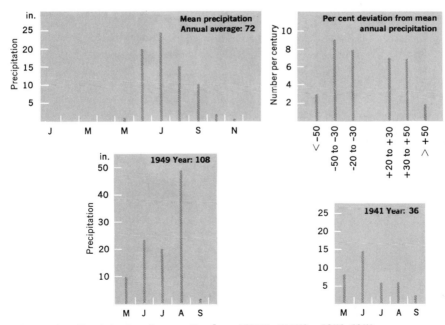

Fig. 10.10 *Precipitation data at Bombay (19°N, 73°E), 1851–1950.*

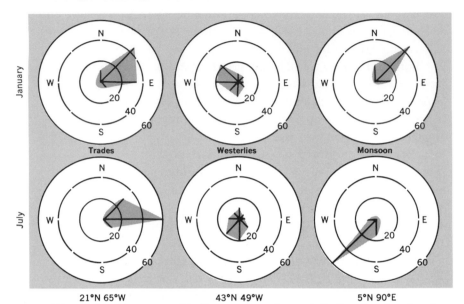

Fig. 10.11 Frequency distribution of surface wind direction for the three indicated regimes in January and July. The shafts show the direction from which the wind comes (see also Appendix I); the circles denote the per cent frequency with which the wind blows from a given direction on the 8-point compass (N, NE, E, etc.); for instance, the trade wind blows 60 per cent of the time from the east during summer.

continent. For almost a century meteorologists have attempted to predict the monsoon rainfall several months in advance, just because of its critical relation to the vast supply of food required. Excepting areas where the monsoon blows against mountains, the rainy season does not bring copious rain on every day, though showers may occur on most. Tropical depressions bring heavy rainfall (Fig. 8.5). These are "weak" cyclones, but only in terms of the wind field; even wind speeds of minimal gale force are rare. But half or more of the monthly precipitation may be delivered by one such disturbance during 2 or 3 days. Between such depressions, interruptions of the monsoon occur that may last 2 weeks and even more.

Because the occasional disturbance holds a key position in producing rain, monsoon precipitation is very variable. In contrast to locations with two rainy seasons, the monsoon countries do not have that second chance to recoup deficiencies of the main rainy season. During 1941, when only half of the mean annual precipitation fell at Bombay, the monsoon failed. At the other extreme, 1949 brought one of the highest totals on record. By the end of August only average precipitation had fallen. Then, in September, rainfall exceeded 10 in. on each of 3 succeeding days, when the equatorial trough stagnated near the city. The monthly total was enormous, well above mean annual precipitation in the Northeastern United States. Though precipitation over a large area is less variable than point precipitation (Chapter 12), the record for Bombay nevertheless highlights the cogent reasons for India's great concern with the monsoon rainfall.

TRADE WINDS

As Figs. 1.7 and 1.8 showed, the trade winds blow from the northeast in the Northern Hemisphere and from southeast in the Southern Hemisphere. The equatorward motion is strongest in the eastern parts of the oceans and may disappear over the western portions during summer. Wind direction is nearly constant when compared to that of monsoon and middle-latitude climates (Fig. 10.11). On the rare days when the trade wind fails, weather is "unusual." During the hurricane season, winds from west are always regarded with suspicion; they often indicate formation or approach of a severe storm.

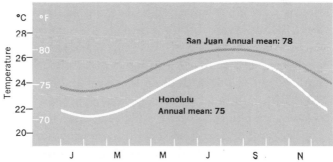

Fig. 10.12 *Seasonal course of surface air temperature at San Juan, West Indies (18°N, 66°W), and at Honolulu, Hawaii (21°N, 158°W).*

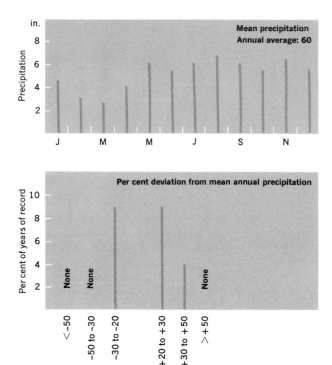

Fig. 10.13   Precipitation data for San Juan (18°N, 66°W),
1900–1950.

Hurricanes fall in the class of weather catastrophe on the trade-wind islands. They have determined the patterns of agriculture on many islands, even though a really severe storm may cross them, on the average, only every 50 or 100 years. On September 13, 1928, the day of San Felipe, a hurricane of great intensity passed over the whole island of Puerto Rico in the West Indies. With winds in the 150 to 200 mph bracket, damage was enormous. The coffee, cocoa, and tobacco industries were wiped out; they have never recovered.

The city of San Juan, on the northern shore of the island, is fully exposed to the trade winds. Temperatures are moderate and the seasonal temperature range is small, only 5 to 6°F (Fig. 10.12). In summer, rains help to keep temperature down. Coldest and warmest months lag behind the solstice by 2 months, showing how the ocean controls temperature.

Rain may fall in every month (Fig. 10.13). Precipitation from hurricanes does not affect the precipitation curve, since they are too infrequent, and weak disturbances often yield rain just as heavy. Droughts of a few months' duration occur often, mainly during the relatively dry winter season. They quickly become severe because of high evaporation by the trade winds. Sometimes, however, January rains bringing as much as 15 in. have prevented annual rainfall totals from falling far below average.

With such favorable conditions, no year from 1900 to 1950 had precipitation more than 30 per cent below average. The problem is to develop enough water storage facilities so that water from rainy months can be held over as a protection against drought. In some years, water must be imported to some of the smaller islands in the

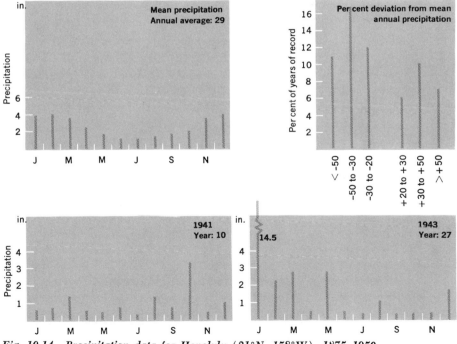

Fig. 10.14   Precipitation data for Honolulu (21°N, 158°W), 1875–1950.

West Indies, where ground water and reservoir storage are inadequate.

Honolulu, pleasantly located in the Hawaiian Island group of the Pacific near latitude 21°N, represents climate in the eastern portion of the subtropical high-pressure cells, dominated by the trade-wind inversion. Hurricanes were unknown around Hawaii before the 1950s, when several storms of minimal hurricane intensity passed near the islands.

Water supply and distribution is the main problem here, too. The truly spectacular orographic control of rainfall is described in the next chapter. Honolulu's average annual rainfall is estimated as equal to that of the surrounding ocean. The seasonal course (Fig. 10.14) is inverse to that of Puerto Rico. Because of the trade-wind inversion, tropical-type disturbances do not occur or are very weak. Only occasionally does a passing disturbance deliver as much as 2 to 3 in. in summer. Most precipitation comes in winter, when the trade inversion is weakest. But the frequency of rain-bearing disturbances is most irregular. In 1941, an adverse anomaly of the general circulation persisted for almost the entire year, and only October had above-average rain. Conditions were not much better in 1943, but in that year very heavy January rainfall, contributing more than half of the year's precipitation, raised the total to the average.

Only 37 per cent of the years from 1875 to 1950 had rainfall within 20 per cent of the mean, in contrast to 78 per cent at San Juan: 11 per cent of the years had precipitation of less than half the annual average. The plantations on the island of Oahu—on which the city of Honolulu with its several hundred thousand inhabitants lies—can exist only because large underground supplies of fresh water are tapped. These are replenished, at least partly, by the heavy mountain precipitation sinking through the porous soil.

WESTERN EDGE OF CONTINENTS: SUBTROPICS

The general circulation strikingly controls climate along the western margins of the continents in the subtropics and lower middle latitudes. First observed and analyzed in the countries bordering on the Mediterranean Sea, this climate recurs along the western edge of all continents, including southwestern Australia and the tip of southern Africa.

Winter rains and summer dryness are the outstanding characteristic. Cyclones moving along low-latitude tracks bring rain when a jet-stream core enters the continents near latitude 30°. The lower the latitude, the less frequent are jet stream and cyclones. Therefore, precipitation decreases equatorward; it averages more than 20 in. at San Francisco, 10 in. at San Diego, and becomes almost nil in northwestern Mexico.

Under the influence of winds from the sea (Fig. 10.15) the temperature is generally mild. Very cold weather can develop in the Mediterranean Sea itself during cold outbreaks from Siberia. The Rocky Mountains shield the United States West Coast from such cold air invasions (Chapter 9). Severe "freezes" occur only rarely in southern California.

Along the coasts of California, Chile, and northern and southern Africa, an extensive fog regime prevails during summer; along por-

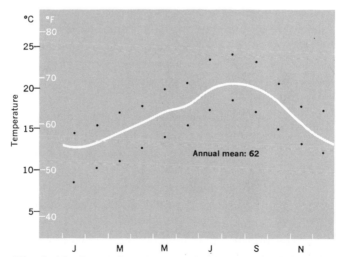

Fig. 10.15   Seasonal course of surface air temperature at San Diego, California (33°N, 117°W). Dots denote highest and lowest average temperature observed for each month, 1851–1950.

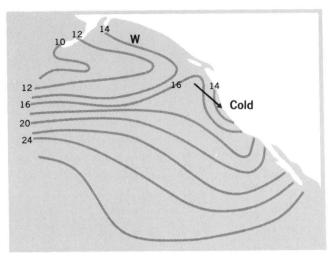

Fig. 10.16   Sea surface temperatures (°C) off the Pacific coast of North America during July, 1957. Arrow shows principal air movement causing upwelling of cold water along coast.

tions of the Southern Hemisphere coasts, which protrude westward with decreasing latitude, it persists through the year. There rainfall is almost nil; but the ground receives some moisture from fog or low stratus, permitting sparse vegetation to grow. The fog forms offshore, where air moves equatorward east of the strong subtropical high-pressure centers. Because of frictional drag by the winds, the surface water is driven away from shore (Fig. 10.16), and colder water wells up along the coasts. Fog forms when the air passes over the cold water.

The low ocean temperatures produce cold summers. San Francisco's mean summer temperature of 58 to 59°F (14 to 15°C) is nearly 20°F (11°C) lower than that of Washington, D.C., at the same latitude. But the coastal strip with the foggy regime is narrow; at Sacramento, 80 miles northeast of San Francisco, summer temperatures equal those at Washington. Daily maximum temperatures of 100°F are common.

The unusual precipitation regime, with almost dry summers, also is very unsteady from year to year. San Diego's record (Fig. 10.17) is extreme; 58 years between 1851 and 1950 had rainfall deviating by more than 20 per cent from the 100-year average. It is generally axiomatic that the lower the average precipitation, the greater is the percentage of variability. At San Diego, the year with highest precipitation had 27 in., the year with lowest precipitation 3 in. Eight years had precipitation less than half of average. Clearly, San Diego must depend on storage in the California mountains and import of water from distant mountain ranges for its water supply; desalinated sea water may eventually be an important source.

WESTERN EDGE OF CONTINENTS: HIGHER LATITUDES

Along the American West Coast, the seasonal migration of storm tracks, produced by jet-stream displacement, shifts the main season of precipitation as follows: late summer on the Alaskan peninsula, autumn in southern Alaska, early winter in the Northwestern United States, and midwinter to late winter in California. Europe has a

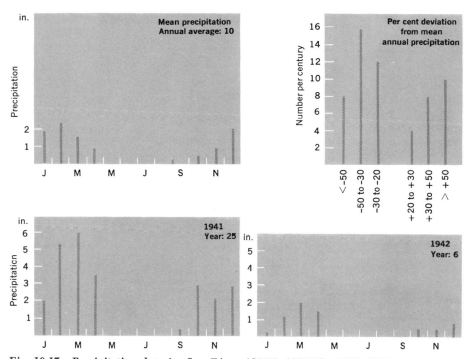

Fig. 10.17   Precipitation data for San Diego (33°N, 117°W), 1851–1950.

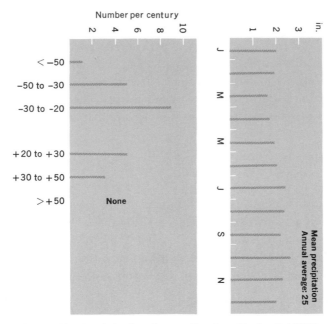

Fig. 10.18   Precipitation data at London, England (51°N, 0°), 1851–1950. (Greenwich Observatory.)

similar transition between Scandinavia and the Mediterranean. Along the coast of Norway, just as along the southern coast of Alaska, a rather dry spring follows heavy autumn rains. The jet stream in spring is located far south and is sometimes divided into two branches, one extending through the Mediterranean and the other over the top of Norway.

London's average annual precipitation of 25 in. may be considered small in view of the city's reputation for cloudy and very damp winters. Here we find only a weak seasonal rhythm of precipitation (Fig. 10.18). With an excellent chance for rain in every month, 78 years during 1851–1950 had precipitation within 20 per cent of the mean, that is, between 20 and 30 in.

In addition to occasional cyclones of great intensity (Chapter 7) and fog or man-made smog (Chapter 11), England's main weather problem comes from occasional long periods of winds from Russia (Chapter 14). These bring snow and cold, for which the country is not well prepared. January or February temperatures fell to below freezing three times during the century of 1851–1950, and they approached the freezing point in several other months. Particularly severe over England and much of Europe were the first three winters of World War II when, with heating fuel and everything else scarce, the following monthly temperatures occurred at London: 30.8°F in January, 1940; 34.1° in January, 1941; 33.5° in January, 1942; followed by 32.2° in February, 1942.

From the range of monthly temperatures that have occurred each month (Fig. 10.19), we see in the first place that temperatures vary more widely in winter than in summer; this is usual. Further, most of the shafts extend farther below than above the curve. The curve represents only the period 1941–1950, and the shafts, the period 1851–1950. Evidently, temperatures were low more often in the early than in the late part of this record. We must conclude that the Greenwich Observatory outside London, where the data were taken, observed a warming trend; among the reasons are

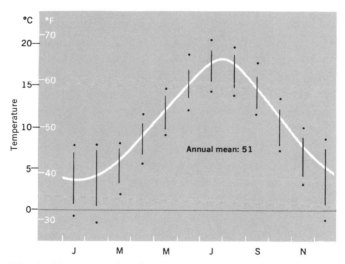

Fig. 10.19 *Seasonal course of surface air temperature at London, 1941–1950. (Greenwich Observatory.) Shafts show the interval, in which the temperature averaged for individual months has remained 90 per cent of the time, 1851–1950. Dots give highest and lowest monthly temperatures on record for the century.*

spreading of the city and a true climatic trend found over most of the Northern Hemisphere at high latitudes. After 1950 this trend leveled off and reversed.

EASTERN EDGE OF NORTH AMERICA

This is our only strictly regional heading, because the climate to be described does not occur along all east coasts. All of eastern Asia, for example, is controlled by the monsoon; South Africa does not extend far enough south; and the coast of South America slopes from northeast to southwest with increasing latitude, whereas it should do the opposite for the east coast climate to appear. Only south-eastern Australia parallels the climate of eastern North America, and even there not nearly so well as the Australian west coast parallels west coast climates.

Because of prevailing offshore winds, eastern North America experiences cold winters and hot summers. Only occasionally does the wind blow from the sea. However, because of the large distance from the source region for very cold air in northwestern Canada, polar air masses are normally warmed by turbulence before they reach the shore. Only occasionally does polar air envelop the East Coast without being modified, sending temperatures very low. New York has experienced −20°F (−29°C), but vegetation there is protected by winter dormancy. Far more serious to agriculture are the severe freezes which occur from time to time along the whole East Coast as far south as northern Florida, where minima of 0°F (−18°C) have been measured.

New York's seasonal temperature range (45°F or 23°C) nearly doubles that of London, and her winters are much colder (Fig. 10.20) in spite of the lower latitude. East Coast winters vary from very cold to very warm (Chapter 14), so that average temperature is a poor guide about conditions to be expected in any one year. Summers bring heat and high humidity; guide books advise tourists to avoid New York (and Washington!) in July and August. Prevailing winds from south to southwest at the western end of the Atlantic high-pressure area import air with high humidity from the Atlantic and the Gulf of Mexico. Heating over land, when solar altitudes

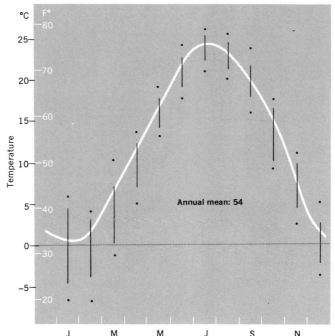

Fig. 10.20   Seasonal course of surface air temperature at New York City (41°N, 74°W), 1941–1950. Shafts and dots for 1851–1950 as in Fig. 10.19.

are high, and strong evapotranspiration from the ground cause further increases of temperature and humidity as the air travels northward from the Gulf states. Temperatures of above 100°F (40°C) have occurred along the whole latitudinal expanse of the Atlantic coast well into Canada.

New York, like London, shows a long-term warming trend. If older temperature records dating back to 1820 are included, the warming trend is even more evident. In this case the situation is a little confused, because the station that kept official records was moved without a period of overlapping record with the previous location—the climatologist's nightmare. As every New Yorker will know, it matters a great deal just where in the city the temperature is read.

Famous for its high precipitation and even distribution of rain-

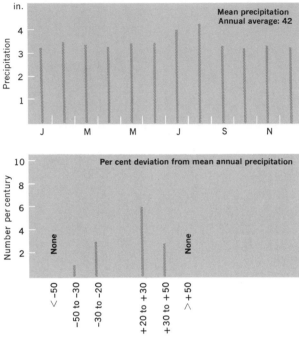

Fig. 10.21   Precipitation data for New York City, 1851–1950.

fall through the year is the East Coast north of Cape Hatteras (Fig. 10.21). In summer, even the arrival of weak troughs in the upper air, preceded by low-level convergence, is enough to generate heavy showers. In winter, cyclones which form in the lee of the Appalachian Mountains over the Carolinas and Virginia produce rain and snow. Such storms often gather great intensity within 12 hr after first developing; they usually move northeastward just off-shore (Fig. 14.12), blanketing the coastal area with heavy precipitation up to 250 miles inland. In 12 to 18 hr, 12 in. of snow may accumulate. Transportation then is disrupted; on a few famous occasions major cities have been immobilized for a day or more by the heavy snow delivery.

These inconveniences are minor compared to the immense value of the cyclones in providing one of the largest and most dependable water supplies of the world. No less than 87 years out of 100 fell

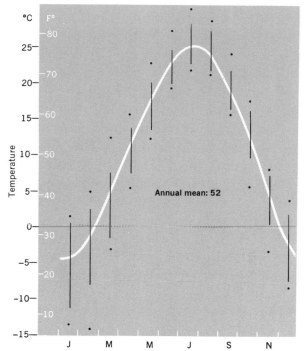

Fig. 10.22 *Seasonal course of surface air temperature at Omaha, Nebraska (41°N, 96°W), 1941–1950. Shafts and dots for 1870–1950, as in Fig. 10.19.*

within 20 per cent of the mean at New York. But the population of the Atlantic seaboard has become so large, and industrial demand for water so heavy, that water shortages keep recurring in spite of the very favorable precipitation climate. The appropriate time unit for discussing water supply there is the month, not the year. A single very dry month such as October, 1963, forces the governors of New England to close the forests because of fire danger. At these times, the water level in reservoirs drops critically.

MIDDLE– AND HIGH–LATITUDE CONTINENTAL INTERIOR

Cold winters and warm summers prevail in the interior of continents. Omaha (Fig. 10.22) will represent the lower middle latitudes,

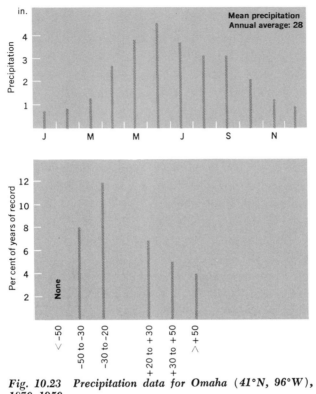

Fig. 10.23   *Precipitation data for Omaha (41°N, 96°W),*
1870–1950.

and Moscow (Fig. 10.24), at latitude 57°N, the severe winter of
Russia, which is matched in the United States in Minnesota and
North Dakota, in spite of their being 10° farther south.

At both locations, the temperature ranges seasonally over a
53°F (27°C) spread, only a little larger than New York's, but much
less than that observed in parts of Canada and Siberia (Fig. 10.3).
January mean temperatures have varied by 30°F (15°C) and more;
thus radiation controls the winter climate very imperfectly even at
these continental locations. The position of troughs and ridges in
the upper westerlies holds the key to whether the winter will be
warm or cold (Chapter 14). It is not the occasional severe cold that

is surprising in the middle of the continents, rather how mild it can sometimes be, even in January.

Though precipitation for both cities is high in summer (Figs. 10.23 and 10.25), high temperatures at Omaha often deplete soil moisture during late summer (Chapter 12). Cyclones along a jet stream above the Midwestern United States produce the precipitation peak in late spring and early summer. Flooding is frequent at that time of year; fields may be so moist that they cannot be plowed until June.

Omaha also lies in the center of a large region in the Western

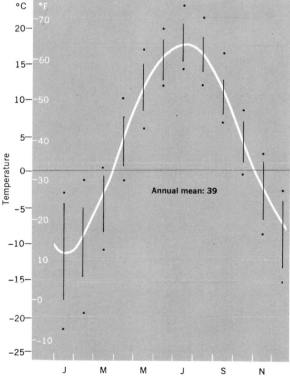

Fig. 10.24   Seasonal course of surface air temperature at Moscow, Soviet Union (57°N, 37°E), 1941–1950. Shafts and dots for 1880–1950, as in Fig. 10.19.

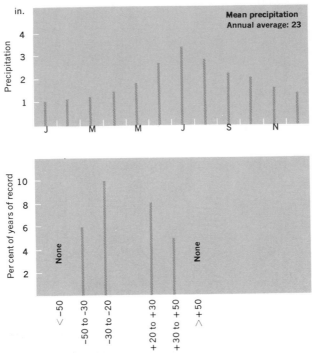

Fig. 10.25   Precipitation data for Moscow, 1880–1950.

Plains states where more than half of the summer precipitation falls at night and where vicious night thunderstorms develop. The plains of Nebraska and adjoining states are exposed to danger from tornadoes and severe hail. During winter, blizzards from Canada sweep down the open prairie with great violence; altogether it is a rough climate, full of extremes and potential for catastrophe.

11

Small-scale Climate

Many controls of weather and climate, from mountain ranges and large lakes to minute topographic features in the lowest few feet above the ground, operate on distance scales smaller than the global patterns discussed in the last chapter. Not all small-scale climate is due to natural processes; man's actions have altered it in many ways.

INFLUENCE OF MOUNTAINS

Precipitation. When a broad air stream is forced over very large mountain ranges, wave motion is initiated in the upper flow that

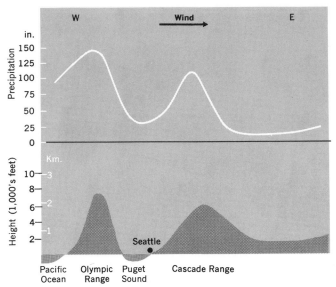

Fig. 11.1 *East-west profile of mountain ranges and of annual precipitation across state of Washington. Profile passes through Seattle (48°N, 122°W).*

can affect weather far beyond the confines of the mountains (Chapter 9). Within the mountains, upward motion increases precipitation on the windward side and diminishes it on the leeward side, introducing sharp climatic divides often over very short distances.

In the Pacific Northwest of the United States, two mountain chains parallel the shoreline. Each has an east-west extent of about 50 miles in the Puget Sound area (Fig. 11.1). Yet their influence on precipitation and vegetation is spectacular. In the coastal (Olympic) range, annual precipitation attains nearly 150 in.[1] Though the altitude of the highest summit is only 8,000 ft (2,400 m), a system of glaciers lies above a tree line only a few thousand feet above sea level. Precipitation then diminishes abruptly over Puget Sound. Seattle, known for its persistent overcast skies and large number of rainy days in winter, averages little more than 30 in. per year, about the same as Chicago. Just east of Seattle, precipitation again in-

[1] Deposit of water from clouds carried against the mountain sides by the winds (horizontal precipitation) adds substantially to the precipitation total along many mountain ranges.

creases. Thick evergreen forests cover the western slopes of the Cascade range below a tree line near 5,000 ft. In this very humid zone, long streamers of moss hang down from the trees. Above tree line here, too, a large number of glaciers remain, even on mountains only 6,000 to 7,000 ft (2,000 m) high. These glaciers, as those almost everywhere in the world, are in retreat. Beyond the top of the range the thick forest growth gives way to open forest; all tree growth terminates along the eastern base of the Cascades. The plain through which the Columbia River flows is virtually a desert, situated in the *rain shadow* of the Cascades.

The world's heaviest rainfalls are recorded in tropical mountains. Often quoted is the more than 400-in. annual rainfall at Cherrapunji in northeastern India, where the southwest monsoon ascends the valleys and foothills of the Himalayas. But even this record has been outdone in the Hawaiian Islands, where the peak on Kauai (Fig. 11.2) receives close to 500 in. per year.

The Hawaiian Islands demonstrate an extreme in orographic control of rainfall. They stand in the path of the northeast trades; very heavy precipitation occurs on the sides of the islands which face these winds. Where the mountains are low, rain spills over on the leeward side. Rainfall in Honolulu is 30 in., but less than 10 miles northeast toward the mountains, which barely top 2,000 ft (600 m), it is as high as 150 to 200 in. Climate literally changes by the mile as the traveler ascends from the shore, the sparse natural vegetation and cactus growth giving way to dense tropical jungle.

On the island of Hawaii (Fig. 11.2), two broad volcanoes occupy the bulk of the land. Rising above 13,000 ft (4,000 m), they extend far above the trade-wind inversion, located near 6,000 to 7,000 ft (2,000 m). Ascending air motion is sharply limited by the inversion, and the air flows around, rather than over, the top of the island above the lowest few thousand feet. As precipitation falls off abruptly above the height of the peak rainfall of 300 in. per year, jungle vegetation gives way to barren lava fields. In contrast, precipitation increases to the peak of many other mountains.

At one time, high precipitation on the lower slopes, decreasing above, was considered typical for mountain ranges, the reasoning being that the water vapor available for condensation decreased

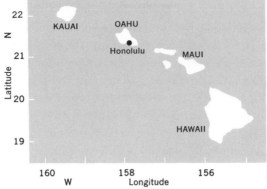

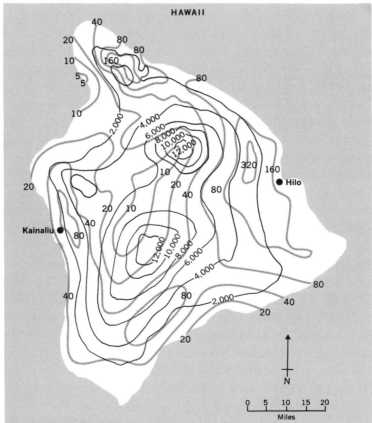

Fig. 11.2   Upper diagram: location of principal islands of the Hawaiian group. Lower diagram: height (feet) and mean annual precipitation (inches) on the island of Hawaii.

upward. But this argument is invalid, since condensation and subsequent precipitation depend on the *upward transport* of moisture. Vertical motion is the decisive factor. In many mountain areas, such as parts of the Rockies and the European Alps, precipitation increases up to the height of land. Engineers involved in controlling streamflow have found much larger water supplies at high altitudes than they would expect on the basis of precipitation charts, which hypothesize decreasing precipitation with increasing altitude.

Mountains can produce many unexpected precipitation patterns. The lee side of Hawaii is arid, except in a narrow belt close to the western, or Kona, coast, where coffee is grown. There the seasonal course of rainfall is inverse to the rhythm of winter rains and summer dryness (Fig. 10.14). A strong sea breeze moves inland against the trade during summer, and this produces high rainfall on the Kona coast (Fig. 11.3). In contrast, the city of Hilo, on the northeastern side of the island, follows the normal rhythm, though rainfall is high in every month because of the windward location.

Precipitation over the Hawaiian Islands averages 70 in. per year, compared to an estimated 25 to 30 in. over the nearby ocean. Thus the mountain effect, averaged over the wet and dry areas of all the islands, more than doubles the precipitation.

Radiation. A mountain range protruding into the atmosphere raises the surface heat source over that of the surrounding land. We might expect to find temperatures to be higher than at comparable elevations in the free atmosphere. Actually, temperature does decrease less with height at the equatorial stations shown in Fig. 10.6 than in the tropical atmosphere above the oceans. Gradually rising land, such as the western plains of the United States, also raises the surface heat source. New York's mean annual temperature is 54°F (12°C); Denver's, at 5,000 ft (1,500 m) above sea level, is almost identical with that of New York, both annually and monthly.

Radiation also produces important variations on much smaller scales. Normally, the mountain atmosphere is "pure" compared to that of the plains, except for high valleys with strong local pollution. Since total moisture of the air is also low, both incoming and outgoing radiation is high compared to the plains near sea level.

Solar radiation on north- and south-facing slopes differs greatly,

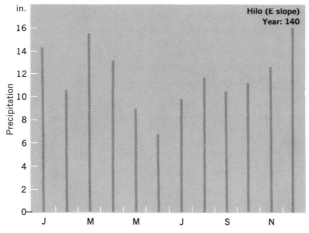

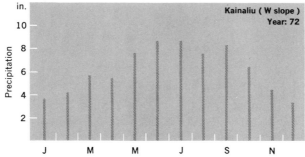

Fig. 11.3   Seasonal course of rainfall at Hilo and Kainaliu on the island of Hawaii. For location see Fig. 11.2.

and the difference increases as latitude increases, where the solar altitude in the noon sky becomes progressively lower. On north-facing slopes (Fig. 11.4), solar rays reach the ground at oblique angles, so that radiation received per unit surface is relatively small. South-facing slopes, in contrast, intercept the solar beam at nearly right angles.

This difference in radiation received by the ground affects vegetation. In high latitudes, south-facing slopes alone receive enough heat to maintain extensive tree stands. At lower latitudes, for instance throughout the Western United States, thick forests grow on north-facing slopes, while the slopes on the opposite side of a valley are often bare or covered with a thin growth of scraggly pine. The moisture budget plays the decisive role. On north-facing slopes, precipitation suffices for plant transpiration, even where rainfall is low and the number of sunny days large. South-facing slopes, however, are so deficient in water because of the heat that only cactus and weeds can grow in many places.

In the Rocky Mountains, especially in their central and southern parts, a double tree line commonly appears. Throughout the broad valleys and lower slopes, temperature is too high and rainfall too low for tree growth. The upper tree line lies near 11,500 ft (3,500 m). Between these two limits is the zone of forest vegetation.

Winds. Mountain slopes are relatively protected from the large daily range of temperature and danger of frost, even in midsummer, prevailing in valley bottoms. During summer mornings, updrafts— the *valley breeze*—develop, ventilating the slopes (Fig. 11.5). At the height of land the valley breeze may encounter an upper wind blowing from the opposite direction. Both currents then join in a wide rising arc, visible when cumuli form.

After sunset, a shallow layer of cold air forms quickly on the slopes. Relatively heavy, it begins to drain down the mountain side into the narrow mountain valleys; from these, violent winds may issue into the plains below, with speeds higher than 40 mph. However, if the cold air drains into a valley without outlet, the cold layer

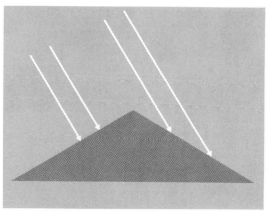

Fig. 11.4 Difference in radiation received on slopes facing and turned away from sun.

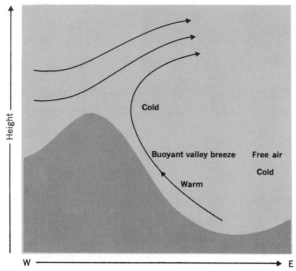

Fig. 11.5   Valley breeze and deflection by upper west-erly current.

at the bottom becomes deeper through the night; here frost danger is most common.

The mountains also give rise to strong downslope winds during cyclone and front passages. When a cyclone moves into, or develops in, the lee of a mountain range, air is drawn toward the low pressure down the slopes from the top of the range or beyond. Heated adiabatically, the descending current arrives on the lee side bringing much higher temperatures, especially in winter. Figure 11.6 shows the arrival of a warm current, called *chinook* in the western United States and *foehn* in the European Alps, to the plain just east of the Colorado front range. Temperatures had fallen to 20°F (−7°C) on the evening of January 30, 1965. Then gusty winds from the west set in suddenly, and, near midnight, the temperature shot up above freezing to 50°F (10°C). Relative humidity dropped from 85 to 30 per cent; low relative humidity always results from compression heating. During the ensuing hours of the night and following morning the wind blew in great gusts up to 87 mph, doing much damage and raising a blinding duststorm. Then, shortly after noon on January 31, the chinook situation ended suddenly as a cold

front passed from the north; temperature dropped just as abruptly
and by about the same amount around 1 P.M. of that day as it had
risen during the preceding night.

In the middle of the nineteenth century the foehn in the northern valleys of the Alps was thought to be a hot, dry wind blowing
up from Africa, until it was discovered that no such hot wind blew
over northern Italy. Next, it was argued that rain heated the air
on the windward side of the mountains and that subsequent compression on the lee side produced foehn temperatures and humidities.

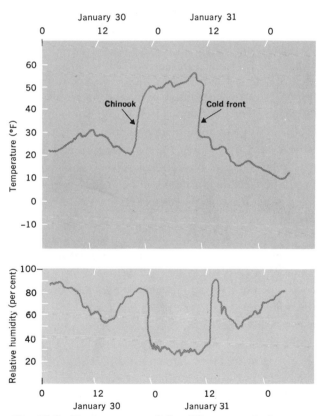

*Fig. 11.6   Temperature and humidity trace during onset
of chinook January 30–31, 1965, at Colorado State University, just east of the Colorado Rockies. The temperature
jump occurred around midnight; this record is far from
extreme. (Courtesy Arnold Finklin.)*

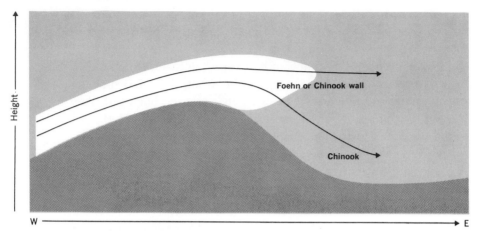

Fig. 11.7   Illustrating flow across mountains and stationary cloud mass (white) during foehn or chinook.

Indeed, during a foehn, a precipitating cloud bank, the *foehn wall,* often lies over the ridges (Fig. 11.7). This cloud remains stationary; the front edge continually evaporates as the wind carries cloud matter forward and down. Nevertheless, many foehns occur without precipitation; it is merely necessary that downward motion extend over a vertical distance long enough for compression heating to raise the temperature of the descending current higher than that in the plains.

The violent, gusty winds of foehn or chinook, at times with speeds above 100 mph, have not been explained. The chinook is of some economic value, since it brings relief from winter cold; snow cover evaporates, and livestock can graze through the winter on the open ranges. On the other hand, soil moisture is badly depleted, and evaporation of the snow cover severely reduces the amount of water which actually gets into the soil. The impact of chinooks after spring planting often damages or kills the seeds. Extreme fire hazard comes to the Alpine valleys when the snow cover vanishes with the fierce, dry winds. Man becomes very irritable, and many persons become ill, though the exact reasons are not known.

The foehn is not restricted to the cold season. Hot winds from the mountains during summer contribute to the dust bowl danger in Texas, Oklahoma, and southern Colorado, and ill-famed is the

Santa Ana wind of southern California. Toward the end of the long, dry summer in California, an upper anticyclone often lies over the center of the Rocky Mountains. The east winds south of this high-pressure area descend from the interior highland deserts toward the shore. Compression heating raises temperatures to 105 to 110°F (40°C), even on the coast. Large fires then break out, as strong, hot winds and very low humidity combine with soils and plant life at their driest.

Downslope winds also can bring cold blasts—the mountain breeze on a larger scale. If a very cold air mass appears at the height of land, it may be colder, even after compression heating, than the air it displaces on the lee side (Fig. 11.8). The Adriatic coast of Yugoslavia is exposed to polar air invasions from Russia during winter. When a cold front arrives from the northeast, the cold air descends the slope from the 3,000-ft-high plateau to the coast. Downward buoyancy develops and the air current, the *bora*, may rush down to the sea at a speed of 100 mph. Over North America such winds are less common. Occasionally, however, the Columbia

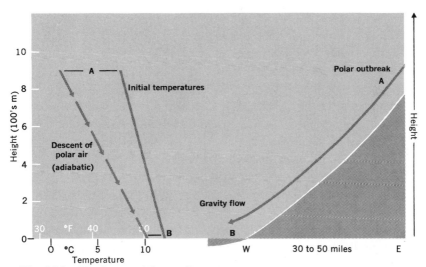

Fig. 11.8   The bora. Right: outline of terrain slope of Yugoslav coast with streamline showing descent of air, from A to B. Left: initial temperature height curve following slope from A to B and compression heating of very cold air mass arriving from east.

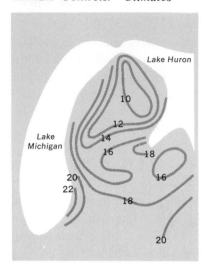

Fig. 11.9 Mean minimum temperatures on the Michigan peninsula during winter (°F). (Courtesy U.S.
Weather Bureau.)

River gorge experiences violent downward winds, channeled by
the steep mountain sides.

INFLUENCE OF WATER BODIES

Temperature. Oceanic climates are milder than continental
climates at the same latitude. Under the influence of winds from the
sea, winter temperatures are higher and summer temperatures cooler
(Chapter 10). Inland lakes produce a similar effect. The peninsula
of Michigan lies between Lakes Huron and Michigan. During winter, minimum temperatures average 5 to 10°F (3 to 5°C) colder in
the middle of the peninsula than they do on the shore (Fig. 11.9);
with prevailing westerly winds, the Lake Michigan shore is about
2°F (1°C) warmer than the Lake Huron shore. Altogether, a pronounced east-west pattern is added to the normal temperature decrease toward north.

During summer, the opposite differences are found between
shore and interior, though they are weaker. Nevertheless, a drive
down the last few miles toward the shore usually brings relief from
summer heat. The sea or lake breeze moderates summer temperatures along lake shores and ocean beaches. Daytime radiation heats

the air over land, while, over water, the air temperature remains nearly constant. With the warming, pressure above 1,000 to 3,000 ft (300 to 900 m) height rises a little over land as the air expands, and the air at these heights is accelerated toward the water (Fig. 11.10). In turn, surface pressure over the land drops, accelerating air near the ground from water toward shore. And so the sea or lake breeze is initiated. In middle and high latitudes, the sea breeze may penetrate inland about 30 to 40 miles. Turning clockwise under the influence of the Coriolis force, it eventually moves parallel to the shore.

Fog. Most coastal areas in higher latitudes have frequent fog. During the summer, warm air moving over colder water is the predominant cause. In autumn and winter, fog often occurs through radiation cooling of air that has moved inland with a relatively high moisture content. At Tatoosh Island, just off the northwest tip of the United States, late summer fogs are frequent when west and northwest winds blow across the cold coastal waters off the Pacific Coast (Fig. 11.11; see also Fig. 10.16). But the picture is quite different at Spokane, in the eastern part of the state of Washington. There, radiation cooling leads to a large number of days with fog during winter; the other seasons are virtually fog-free.

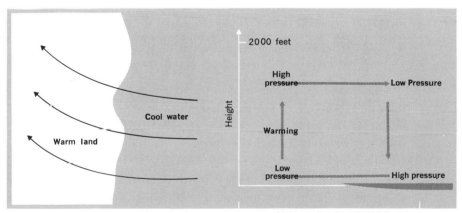

Horizontal distance 10 miles

Fig. 11.10 Illustrating the sea breeze. Left: horizontal view showing turning of sea breeze under influence of earth's rotation. Right: vertical view along line normal to shore.

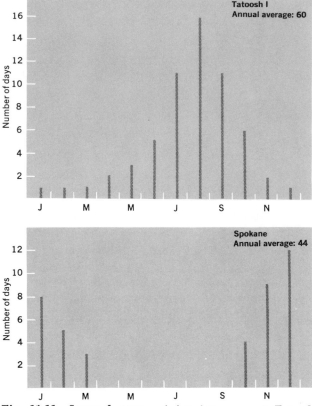

Fig. 11.11 Seasonal course of fog frequency at Tatoosh Island, off the northwestern tip of the United States, and at Spokane (48°N, 118°W), in the interior of Washington.

Lake Snows. During cold outbreaks over open bodies of water such as the southern Great Lakes, the temperature difference between air and water may exceed 50°F (25°C). The polar air rushing over the water is heated very rapidly; Arctic sea smoke attests to equally rapid evaporation. In such unstable air, cumulus clouds and heavy snow showers develop toward the lee shore. Snowfalls of 20 to 30 in. have been measured at Buffalo, New York, in 24 hr during west-wind situations, when the cold air blows down the whole length of Lake Erie.

Convection bands, a result of shoreline contours and even minor topographic features, may extend 50 miles downwind from lakes, yet have widths of only a few miles. One well-known band recurs in the same location on the southeast side of Lake Michigan during west-northwest winds; the band is oriented along the wind. No less than 37 in. of snow was recorded here during a single storm in February, 1958. This equaled the mean February precipitation, which in this narrow lake-snow corridor is 1 in. (of water) higher than in the areas around it. The author came through the area by railroad just after the storm and found it an awesome sight. Within a few miles the train passed from nearly bare countryside to the corridor, where houses, cars, and roads were virtually buried. Plows had piled snow so high on the side of the tracks that the train seemed to be moving in a tunnel. Then, just as abruptly, the whole spectacle ended.

FOREST CLIMATE

Most plant life is found in the first 6 ft (2 m) above the ground, and nearly all of it in the first 300 ft (100 m). The nature of the soil, the interaction between ground and atmosphere, and the influence of local topography and man-made structures produce a great variety of local climates. In considering the relation of climate to vegetation, our interest centers on the warm part of the year, the growing season.

In a high forest where the trees form a rather solid canopy, the radiating surface is, in effect, transferred from the ground to the treetops, which intercept nearly all sunlight (Fig. 11.12). Highest temperatures inside the forest occur at the top of the canopy. Compared to bare ground outside the forest, temperature near the surface remains high at night and low by day, depending, of course, on type, height, and extent of the forest. In some forests in middle latitudes the maximum daily temperature averages about 5°F (3°C) lower in midsummer than over open country nearby; on hot days the difference may be 10°F (5°C) and more.

Relative humidity averages 5 to 10 per cent lower outside than inside the forest (Fig. 11.13), where air movement is greatly retarded (Fig. 11.14). Within the canopy, wind speed quickly drops

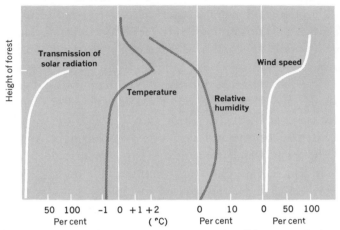

Fig. 11.12   The effect of forest cover with solid canopy during a summer day. Solar radiation transmitted, in percentages of radiation received at the top of the canopy; temperature, zero setting on temperature above vegetation; relative humidity, zero setting on relative humidity near the surface; wind speed, in percentages of wind speed above forest.

to only a few per cent of that above it (Fig. 11.12). Evidently the forest creates its own local climate.

In midsummer, soil temperature measures as much as 10°F (5°C) lower inside the forest than in the surrounding open fields (Fig. 11.15). Through lower soil temperatures and lower wind speeds, evaporation inside the forest is also much reduced (Fig. 11.16). Thus the forest conserves its moisture for the maintenance and growth of the trees. Forests diminish all weather extremes. Where forest cover does not exist—either because of cutting or through natural absence—snow melts early. Where solar radiation on deforested areas is especially intense, snow cover simply evaporates, leaving no usable moisture at all. In summer, droughts are intensified, while heavy rains bring flash floods where the forest is no longer available to contain the precipitation. On the other hand, the diminished need for water to sustain forests, and unhindered runoff, are thought to be the principal factors in the increases of annual water delivery to storage reservoirs in various mountain areas of the United States, where parts of forests have been cut

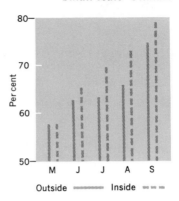

Fig. 11.13 *Average relative humidity measured at 5 P.M. inside (dashed) and outside (solid) of forest during summer months. The difference is largest in mid-summer when the forest is in full foliage. Upper Peninsula Experimental Forest, Dukes, Marquette County, Michigan. Record for 1926–1936. Birch, beech, and maple forest. (From* Climate and Man, *Yearbook of Agriculture, Government Printing Office, Washington, D.C., 1941.)*

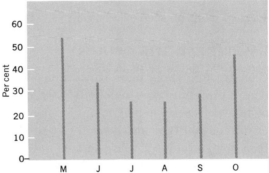

Fig. 11.14 *Ratio of average daily wind speed inside to outside of forest measured at 15 ft above the ground. Data source as in Fig. 11.13.*

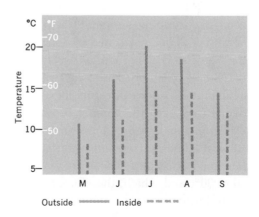

Fig. 11.15 *Average daily soil temperature to a depth of 6 in. inside and outside of forest. Notation and data source as in Fig. 11.13.*

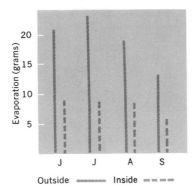

Fig. 11.16 Average daily evaporation inside and outside of forest as measured with a Livingston atmometer (evaporimeter). Notation and data source as in Fig. 11.13.

experimentally. Such increases have amounted to as much as 25 to 50 per cent. It appears doubtful, however, that such schemes could succeed when applied on a larger scale.

LAYER NEAR THE GROUND

Climate often varies more between man's head and his toes than it does horizontally over hundreds of miles. The outstanding feature of the surface layer is its daily temperature range. Depending, of course, on soil type and general climate, the daily range may more than double from 6 ft (2m) to 1 in. above the ground (Fig. 11.17). In the middle of a summer day, temperature can decrease 10°F (5°C) over this distance above bare soil.

Even slight topographic features affect temperature. On low spots in fields the growth of wheat, corn, and vegetables is often sparse, for a depression of a few feet can induce drainage winds at night, dropping temperatures 5 to 10°F (3 to 5°C) below those around it. This, then, may reduce the frost-free summer period in the depression by perhaps a third to a half.

Small hills and depressions receive varying solar radiation just as mountain slopes do (Fig. 11.4), and the water requirements of plants vary with the amount of radiation that reaches them. Water needs on south-facing slopes increase rapidly as latitude decreases. In most climates, frequent watering is needed, for instance, to maintain good grass on portions of lawns which face the sun at angles of 20 to 30°, and which, therefore, receive nearly maximum solar radiation during summer.

The daily wind variation acts to augment evaporation, through turbulent mixing, just at the same time of day when the vapor pressure over plants and moist ground is highest under the influence of radiation. Normally, wind increases most rapidly between the ground and 6 ft (2m) height (Fig. 11.18). On summer afternoons wind speed may reach 10 mph just a few inches above grass when the wind at anemometer level is 20 mph.

Soil Temperatures. Even large seasonal ranges of air temperature just above the surface quickly damp out in the ground, which is normally a poor heat conductor. Measurements made near Chicago show that an annual temperature range of 57°F (32°C) in the air is reduced to half this value at just 3 ft (1 m) depth (Fig.

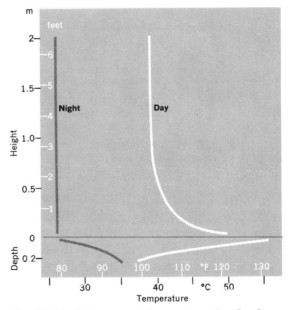

Fig. 11.17 Extremes of temperature in the layer nearest the ground. Vertical temperature structure in the lowest 2 m (6 ft) at time of maximum and minimum temperature observed near Yuma, Arizona (33°N, 115°W), during July and August, 1956, over sandy soil. The night temperature inversion is very weak in this case. Profiles based on recordings at ten levels down to 20 cm in the soil. (From Arthur V. Dodd, U.S. Army Natick Laboratories.)

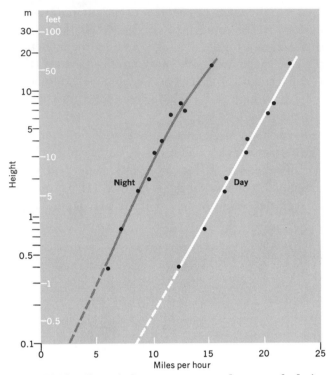

Fig. 11.18 The wind structure near the ground during day and night. Average of measurements during July and August, 1953, made at O'Neill in eastern plains of Nebraska.

11.19). At 27 ft (8 m), temperature varies only by about 1°F. So gradual is the annual intrusion of heating and cooling into the ground that the temperature cycle reverses with depth. At 10 ft (3 m), the temperature minimum occurs in March and April, and the maximum in September and October. By 30 ft (9 m) of depth, the reversal is complete, with highest temperature in February and lowest in August.

Vast areas of Canada and Siberia, with extreme winter temperatures, have permanently frozen soil called *permafrost*—about one-fifth of the world's land. The intrusion of frost into the ground is so strong, in spite of some snow cover, that summer warming is not enough to thaw the ground below about 3 ft (1 m) depth. Since water cannot sink into frozen soil, these areas become swamps during the warm season rains. The Russians have increased the land available for agriculture by installing extensive drainage systems in these areas and by powdering the snow with black dirt from aircraft, increasing the rate of spring snow melt.

CITY CLIMATE

Most of man's weather modifications, intentional and unintentional, have been less successful than the Russian experiment with frozen soils. A majority of the population in industrial countries lives in cities, most of which are growing at a fast rate. Combustion products, the high heat capacity of stone and concrete, and reduction of wind by buildings have helped to raise mean annual temperatures in cities by 1 to 2°F over those in suburbs and neighboring country. Nighttime minima during winter are especially affected by these factors. A typical forecast is, "Chicago temperature tonight near 15°, 5 to 10° colder in suburbs."

In summer, evening cooling is also slower in the city than outside, although highest temperatures may be equal. After the ex-

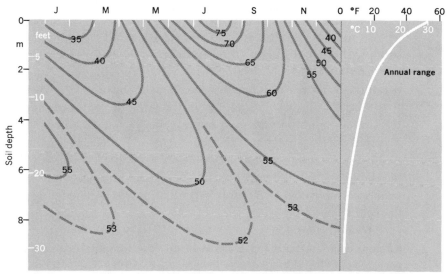

Fig. 11.19 *Seasonal course of temperature (°F) in the soil to a depth of 9 m measured in open country at Argonne National Laboratory near Chicago, Illinois. Right: annual temperature range. (Adapted from J. E. Carson.)*

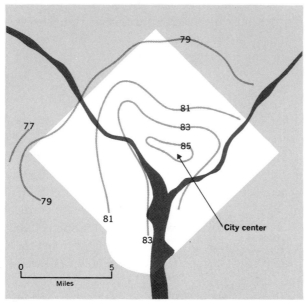

Fig. 11.20 Temperature distribution (°F) in Washington, D.C. and suburbs at 10 P.M. local time on August 11, 1949, showing city heat island. (After Helmut E. Landsberg.) Square area: District of Columbia.

tensive stone-covered areas have absorbed heat all day, they radiate strongly through the night. Temperature inversions may form shortly after sunset in the suburbs and bring relief from the heat, but temperature inside the city remains near maximum until late evening. It is then that heat and humidity in the Atlantic seaboard cities of the United States become most oppressive. The city is a *heat island,* depicted for Washington, D.C., on August 11, 1949, in Fig. 11.20. At 10 P.M. the center of town was 6 to 8°F (3 to 4°C) warmer than the suburbs; this difference is by no means unusual. Only when wind rises above 15 to 20 mph is ventilation strong enough so that the heat island disappears.

Air Pollution. Fog contributes to relatively high night temperatures in cities. After a fog blanket forms, the temperature falls only very slowly. London had 940 hr per year during 1947–1956 when visibility was less than 1,000 m (3,300 ft), twice the number observed in nearby rural areas. City pollution sources send large numbers of nuclei into the air; condensation then begins at relative humidities well below 100 per cent, contributing to low visibility.

A friendly term coined for the mixture of soot with fog-like condensation is *smog;* its meaning has broadened to include the visible product of air pollution in general. In London, smog is not a recent acquisition. We hear about the smoke pall of the seventeenth century: "The weary traveler, at many miles distance, sooner smells, than sees the city to which he repairs. This is the pernicious smoke which foils all her Glory, superinducing a sooty crust or fur upon all that it lights." [2] This description and others, as charmingly frank, apply with added emphasis in the twentieth century. We see the average smoke concentration over London for the 1957–1958 winter in Fig. 11.21. London receives an annual "sooty crust" in excess of 100,000 tons.

[2] John Evelyn in 1661.

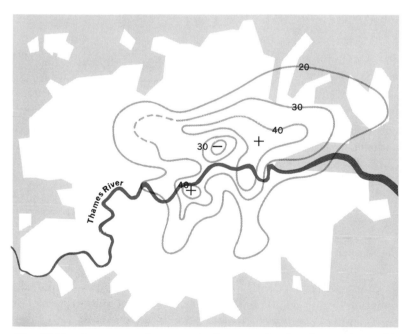

Fig. 11.21 Average smoke concentration over London (grams per cubic kilometer), October, 1957, to March, 1958. (After T. J. Chandler, Geographical Journal, London, *1962.)*

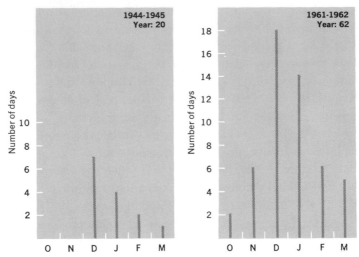

*Fig. 11.22   Number of days with visibility less than 2,000 m
(6,600 ft) at Tokyo, averaged for each month of the pollution
season during 1944–1945 and 1961–1962. (Data courtesy of M.
Yoshitake and M. Yanai.)*

The number of smogs grows with the size and intensity of the
pollution source. When, toward the end of World War II, industrial
activity in Tokyo was depressed, the air was very clean (Fig. 11.22).
By the early 1960s, revival of industry and growth of the metropolitan area had reinstated the sooty air typical of most large cities;
notice the large number of days when visibility was less than
2,000 m (6,000 ft) in Fig. 11.22. Such pollution reduces the hours
of sunshine and the amount of solar radiation the ground receives.
In most climates, smog incidence is highest in winter, and sunshine
then may be decreased by 50 per cent.

On many winter days the intensity of pollution by far exceeds
that shown in Fig. 11.21. One ominous feature of twentieth-century
urban life is the pollution disasters that have taken many lives.
Sickness and even death can result from the gradual buildup of
pollution during windless periods. Over London, there was less than
one complete change of air in 4 days during December, 1952! The
accumulated weight of smoke particles in the air during those days
was estimated to be 380 tons, about 10 times the average weight

computed from Fig. 11.21. Poisonous gases issuing from industrial stacks can also lead to disaster; this happened at Donora, Pennsylvania, in 1948.

The demonstrated dangers of pollution to life, health, and property have led to an intensive search for effective controls. To formulate and enforce adequate laws, the nature of pollution over any metropolitan area must be clearly understood. The problem, essentially, has two parts: (1) diffusion of gases and particulate matter emitted from individual sources, and (2) the buildup of a generally polluted air mass accumulating its ingredients from numerous sources. A great deal of attention has been given to the first problem, less to the second.

Diffusion from stacks can be studied experimentally, for instance, by releasing chemical smoke from meteorological towers originally built to investigate the spread of atomic material. Figure 11.23 shows how rapidly an oil smoke diffused after its daytime release from a tower on Long Island, New York. The temperature lapse rate exceeded the adiabatic; wind speed above 10 mph ensured transport of the effluent away from the source. Under these conditions turbulence dispersed the plume quickly, as its downstream broadening indicates. At night, with a temperature inversion and light wind, such plumes will broaden very little, and they may even bend downward to the ground. The weather conditions which lead to serious health danger from such a source are known in principle; they can be identified specifically everywhere.

City-wide accumulation of pollution is more difficult to analyze because of the multiplicity of sources. Further, local wind regimes give each metropolitan area individual problems. Industrial stacks, automotive traffic, and home incinerators are cited as the principal contributors to pollution. Of these, home incinerators are most readily eliminated through metropolitan waste collection; they are, however, only a minor nuisance, as Los Angeles has found.

If we are to explain the composition of pollution in a given mass of air, it is necessary to sample both particulate matter and gases, and to construct air trajectories showing how the pollution accumulates. Recurring heavy pollution over one part of a city by no means indicates that the pollution originated there, which is

Fig. 11.23   Diffusion of oil smoke released during daytime at height of 350 ft (110 m) from the meteorological tower at Brookhaven National Laboratory. Wind speed was about 10 mph and the temperature lapse rate was greater than adiabatic, so that the smoke diffused rapidly. (Courtesy Maynard E. Smith, Brookhaven National Laboratory.)

obvious when the polluted mass moves over adjoining country with no pollution sources at all. In Denver, just east of the Rocky Mountains, where local winds play a large role in channeling pollution, we see how important it is to study such circulations in order to control pollution eventually. The city straddles the South Platte River, which flows northeastward (Fig. 11.24). During winter nights, air drains toward the river bottom and then northeast down the terrain slope. During the day, wind direction often reverses completely in the afternoon; the air which has moved north of town during the night returns.

Figure 11.24 shows an early morning trajectory during a typical pollution situation—fair-weather anticyclonic conditions and local wind systems predominant over large-scale wind. The trajectory, an average from several pollution episodes, took 5 hr to cross the city from south to north. To its left, values of the "soiling index" have

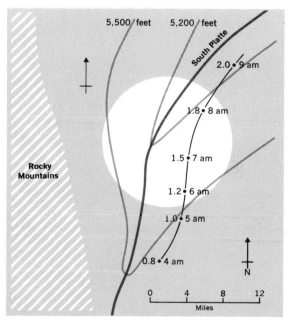

Fig. 11.24 *Early morning trajectory of air across Denver, Colorado, average for 5 days during heavy pollution. Light, circular section is outline of city area. Values of soiling index are plotted to left of trajectory.*

been plotted, a rough measure of particulate matter in the air. These values, interpolated from a sparse network of sampling stations, must be viewed mainly as illustrating technique. If realistic, however, Fig. 11.24 demonstrates that material accumulated along the entire path and that such accumulation led to the relatively high values of the soiling index in the northern outskirts of the city.

With winds from the south which normally increase during morning, Denver may become pleasantly clear and have a good view of the Rocky Mountains. But the wind reverses after noon, and the polluted mass returns from the north, blotting out the landscape. This pendulum-swing of wind direction carrying the pollution back and forth may continue for 2 or 3 days, until the general weather situation changes as a trough arrives in the upper westerlies from the Pacific Ocean.

part four

Weather and Climate Applied

12

Weather and Water Management

Expanding populations and industry demand more and more water in the modern world. The problem of water shortage, once confined to the marginal and low-precipitation regimes, has invaded regions thought, not long ago, to have abundant water resources. Yet, in the midst of growing concern about water supply, the old problem of flood danger remains alive, a seeming anachronism. Man's desire is for the "ever normal" flow of water; the occurrence of both water shortage and flood stresses that nature is far from providing this ideal state.

FACTORS IN THE WATER BALANCE

The water balance of a watershed depends on four factors: (1) precipitation, (2) evaporation, (3) river and underground runoff, and (4) changes in ground water storage, normally small compared to precipitation and evaporation during a whole year. If so, annual precipitation almost equals annual evaporation plus runoff. Here, the term "annual" usually refers to the *water year*. Most areas of the globe go through an annual cycle of water accumulation and depletion. The beginning of the water year is often defined as the average date that water accumulation begins—September or October in most middle-latitude areas.

Precipitation, evaporation, and runoff have very different modes of occurrence. Precipitation falls intermittently. At Chicago, 1 day out of 3 has precipitation, in the mean; 240 days per year are dry. Of the days with precipitation, a very small number delivers the bulk of the water. If there are 120 days of precipitation, about 15 days will produce half the water, and if annual precipitation is 30 in., the mean daily rate for these 15 days is 1.0 in.

Evaporation, in contrast, is an unspectacular but unceasing process. This becomes oppressively obvious during drought. If the annual evaporation is 18 in., typical of many middle-latitude areas, the average daily evaporation is 0.05 in., lower by more than a factor of 10 compared to precipitation on the days with heavy rain.

Seasonal runoff depends not only on precipitation and evaporation, but also on the extent and geography of the drainage above the place where the runoff is measured, and on the degree of soil saturation, snow melt, vegetation, and other factors. The maximum Colorado River runoff, like that of many rivers, comes in spring and early summer, when soils are nearest saturation and snow melt in the mountains reaches its peak (Fig. 12.1). Rivers flowing eastward from the continental divide carry their highest water at a time when rains are normally highest in the downstream states (Fig. 10.23). Thus, there is a chance of dangerous floods in years when large river flow from the mountains coincides with above-average precipitation over the plains.

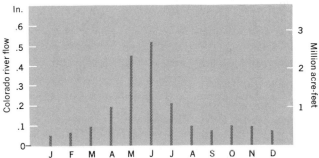

Fig. 12.1 Top: location of Upper Colorado River Basin. Bottom: seasonal course of discharge of the Colorado at Lee's Ferry (left scale gives equivalent precipitation depth). The annual flow is about 10 per cent less than the virgin flow for 1930–1960.

ANNUAL CYCLE OF WATER SUPPLY TO THE GROUND

Evaporation from oceans, lakes, rivers, and other bodies of water depends mainly on the vapor-pressure difference between water and air, and on wind speed (Chapter 4). Over continental areas in middle and high latitudes, the vapor-pressure difference varies widely by seasons. In Lake Michigan, surface water temperatures range from near freezing to 74°F (23°C); thus the vapor pressure

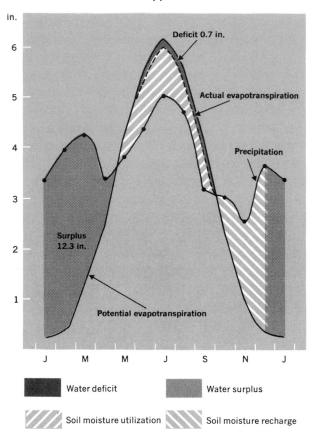

Fig. 12.2 *Seasonal course of precipitation, potential and actual evapotranspiration at Winston-Salem, North Carolina (36°N, 80°W). (Courtesy J. R. Mather and C. W. Thornthwaite Assoc.)*

over the water varies from 6 to 28 millibars. If vapor pressure in the air rises seasonally from 3 to 15 millibars, the difference of vapor pressure between water and air varies from 3 to 13 millibars, or by a factor of 4. This estimate is conservative; evaporation often differs by a factor of 10 between summer and winter.

Transpiration from plants also changes seasonally. During the dormant winter period it is virtually nothing, and it approaches the evaporation rate from water in summer. According to the late American climatologist Thornthwaite, transpiration at the full capacity of plants and evaporation from water bodies and soil are called *potential evapotranspiration.* This term, cumbersome and yet well-established, denotes the largest amount of water that can be evaporated by a given surplus of solar radiation received over radiation emitted from the ground and vegetation. The concept of potential evapotranspiration is meaningful only when applied to areas of at least 10,000 sq miles. Local evaporation from a storage reservoir with dry, hot surroundings, for instance, will greatly exceed the evaporation computed from radiation balance. Hot air blowing across the reservoir at wind speeds above 10 to 15 mph gives off heat to the water by conduction, maintaining surface water temperature against the evaporation. The latter, under such circumstances, may attain 10 ft (3 m) per year and more, and

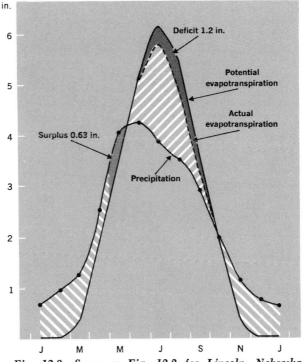

Fig. 12.3 Same as Fig. 12.2 for Lincoln, Nebraska
(41°N, 97°W).

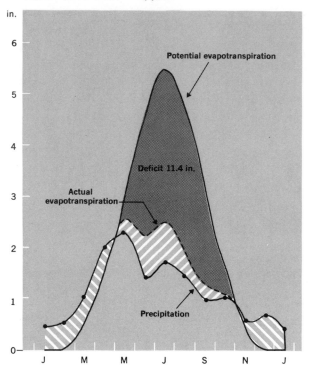

thus may detract substantially from the storage value of the reservoir.

Figures 12.2 to 12.4 compare the seasonal course of precipitation and potential evapotranspiration for three locations in the United States which have nearly equal potential evapotranspiration for the year. At Winston-Salem, North Carolina, precipitation is high in all months (Fig. 12.2). Although a definite summer peak exists, potential evapotranspiration is so large at that time of year that soil moisture is depleted. Thus, summer is the "dry season." During autumn, potential evapotranspiration falls below precipitation; soil moisture is recharged. When the ground becomes saturated, the excess of precipitation over potential evapotranspiration becomes available for river runoff. Total computed runoff at Winston-Salem is 12 in., or 25 per cent of mean annual rainfall.

North Carolina, of course, has an abundant moisture source, but westward, the water balance becomes gradually more marginal. At Lincoln, Nebraska, soil moisture is recharged only slowly during the cold season (Fig. 12.3); only a small amount of water becomes available for runoff during spring. Precipitation and soil moisture supply are unable to furnish water for maximum plant growth in midsummer.

At Denver, Colorado, this deficiency is far more extreme (Fig. 12.4). Soil moisture recharge is not enough to saturate the soil, and, during summer, drought prevails. As summer proceeds, the plains area turns brown except where irrigation water maintains green fields and pastures. We see that whether or not precipitation is adequate for plant growth is a question of potential evapotranspiration. Rainfall of 60 in. per year and even more supports only brush-type vegetation in parts of the trade-wind belt where potential evapotranspiration is very high.

River discharge provides the most reliable information for determining the fraction of mean annual precipitation which actually evaporates. Over the western plains of the United States very little water goes into river discharge (Fig. 12.5). A second evapora-

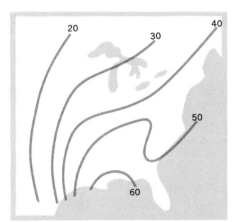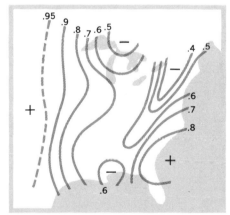

Fig. 12.5 Left: mean annual precipitation (inches) for the Central and Eastern United States. Right: fraction of mean annual precipitation evaporated. Subtraction of these numbers from one gives the fraction of mean annual precipitation carried off by the rivers. (After James E. McDonald, University of Arizona.)

tion peak coincides with the heavy rainfall regime of the East Coast. Between these two regions, extending southwestward from New England along the Appalachian mountains, there is a strip of minimum evaporation-precipitation ratio; this strip reflects high rainfall and, in the mountains, relatively low temperatures. There lies the major source of water for the eastern streams.

For the United States as a whole, rainfall is 30 in. per year, and runoff into the oceans, 8 in. A little more than 25 per cent of the precipitated water is thus returned to the oceans by the rivers.

Colorado Basin Discharge. Throughout the arid Southwestern United States, the Colorado River is a main support for the enormous growth of population, agriculture, and industry. Averaged over the Upper Basin of the Colorado, annual precipitation is 16 in. (Fig. 12.6). Hydrologists compute a quantity known as *virgin river flow,* which is the discharge that would be taking place if man had not arrived on the scene and interfered. For the period 1930–1960 this reconstructed flow was 2.2 in. per year for the Colorado. The actual flow around 1960 was about 20 per cent less.

Compared with the ratio of *actual* runoff to precipitation in the mountains of the Eastern United States (Fig. 12.5), even the ratio of *virgin* runoff to precipitation is very low for the Colorado— only 14 per cent. Now, if evaporation could be reduced by only a small fraction, such as 2 in. out of 15 in. evaporation, the water available to the lower basin states of California and Arizona could be doubled without loss to the Upper Basin states. Here lies the most promising approach to increasing the Colorado's water supply artificially. Storage reservoirs are particular offenders against the natural hydrologic balance, since water evaporates from them at high rates. The hydrologist Langbein has proved that water storage cannot be increased without limit in a river basin. As the total evaporating surface increases, the storage gain diminishes. Eventually a point is reached at which new reservoirs can provide little or no additional water storage.

In view of this situation many schemes have been advanced for reducing evaporation. These include controlling vegetation along rivers, cutting forests (see Chapter 11), storing water underground, spreading certain chemical films on reservoirs, and establishing reservoirs, where possible, at high instead of low elevations, with their relatively low temperatures.

PRECIPITATION ANALYSIS

An important requirement for all phases of life dependent on water is *reliability* of precipitation. Yet this is precisely what is not observed. Even over spans of a year, when there is plenty of time for dry and wet spells to cancel out, precipitation departs widely from the average, as we saw in Chapter 10. There we examined the record of individual rain gauges. Since, from the viewpoint of water resources management, rainfall over a whole watershed is more important, we shall continue to study the record of the Colorado River Basin.

Over the 30-year period, 1930–1960, annual water-year precipitation averaged 16 in. in the Upper Colorado Basin. Half of the years had precipitation within 10 per cent of the mean (Fig. 12.6); 65 per cent of average was received in the year with lowest precipitation. Thus, precipitation over a large area varies much less from

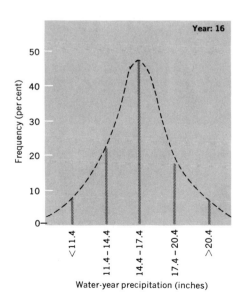

Fig. 12.6 Frequency distribution of water-year precipitation averaged over the Colorado River Basin above Lee's Ferry, Arizona (see Fig. 12.1). Period 1930–1960. (After W. E. Marlatt, Colorado State University.)

year to year than precipitation at individual stations in a similar climate.

Long-period Trends. When precipitation departs from the average for longer periods of time, critical water shortages can arise. Southern California is an outstanding example, and the Colorado River is of key importance to its economy and growth. The increasing population is so large that rainfall in the nearby mountains has not met water requirements for many years. In the early 1920s the Colorado River Compact divided the flow of the stream among the states concerned. California has taken her share 500 miles to Los Angeles and other cities through great aqueducts. So serious would be a sustained shortage in this supply, that two huge storage basins have been built having a combined capacity of no less than 5 years' average annual runoff for 1930–1960.[1] The great fear of water deficiency has resulted partially from the fact that the compact to share the Colorado's water was based on a runoff peak that was sustained for some years prior to the agreement and has not been reached since.

Annual precipitation for the Upper Basin and runoff at Lee's Ferry (Fig. 12.6) have been plotted cumulatively for the period 1930–1960 in Fig. 12.7; the last value gives the 30-year total. If curves best approximated one or both of these plots, a trend toward increasing or decreasing precipitation or runoff would be revealed. Since straight lines give the best approximation, we see that annual values have not altered significantly during those 30 years.

There is, however, an indication of shorter-period fluctuations. In Fig. 12.8, departures from the 30-year mean precipitation and virgin streamflow have been accumulated through the period. By definition, the sum of the deviations must be zero; beginning and end points of all four plots are therefore located at zero. Only the trend given by the slope of the curves matters in evaluating Fig. 12.8, not the absolute values. It so happens that these are mostly negative; this is so merely because the record available for analysis started with some dry years. Where the curves slope toward lower

[1] Lake Mead and Lake Powell, located above Hoover (Boulder) Dam and Glen Canyon Dam, respectively.

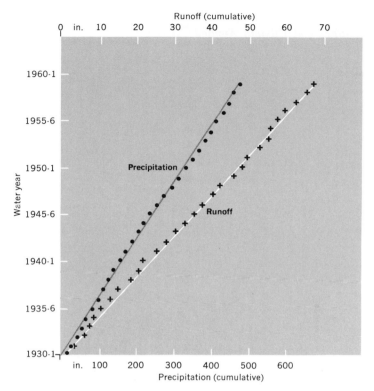

Fig. 12.7 Cumulative water-year precipitation and virgin runoff of the Colorado summed in time sequence, 1930–1960. The difference in the slopes is irrelevant, resulting merely from the scaling of the diagram. Important is that both sets of data are best approximated by straight lines.

values, the variable is below the 30-year mean; with an upward slope, it is above average.

Annual precipitation was below average from 1930 to 1940 and above average thereafter. Various interruptions of the 10-year trends occurred, for instance, from 1934 to 1937 and from 1951 to 1955. All such fluctuations are randomly distributed in time. In spite of a great many efforts to find predictable cycles, time series have produced none that have withstood the test of time. Nor does the diagram give any information on precipitation trends prior or subsequent to 1930–1960.

Winter precipitation in Fig. 12.8 is entirely in phase with annual precipitation. Both curves touch an accumulated bottom of −15 in. in 1939. In contrast, the curve for summer is almost indiffer-

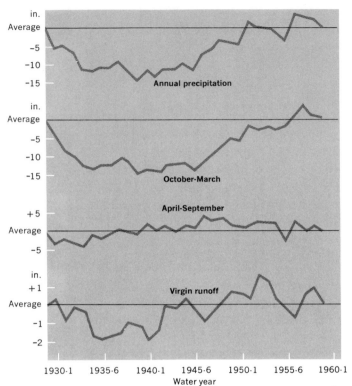

Fig. 12.8   Cumulative summation in time sequence of annual, winter (October to March) and summer (April to September) precipitation, and of virgin runoff of the Colorado at Lee's Ferry, in terms of deviations from the average, 1930–1960. In this diagram all curves must begin and end at zero.

ent; winter storms determine the long-period trend almost exclusively. The general trend of the virgin-runoff curve follows that of annual and of winter rainfall. During 1930–1940, a deficiency of 2 in. was accumulated, which is a year's average virgin runoff. Thus protective measures against prolonged drought for the Southwestern states are definitely warranted.

Rainstorms. Throughout the year, a succession of troughs in the middle and upper troposphere crosses the watersheds of the world. A few of these troughs, usually coupled with cyclones, deliver the bulk of the water, but most are weak or touch a watershed only marginally, bringing little rainfall.

In the Upper Colorado Basin, the weak troughs and orographic influences combine to produce small amounts of precipitation on many days in the year. This background, or *noise*, precipitation is quite substantial in the mountainous basin; it is about one-third of mean annual rainfall, varying little from year to year. Most of the variability in Fig. 12.6 results from occurrence or nonoccurrence of a few days with heavy precipitation. On such days, a large fraction of the basin, up to 100 per cent, is blanketed by rain or snow (Fig. 12.9).

Events that bring general precipitation—mainly, the passage of large upper-air troughs—are often called *rainstorms* in work concerned with studying the yield of such disturbances. We shall use this name, even though much precipitation is in the form of snow. A single storm may pass over the area in only 2 days. Often, however, several disturbances follow in quick succession, with precipitation stopping only intermittently. If we classify such a sequence as a single rainstorm, we find that storm yield increases with the stórm duration (Fig. 12.10). Largest yields are derived from precipitation favoring large-scale weather situations that last about a week, rather than from heavy downpours on a single day.

Annual precipitation above the noise level and number of rainstorms per year are well correlated (Fig. 12.11). The number of storms ranged between 15 and 35 per year during 1930–1960. In

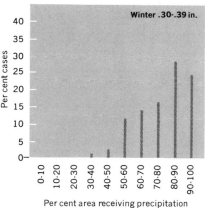

Fig. 12.9 Per cent of area of the Upper Colorado River Basin receiving precipitation on days, when the basin-averaged precipitation is 0.30 to 0.39 in., 1930–1960. Over 80 per cent of the area had precipitation on more than half of the cases (66 cases in 30 years). (After W. E. Marlatt.)

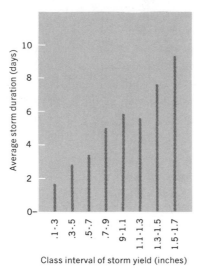

Class interval of storm yield (inches)

Fig. 12.10 Relation between dura-tion and yield of rainstorms for the Upper Colorado Basin, 1930–1960.

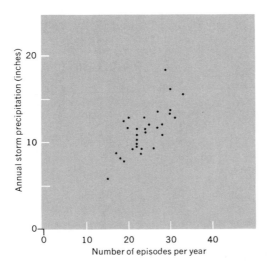

Fig. 12.11 Scatter dia-gram showing number of rainstorms in each year against annual precipita-tion due to rainstorms for the Upper Colorado Basin, 1930–1960.

some years storms persistently skirted the basin; in others they kept passing through it.

Individual rainstorms contribute widely differing amounts to the annual precipitation in all parts of the world. The percentage supplied by large and small storms appears to be fairly constant, irrespective of location of a watershed. Thus Fig. 12.12, representing the Colorado, has general significance. On the average twenty-four rainstorms occur there per year. Of these, twelve storms, or 50 per cent, produce only 25 per cent of the precipitation; six storms,

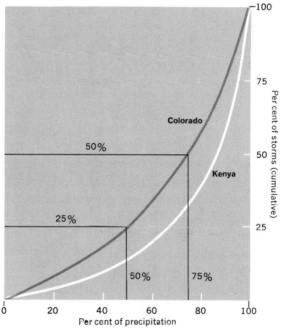

Fig. 12.12   Diagram showing the per cent contribution to precipitation made by rainstorms of different intensity in the Upper Colorado Basin (gray) and in the Kenya Highlands (white, Fig. 8.1). For construction of this diagram all rainstorms are ordered according to their water yield, from highest to lowest rank. We see that the 25 per cent of storms with highest yield contributed half of the Colorado's precipitation; the 50 per cent of storms with lowest yield only contributed 25 per cent. The Kenya situation is even more extreme, owing to the smaller size of the area for which the computations were made.

or 25 per cent, produce half of the precipitation. This result shows why the reliability of precipitation is often so low. If only two of the big storms fail to materialize in a year, drought may follow. A single large storm lasting a week and producing 1.5 in., or 10 per cent of the mean annual precipitation, can bring annual precipitation into the high brackets.

The second curve for the Kenya Highlands in Fig. 12.12—which is Fig. 8.1 repeated—is even more extreme than the curve for the Colorado. However, the difference is explained by the sizes of the areas involved: the larger a basin, the more precipitation in one portion will compensate for deficiencies in other parts of the watershed.

FLOOD PREVENTION

The Colorado River watershed above Arizona covers an area of 100,000 square miles, which has many small and large tributaries of the main stream. Even for the whole large basin, the most potent single rainstorm seldom produces less, and usually produces more, than 10 per cent of annual precipitation, though the water yield from the largest storm is poorly correlated with annual precipitation (Fig. 12.13). In a small headwater basin where the area is, perhaps, 1 per cent of that of the Colorado, the largest storm may deliver a much larger fraction of its annual rainfall, occasionally as much as a third. Moreover, this fraction tends to increase with the aridity of an area.

In the Colorado Basin, the peak runoff from all tributaries is not likely to arrive simultaneously at the main reservoir. Some tributaries discharge more water than others, and peak discharges are staggered according to location and to the time the flood of each tributary crests. Since the two reservoirs of the Colorado have a combined capacity of 5 years mean annual river flow, all danger of flooding in Arizona and California appears to have been thoroughly erased.

Such mammoth protection definitely is not achieved in the small, upper watersheds, where assurance against long drought is much harder to procure. Flood prevention tends to be the dominat-

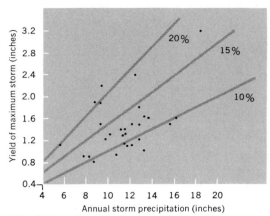

Fig. 12.13   Scatter diagram of annual storm pre-cipitation against yield of largest storm in each water year for the Upper Colorado Basin, 1930–1960. Straight lines give per cent contributed by largest storm to annual precipitation.

ing factor in many instances of reservoir construction. In a drainage area 10 by 30 miles intense precipitation may fall in a few hours, producing 1 to 3 in., rarely 6 or 10 in., and the whole rain-producing storm may pass in less than a day. The ensuing flood is controlled by releasing a major portion of water stored downstream in order to make room for the new masses of water. But dam and spillway design for guarding against flood disasters must involve a decision about the necessary degree of protection against extremes and what risks should be taken. Construction of coastal protection works discussed in Chapter 7 involves such a decision, based on both the economic and the physical situation.

The problem, then, is to determine the intensity and frequency of extreme weather events. From streamflow and precipitation observations gathered throughout the world, hydrologic engineers estimate the probability of floods having a return period of 1, 10, 100 years, etc. Physical studies of weather disturbances are another way to reach flood estimates. Such studies include important local factors, especially topography, winds, and moisture content of the air masses involved.

One physical method consists in *storm transposition*. When

specifications for dam construction are needed in a basin, and no adequate records of streamflow and precipitation are available, it may be possible to locate another basin similarly situated with respect to the general circulation, where records of earlier floods exist. When the basin area is over 1,000 square miles, great floods are usually produced by passage of severe cyclones or upper troughs. From the records a model of an extreme cyclone can be composed and then transplanted to the basin for which flood danger is to be estimated.

A further step is to compute an energy budget for the cyclone. Such a calculation was made, for instance, for one of the tributaries of the Orinoco River in northern South America. Heavy rains in this watershed, located on the eastern slope of the Andes, are brought on by cyclones traveling northwestward along the equatorial low-pressure trough between May and November (Fig. 8.4). Heat released during condensation furnishes the source of energy for the winds of these cyclones. The cyclones will attain their maximum intensity when the work done through condensation heating can no longer increase the wind energy against dissipation by friction. If we know the wind and precipitation for an equatorial cyclone of average intensity, we can inquire what would happen if this cyclone increased to two, three, or four times the average strength. Doubling the winds will approximately double the rainfall. Energy dissipation by friction, however, will increase by as much as a factor 10, because the dissipation increases with the cube of the wind speed. Thus there is always an upper limit of cyclone growth. In the Venezuelan case, a storm of twice the average intensity could maintain itself, while a cyclone with three times the average intensity—almost that of a hurricane—would fall apart. This constraint upon storm growth prescribes the limit of water yield by a cyclone crossing the basin.

13

Aerospace Weather

For many years, upper-air weather-observing networks expanded as aviation grew. Stations were established to measure winds aloft along the air routes, at first in the lowest 10,000 ft (3,000 m). But flight altitudes kept rising; then radar became a tool for measuring upper winds. By the 1950s observations through most of the troposphere were routine in many countries.

The design and operation of supersonic aircraft, missiles, and other types of craft require added meteorological support and knowledge. While increasingly complex and rapid vehicles fly through the upper atmosphere—and out of and into it—the fleet of aircraft operating in the low atmosphere, where pressurizing is not needed, continues to expand. The whole of the atmosphere has become user space. Weather problems depend on the atmospheric layer or layers traversed by a vehicle, and on its design and performance. There remains, however, one phase of operations all manned vehicles share: terminal-area operations.

WEATHER FACTORS DURING TAKE–OFF AND LANDING

Altimetry. Aeronautical engineers call height in the standard atmosphere (Appendix II) *pressure-altitude;* they also refer to pressure in those terms. Thus, the scale of a barometer may be graduated in units of pressure-altitude instead of pressure; the instrument, usually an aneroid, then is called an *altimeter.*

By the definition of pressure-altitude, the indicated height is always that of a given pressure surface above sea level *in the standard atmosphere.* When the sea-level pressure deviates from the standard value of 1,013.25 millibars (29.92 in. of mercury), or when the mean temperature between the surface and the flight level differs from that of Fig. 1.14, the altimeter will not indicate the correct height.

If an aircraft stands on the ground at sea level, its actual height is, of course, zero. If the airport has higher than standard atmosphere pressure, if it is 1,030 millibars (30.42 in.), the altimeter will show the aircraft located about 450 ft (140 m) below sea level! With a pressure of 1,000 millibars (29.53 in.), the altimeter indicates that the plane is 360 ft (110 m) up in the air. Obviously, this erroneous information must be corrected. Altimeters have a dial which permits pilots to adjust indicated altitude to zero. The amount by which the altimeter is corrected is called the altimeter setting; in our example, +450 ft for the high pressure and −360 ft for the low pressure. Usually, the altimeter setting will differ at the point of departure and at the destination. If an aircraft starts at sea level, where pressure is 1,030 millibars and ends at sea level at 1,000 millibars, the altimeter will still indicate an 810-ft height when the plane lands unless corrected en route. Most countries have aviation weather services from which a pilot can obtain, via radio, altimeter corrections.

The altimeter setting merely assures that the altimeter, upon landing at sea level, will read zero, or that, when the airport lies above sea level, the altimeter will point to the altitude of the airport when the plane touches ground. It need not indicate the altitude of aircraft in flight above the ground, even when the ground is near sea level. We found in Chapter 3 (Fig. 3.3) that surfaces of constant pressure are spaced farther apart vertically when temperature is high than when it is low. Thus, when the mean temperature between sea level and flight altitude is greater than it is in the standard atmosphere, the altitude of the aircraft will be higher than the altimeter indicates; at colder temperatures, it will be lower.

The mean temperature between sea level and the pressure-altitude of an aircraft is not routinely furnished by flight-advisory weather services. Therefore, a pilot does not know his altitude precisely, except when his craft is equipped with a radio-altimeter which measures height above ground directly through reflection of electric waves. However, solutions can be given for specific problems. Consider the case of a pilot flying at an indicated altitude of 1,000 ft (300 m), determined from the altimeter setting. He needs to drop below the base of a cloud deck for a landing approach. How high is he really above the ground when starting this maneuver? Figure 13.1 shows that he is within 100 ft (30 m) of standard atmosphere altitude for a very wide range of temperatures, from 0° to 100°F (−18° to 38°C). A good thermometer aboard the aircraft is sufficient to determine temperature in this particular case. Figure 13.1, of course, can be extended to give the heights for much higher or lower temperatures.

Terminal Weather. Low ceilings and visibilities cause the major traffic disruptions at air terminals; this problem has remained unchanged over the years. Landing is generally restricted when the ceiling, or height of low cloud base with more than six-tenths of the sky covered by cloud, drops below 1,000 ft (300 m) above the ground, or when horizontal visibility is reduced to less than 3 miles. Fog is most dangerous, since it can bring zero ceiling and visibility. Smog, blowing or falling snow, and dust storms also can generate

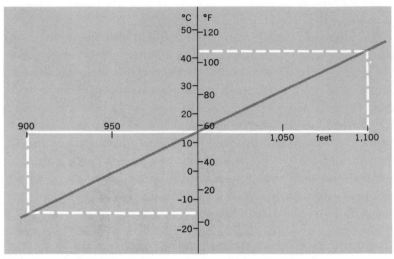

Fig. 13.1 Actual altitude of aircraft above ground, given the air temperature, if the altimeter, after appropriate altimeter correction, indicates 1,000 ft. Dashed lines give two extreme examples.

very poor landing conditions. Freezing rain that covers the runways with a sheet of ice may force closing of an airport, although this is a rare event.

Much effort has been expended in developing methods for predicting weather at airports. Some studies have been very successful, notably during low stratus and fog situations connected with cyclones and their fronts. Nevertheless, local air currents and random factors often complicate the picture. A large fog bank may end suddenly a few miles from an airport on one day; under similar general conditions, it may just cover the field on another. Therefore, aircraft must carry enough fuel to reach an alternate airport.

Ideally, this alternate airport should always be open when the destination airport is closed. In practice, this ideal is sometimes approached, mainly when topographic features lend a helping hand. On Iceland, in the North Atlantic, two fields located on opposite sides of the island are separated by mountains up to 5,000 ft (1,500 m) high. Reykjavik, on the southwest shore (Fig. 13.2), has ceilings below 1,000 ft in 16 per cent of the morning and evening observations during summer. At Akureyri, facing north, low ceilings prevail 12 per cent of the time. However, the probability that both fields will have low ceilings at the same time is only 2 per cent. When winds blow onshore at one field, they blow offshore at the other.

Where the situation is not so favorable, aircraft must carry reserve fuel for long distance travel to a safe alternate destination. Over the Eastern United States, fog and low ceilings at times may envelop a very large area; this happened on January 5–6, 1962,

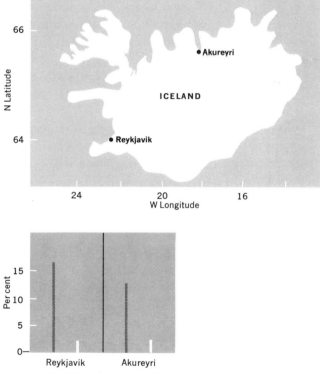

Fig. 13.2 Top: location of two air fields on Iceland, one near shore facing west, the other north. Bottom: gray bars show per cent of time ceiling is below 1,000 ft (300 m) at morning and evening observation at each station from May to August; white bars show per cent of time both stations have ceiling below 1,000 ft simultaneously. (After W. C. Jacobs, American Meteorological Society Monograph No. 1, 1947.)

illustrated in Figs. 7.8 to 7.11. Some terminals can land aircraft even during fog with instrument landing systems (ILS) and ground control approach (GCA) methods. These techniques, however, are time-consuming and slow down the acceptance rate at airports. Frequently, they can be employed only when the ceiling remains above 100 ft and visibility above ¼ mile.

In some circumstances, weather may be locally controlled; we noted in Chapter 5 that certain types of fog may be dispelled, at least temporarily. Where such relief cannot be provided, it has been proposed to hold aircraft at their point of origin until the weather at the destination clears. This solution will work in obvious cases—when, for example, arrival of a cold front will clear away a foggy warm air mass. Often, however, weather remains a question mark for many hours. Ceilings alternately rise and fall below acceptable levels because of random wind eddies. In such cases, only an aircraft near the terminal and ready to land can avail itself of the breaks in the weather.

Wind. Serious danger from wind arises, even at large fields with many runways, when strong squalls preceding thunderstorms arrive suddenly. This danger often can be foreseen, mainly at terminals where radar tracks the approach of severe cumulus-type clouds. At small airfields with only one runway, strong crosswinds can also inhibit landing. The problem of designing airports to guard against such crosscurrents will be considered in the next chapter.

Pilots ascending or descending through the lowest 2,000 to 3,000 ft (600 to 900 m) above the ground will observe that the wind frequently turns quickly with height—clockwise with increasing height in the Northern Hemisphere and counterclockwise in the Southern Hemisphere. This happens regularly in a *stable* atmosphere, when there is no vertical overturning. The change of wind direction with height, which may amount to 50 to 60°, is due to the decrease with height of the effect of ground friction. In Fig. 13.3 we find a 55° turning; the top of the friction layer is situated at 3,000 ft (900 m), a normal occurrence when the wind blows with a component from south in the middle and high latitudes of the Northern Hemisphere during the cold season. Warm air then moves over a cold surface, and the atmosphere is thermally stable. Behind cold fronts and in the trade-wind belt, where the air is turbulent, the wind turns very little or not at all, up to the top of the unstable layer.

WEATHER HAZARDS EN ROUTE: ICING

Aircraft which normally cruise above 25,000 to 30,000 ft (7,500 to 9,000 m) pressure-altitude can nearly always climb above cloud layers with icing danger. Vehicles that fly at lower levels, however, remain exposed to this hazard, one of the major problems for aircraft over the years. Icing increases the weight of aircraft; it changes the aerodynamic characteristics of the wings and other surfaces

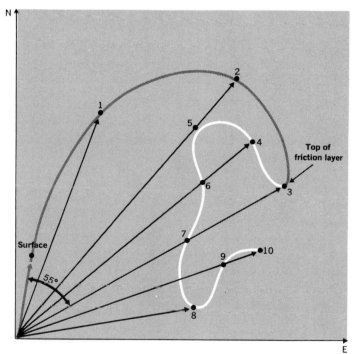

Fig. 13.3   Pilot balloon observation at Chicago Midway airport on January 17, 1942. (After V. J. Oliver.) Height indicated along curve in 1,000s of ft. Arrows are wind vectors pointing to direction toward which wind blows. Curved line gives envelope on which all winds at intermediate levels lie. Top of friction layer is at 3,000 feet where clockwise turning of wind with height first terminates.

of the craft. Two types of icing form on these surfaces: rime, and glaze, or clear icing.

Rime forms when a plane flies through a stratus deck with many supercooled water droplets too small to precipitate. These freeze when they strike the cold body of the airplane. Irregularly shaped masses of small ice pellets accumulate, mainly on the leading edges of the wings; deicing equipment can usually remove these clusters.

An aircraft encounters glaze danger when it flies through a cloud with precipitation-size water drops at temperatures below freezing. Such drops break up on striking the plane, and the resulting coat of ice is difficult to remove. Clear ice can accumulate rapidly, especially when rain from cumulus-type clouds above a warm-front surface falls through a cold layer underneath. During the warmer months, the best escape route is normally downward, because low-level temperatures are above freezing. In winter situations, when temperatures are below freezing at all heights, aircraft will be above the layers most dangerous for icing if flown at temperatures of 15°F (−9°C) or lower in stratus-type clouds.

WEATHER HAZARDS EN ROUTE: TURBULENCE

The greatest in-flight danger is turbulence, and it has destroyed many vehicles. The motions of an aircraft, which those aboard interpret as turbulence, arise in part from natural turbulence in the air and in part from aircraft structure and pilot maneuver. Therefore it has proved to be a very difficult task to specify whether and where turbulence will occur in many types of weather situations. Nevertheless, we can make a gross distinction between three principal types of turbulence: (1) in-cloud, (2) clear-air, and (3) mountain-induced.

In-cloud Turbulence. When an aircraft approaches a cloud layer, it normally begins to encounter *bumpiness* even before entering the cloud. Rapid alternation of upward and downward accelerations produces a washboard or cobblestone effect when traveling in stratocumulus (Fig. 4.14); such turbulence may persist for hundreds of miles. A plane moving at 250 knots with respect to the air will experience a bump every 1 or 2 sec, so that the wavelength of the turbulent air motion is about 300 to 600 ft (100 to 200 m). There is always a spectrum of intensity as well as of distance between bumps. Often the intensity of turbulence has been divided into three classes: light—acceleration less than $\frac{2}{10}$ that of gravity; medium—acceleration $\frac{2}{10}$ to $\frac{5}{10}$ that of gravity; heavy—stronger accelerations. Instruments measuring acceleration have shown that turbulence is generally light in clouds such as strato-cumulus and trade-wind cumulus; however, accelerations in the medium range also occur there.

Cumulonimbus clouds, especially when they contain active thunderstorm cells, always have been the bane of aviation, and with much justification. When severe, they may combine heavy turbulence with hail and icing, and it is not always possible to fly above a thunderstorm, even in subsonic jets. The violent thunderstorms of spring and early summer in the Midwestern United States break through the tropopause at about 40,000 ft (12,000 m) pressure-altitude or a little higher. Cloud tops above 50,000 ft (15,000 m) have been reported. Heavy turbulence is likely to occupy parts of the entire air space from 20,000 ft (6,000 m), or lower, to the tropopause and beyond, a dangerous situation for jet aircraft whose wings are not stressed against extreme accelerations. An increasing number of such aircraft carry weather radar, which shows the heavy precipitation areas; this permits pilots to steer around thunderstorm cells as shown in Fig. 5.5. It is one advantage of severe cumulus weather that it is concentrated in small areas. Cloud development and turbulence are suppressed over large areas on the outside of thunderstorms. These fair-weather corridors may be 30 miles and more across, and they can serve as channels through which aircraft, guided by radar, can pass, avoiding the intense centers of convection with their lightning, hail, and turbulence. The aircraft may be in thick cirrus flowing from the cumulonimbus anvil, but this is harmless.

When thunderstorm cells consolidate into a squall line (Figs. 5.7 and 5.8), as they often do in spring over the Midwestern United States, the path across the line may be closed to aircraft.

Clear-air Turbulence. From the first days of aviation, pilots have learned to contend with the thermal and mechanical turbulence near the ground, discussed in Chapter 3. It was expected that above the lowest few thousand feet, and especially in the upper troposphere and stratosphere, the atmosphere would be nonturbulent outside of clouds. Great surprise, and much disbelief, was the first response when pilots flying near 30,000 ft (9,000 m) began to report frequent light turbulence and occasional heavy turbulence in clear air. All illusions about the quiet upper atmosphere had to be discarded. High-flying vehicles must be designed to withstand the clear-air turbulence which is encountered without warning. Such turbulence must also be taken into account in the design of missile guidance systems.

In the search for a source of clear-air turbulence, the jet stream has been frequently studied. Indeed, some concentration of turbulence often accompanies jet-stream cores. Aircraft, however, often fly across or along jet streams without meeting any turbulence; many condensation trails show little, if any, of the distortion to be expected under turbulent conditions. Further, fatal accidents ascribed to clear-air turbulence have occurred at sites far removed from any jet stream. Our understanding of clear-air turbulence is evidently incomplete. Besides, many of the accelerations experienced by aircraft in the high troposphere and stratosphere may not be due to turbulence. Wave motion may develop in the air under the influence of gravity in a shallow layer of, perhaps, not more than a few hundred feet thickness, when the layer has a temperature inversion. Aircraft flying through the successive crests and troughs will experience accelerations that convey the impression of turbulence to those aboard.

Mountain Waves. Just downstream from mountain ranges, very spectacular lens-shaped clouds form when a strong current, usually with a jet-stream center, crosses the range at more or less right angles. These clouds are *stationary;* ascent must take place at their upstream end and descent at their downstream end in order for them to remain in the same location against a strong wind. Stationary clouds reveal wave motion in the upper-air flow in the lee of mountain ranges; the waves may extend to the tropopause, even when the mountains are only a few thousand feet high.

At low levels, the air descends the mountain range, often as foehn or chinook (Chapter 11), so that the cloud deck formed on the windward side of the mountains disappears (Fig. 11.7). At higher altitudes, the lee-side descent disappears and actually becomes ascent some miles downstream from the high mountain ridges. Here the lenticular clouds form, often in two or more layers and in several rows downstream (Fig. 13.4). In severe cases, a low-level countercurrent against the mountains develops near the ground, forming a *rotor* (Fig. 13.5). Then a tremendous cloud, sometimes of imposing and awesome appearance, parallels the mountain range in the middle of the troposphere—the *rotor cloud* (Fig. 13.6).

The *mountain wave,* observed in all parts of the world, can pose severe danger for aircraft, as well as provide spectacular sights and pictures. Even though flight in the lenticular wave clouds may be smooth, the vertical velocities, similar to thunderstorm drafts, may attain extraordinary strength. Vertical draft speeds of more than 10 mph are common; they have reached 50 mph on occasion. Such strong downdrafts are a serious aviation hazard; further, the rotors

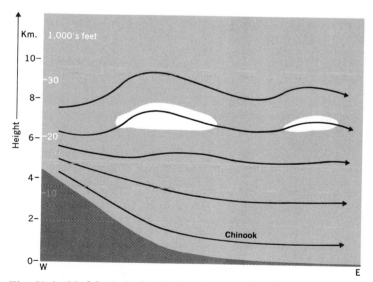

Fig. 13.4   Model of air flow in lee of mountains illustrating formation of lenticular lee wave clouds above low-level chinook. White areas: clouds.

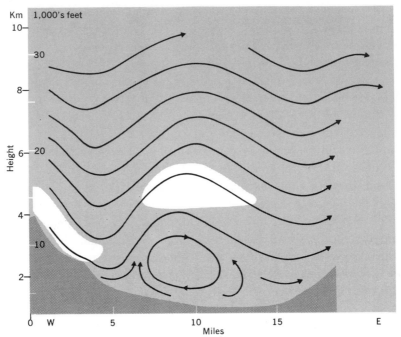

Fig. 13.5 The air flow as determined by glider east of the Sierra Nevada of California near Bishop on February 16, 1952. White areas: clouds. (After Harold E. Klieforth.)

are highly turbulent. On the lee side of the Sierra Nevada of central California accelerations have been encountered as much as five times that of gravity. It is small wonder that here is a paradise for sailplanes and that much of the research in exploring the waves has been conducted with such craft. All world glider records have been established in mountain waves; flights have penetrated the tropopause and reached heights well beyond 40,000 ft (12,000 m).

FLIGHT PLANNING AND THE JET STREAM

Ground Speed. The velocity at which an airborne vehicle moves relative to the ground is its *ground speed.* When there is no wind blowing, the vehicle will travel at the same rate through the air and over the ground. However, when wind is blowing, ground speed and speed with respect to the air differ. The ground speed exceeds *true air speed* when the wind is at the tail of an airplane; it is less than true air speed against a head wind. An aircraft going west at 200 knots will remain stationary over the same spot on earth when it flies against a 200-knot wind from west. The aircraft will also be retarded when there is a crosswind from north or south; it must head into this wind in order not to be driven off course.

Ideally, a plane is dispatched to reach its destination in the shortest possible time, that is, at maximum ground speed. This, however, may be very costly in fuel and severely limit the cruising range. For most types of missions, aircraft is flown near the altitude where it performs most economically, provided traffic permits. After selection of an optimum cruising altitude, the plane then may be routed to assure best use of the winds at that level. Of course, wind is by no means the only factor determining actual flight levels and routes. Safety in the crowded air space weighs most heavily. Our

Fig. 13.6   Rotor cloud near Bishop, California, May 19, 1962. The Sierra Nevada are to the right in picture. (Courtesy Harold E. Klieforth.)

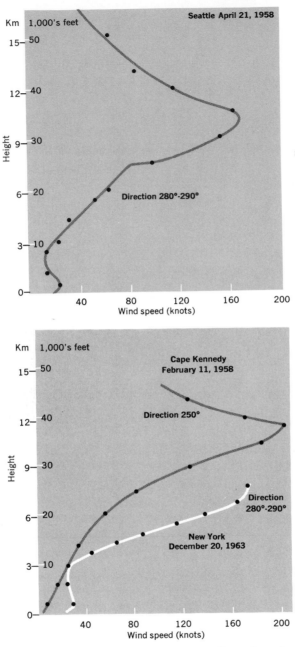

Fig. 13.7   Three examples of wind soundings through jet streams. Upper diagram: Seattle, typical profile of strong jet. Lower diagram: Cape Kennedy, an exceptionally strong jet stream; New York, a current with unusually low base. Wind direction, indicated on the 360° compass (Appendix I), was nearly constant through the jet-stream layer in each case; this happens always.

concern here, however, is limited to the importance of wind in relation to flight planning.

Optimum Cruise Altitude. The subsonic jet aircraft flies at true air speeds of 450 to 500 knots. Its most economical operating altitude generally lies between 30,000 and 40,000 ft (9 and 12 km) pressure-altitude, which is also the height range for the core of most jet streams. Thus wind remains an important factor, even for such fast aircraft, since they consume fuel very rapidly.

When a jet stream is present, wind usually, though not always, increases with height most sharply above 20,000 ft (6 km). On February 11, 1958, for instance, wind speed rose from nearly zero to 60 knots at 20,000 ft at Cape Kennedy (Fig. 13.7); it then increased from 60 to 210 knots between 20,000 and 38,000 ft. Wind direction remained nearly constant above 10,000 ft, and this occurs in all jet streams in middle and high latitudes.

Figure 13.8 shows the performance characteristics of a well-known subsonic jet. The objective is to fly the longest distance possible with a given load of fuel (maximum range power setting). If there is no wind, the aircraft flies most economically near 35,000 ft pressure-altitude, as seen from the straight vertical line at zero wind speed in Fig. 13.8.[1] At that altitude, it gains about 1.5 miles per 100 lb of fuel burned over the amount it uses at 20,000 ft. Considering that the aircraft consumes about 100 lb of fuel in 5 miles when traveling at optimum cruise altitude, the efficiency gained through climbing to this level is indeed significant.

If the Seattle jet stream of Fig. 13.7 is superimposed on Fig. 13.8 as tail wind, the gain in efficiency is 3 miles ground distance per 100 lb of fuel, or twice the gain under no-wind conditions between 20,000 and 35,000 ft pressure-altitude. This difference is very large; evidently, the jet-stream core is the optimum cruise level. Flying westward against this jet stream, however, the aircraft might as well stay at 20,000 ft; the fuel expended in climbing higher brings no return in terms of economy.

Minimum Flight Path. An aircraft crossing the United States from San Francisco to New York at a true air speed of 500 knots

---

[1] The optimum altitude varies somewhat depending on the total weight of the aircraft.

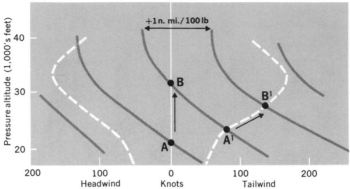

Fig. 13.8 Locating the optimum cruise level for a subsonic jet aircraft. The slanting solid curves give the efficiency gained through climbing, in units of one mile of ground distance per 100 pounds of fuel consumed. In case of no wind, the straight line at zero wind speed applies. Going, for instance, from altitude marked "A" to altitude marked "B" along the line, the performance gain is 1 mile per 100 pounds of fuel. The Seattle sounding of Fig. 13.7 is shown (dashed) both as tail wind and head wind. Going along the tail wind from A' to B', a much shorter vertical distance than A-B, the performance gain also is 1 mile per 100 pounds of fuel. Along the head wind profile, corresponding points cannot be located below the level of strongest wind.

needs less than 4 hr for the flight in a 150-knot westerly jet stream. In the opposite direction, the flight takes nearly 7 hr. Thus, it should be worthwhile to dispatch subsonic jets along routes other than minimum distance, or great circle track, in order to ride or avoid a jet stream. Similar considerations apply for a piston-powered aircraft flying, for instance, at 18,000 ft pressure-altitude, when the plane is contending with a wind field such as shown in Fig. 13.11.

If the fast air current is not too broad, geometry strongly favors such deviations. For instance, if a plane deviates from a 3,000-mile great circle route by 300 miles along the path shown in Fig. 13.9, its total ground distance flown increases only by 2 per cent, or 60 miles. If the flying time on the great circle is 6 hr, the deviating aircraft must realize a 10-knot wind advantage in order to arrive at the same time as another vehicle flying on the great circle. With larger wind advantages, it will arrive sooner. The question then is whether jet streams are sufficiently narrow to make deviations worthwhile.

Figure 13.10 shows wind direction and speed at 200 millibars (near 39,000 ft pressure-altitude) for November 10, 1963. Two jet streams, with core speed above 125 knots, were located in the ridges of a wave pattern whose trough was over the Central United States; such speeds are commonplace during winter. We shall consider the routes Houston–New York and Seattle–Chicago. These routes parallel the jet streams and also coincide fairly well with the great circle tracks. Hence, the downstream flights on the great circle are fast, and the return trips are slow.

We shall select a subsonic jet for calculation, flying with 75 per cent of the speed of sound, or 450 knots true air speed, at the prevailing temperatures. Along the Houston–New York route the mean head wind or tail wind is 105 knots; ground speed averages 555 knots going downstream and 345 knots going upstream. Flight durations are 2.3 and 3.8 hr, respectively. The alternate return path to the north and west of the great circle route is about 10 per cent (130 miles) longer. A plane flying this route encounters strong head winds in the east. Where the track bends southward just below the Great Lakes, the head wind quickly disappears, and is succeeded by a tail wind. Averaged over the route, the head wind is 35 knots. At a ground speed of 415 knots, or 70 knots more than along the great circle route, the plane covers the longer distance in 3.4 hr;

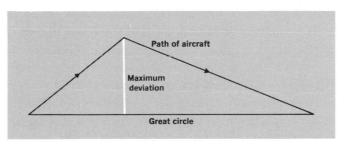

Fig. 13.9 *Example of route (shown with arrows) deviating from minimum distance (great circle) track in order to utilize or avoid jet-stream winds.*

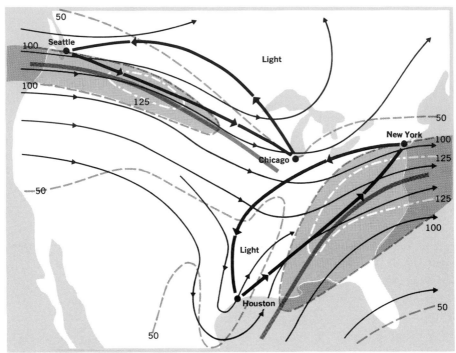

Fig. 13.10 *Illustrating minimum flight planning. Streamlines and lines of equal wind speed (knots) at 200 millibars (40,000 ft pressure-altitude) on November 10, 1963. Jet-stream axes denoted by heavy gray lines; areas with wind speed above 100 knots shaded. Curves with arrows show great circle paths Houston-New York and Seattle-Chicago, also return routes, which avoid going upstream against jet streams.*

this is 24 min less than the time needed on the direct route—a marked gain in performance on this relatively short flight.

On the Seattle–Chicago route, the computations yield similar results. Here, the mean jet-stream speed is 115 knots along the great circle route. Eastbound time is 2.6 hr and westbound time, 4.5 hr. The length of the northern return route is 1,650 miles, avoiding the jet stream entirely. This, again, is 10 per cent longer than the great circle route. Assuming that the international travel is permitted, the time against an average headwind of 30 knots is 3.9 hr or 36 min less than on the great circle.

Clearly, the benefits to be obtained through full use of the wind field will be still larger for strong jet streams and long flights, especially across oceans. However, referring again to Fig. 13.11, we see that a westbound piston plane from New York also will reduce its head wind from 110 to only 30 knots by deviating just 50 miles to the north.

JET STREAM AND MISSILE TRAJECTORIES

The atmosphere places many obstacles in the path of missile releases. Among these are surface winds at the launch site, turbulence in troposphere and stratosphere, and jet-stream winds. When winds are very strong, unguided missiles will be driven off course; even the guidance system of guided missiles may not always be able to control the missile trajectory through an extreme jet stream.

At least for certain types of missiles, the momentum of the air (see Chapter 3) is the important factor affecting the trajectory. Because air density decreases upward (Fig. 1.16), the momentum

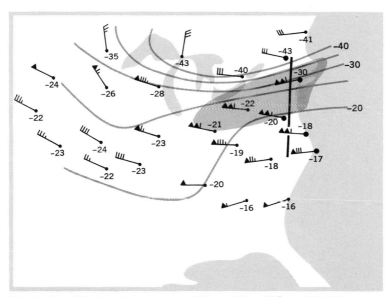

Fig. 13.11   Winds and isotherms (°C) at 500 millibars (18,000 ft pressure-altitude), on December 20, 1963. Area with large increase of momentum with height shaded. Note very sharp drop of wind speed north of jet stream.

also will decrease upward, unless the wind increases strongly with height. This happens below jet-stream cores when the shear of the wind is very large, for instance in the three wind profiles of Fig. 13.7.

Conditions for missile flight are most adverse when the momentum increases with height. This is most likely to happen in situations when the bottom of a jet stream is situated in the layer between 10,000 and 20,000 ft (3,000 and 6,000 m) pressure-altitude, much lower than usual. Here air density is still high, compared to the upper troposphere.

We see such a low bottom in the New York sounding of December 20, 1963 (Fig. 13.7). Wind speed on that day already exceeded 100 knots at 18,000 ft (500 millibars); such strong winds extended westward nearly to Lake Michigan (Fig. 13.11). A vertical cross

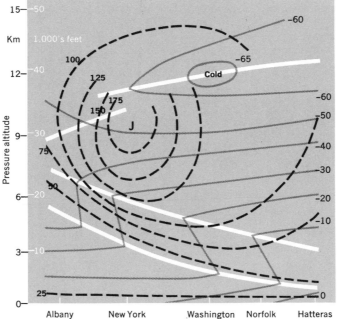

Fig. 13.12 Vertical cross section of temperature (°C) and of wind speed (dashed, knots) along line drawn near U.S. East Coast in Fig. 13.11 Boundaries of front and tropopauses marked with white lines; frontal layer shaded.

section along the East Coast (Fig. 13.12) shows a strong front sloping upward toward the north. In the northern portion of the frontal layer, wind speed increased from about 40 to over 100 knots from lower to upper boundary of the front. Above the front, wind speed continued increasing below the intense jet-stream center over New York. In contrast, highest speeds were already attained a short distance over the frontal boundary at Washington and Norfolk and then remained uniform in a deep layer of the middle and upper troposphere.

The momentum cross section computed from Fig. 13.12 with the density-temperature relation of Fig. 1.16 shows a core with maximum momentum just above the front at New York (Fig. 13.13). Though the wind there could not be measured through the whole jet-stream core because of the very strong velocities, the tempera-

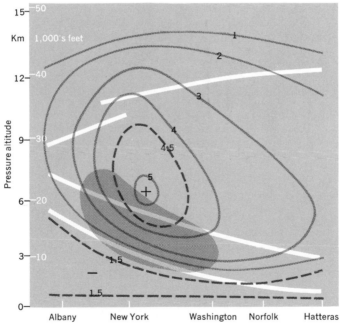

Fig. 13.13 Vertical cross section of momentum corresponding to Fig. 13.12. Shaded: layer where momentum increases most rapidly upward. The direction is constant and nearly from west. Unit is that of specific momentum, grams per square centimeter per second.

ture field at upper levels indicates that the top of the sounding in Fig. 13.7 was close to the level of strongest geostrophic wind (Chapter 6). This assumption was used in constructing Fig. 13.13.

Almost the entire increase of momentum with height is concentrated in the frontal zone, and the level of strongest momentum lies well below the level of strongest wind. The shading shows the layer through which missiles can pass only with difficulty. This layer had a north-south extent of less than 200 miles, but it extended westward almost to the Great Lakes (shaded region in Fig. 13.12) and, of course, an unknown distance eastward into the Atlantic Ocean.

14

The Weather Factor
in Design
and Operations

Weather is an important ingredient in making decisions. In planning, questions such as these are asked: how high to build a dam for protection against runoff from an extreme storm; how to lay out a highway through a valley to avoid frequent radiation fog; what crop to plant in view of the probable length of the growing season; how to design a smoke stack against poisonous pollution; what preventive measures to take so that machinery is kept from disintegrating in the tropics.

Decisions involving the weather factor in operations might be the following: should frost protection measures be started against a threatening freeze in the citrus groves; should offshore oil platforms be evacuated in the face of a hurricane threat; should the snow removal crews be called out to battle an impending storm with possibly heavy snowfall; and, on another time scale, should fuel oil storage be raised above normal in New England to prepare for heavy demand when an abnormally cold winter is expected. There are also those questions that forever darken the meteorologist's life: can the laundry hang out for drying; will the weather be fine for the picnic; can the wedding reception be outdoors.

WEATHER CONTROL

The tools for solving weather problems in design and operations are *control, analysis,* and *prediction.* Control, of course, eliminates weather as a variable in decision making. Over the ages man has spent a considerable fraction of his time and energy on controlling weather. Erection of the first shelters eliminated wind and precipitation quite well. From such beginnings we have graduated to fully air-conditioned building with complete control of temperature and humidity as well as of rain, snow, and wind. Some design problems, to be sure, remain, and these are important in analyzing costs: against what maximum and minimum temperatures should an air-conditioning system be effective? What roof construction is needed against snow loading?

Irrigation and desalinization of sea water are other examples of man's effort to overcome problems of weather and climate. Thus, the old saw, "Everybody talks about the weather but no one does anything about it," has never been true.

But in a rather different class of endeavor are man's measures, deliberate or unwitting, that interfere with the natural evolution of weather and climate. In Chapter 2 we raised the question of whether contamination of the atmosphere in the last hundred years has caused the observed global warming. If so, man has exercised an entirely unintentional control. Pollution of the high atmosphere by rocket fuels may well modify the solar radiation penetrating the ionosphere. This will be a matter of growing concern as the number and size of space loads continue to increase.

Deliberate interference with nature aims to promote man's welfare: fog dispersal at airports with cloud seeding; covering of reservoir surfaces with chemical films to reduce evaporation; sprinkling of snow with black dirt from aircraft in spring to accelerate snow melt in cold climates. More grandiose schemes are being proposed from time to time. In assessing their merits, we should be aware that their implementation might conjure up unforeseen and unwanted consequences. Full theoretical exploration is essential; fortunately, laboratory experiments and electronic computers provide the means for rather exhaustive studies. For instance, a physical model of the atmosphere is introduced on a computer; a proposed weather modification experiment is superposed after the model has run for some time without such modification. The computer shows the future state of the model atmosphere for both cases. If the model is realistic, the computation should demonstrate the merits and demerits of the proposed scheme.

ANALYSIS OF WEATHER DATA FOR DESIGN

Statistical analysis is the main tool that enables us to include the weather factor in solutions to design problems. An example will illustrate the technique. During the early 1940s, the United States heavily used a group of air fields in North Africa and the Middle East. Each field had its unique set of local weather factors, which influenced its operations. At Bengazi in Libya (Fig. 14.1), the wind blows steadily from north during summer, often from south to southeast during winter. The single runway of the airport was oriented north-northeast–south-southwest. This orientation proved satisfactory during the eight summer months with steady north wind. Operational difficulties, however, developed in winter. A review of the airport design was undertaken by Samuel B. Solot.

The review showed that wind speed at the airport exceeded 10 mph during winter from 30 to 50 per cent of the time, determined from hourly wind observations. These winds often blew at a large angle across the runway. From the frequency distribution of wind speeds above 10 mph at various wind directions (Fig. 14.1), an alternate runway oriented northwest to southeast was needed for

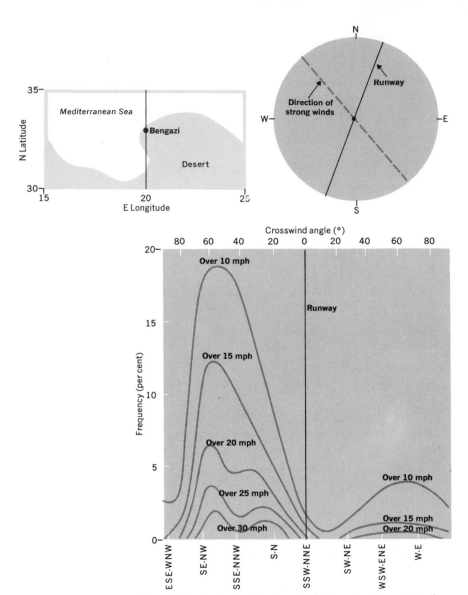

Fig. 14.1 Analysis of airport design at Bengazi, Libya (33°N, 20°E). Upper diagram: location of airport, orientation of runway and most frequent direction of strong winds in winter. Lower diagram: frequency analysis of wind direction at various wind speeds during November. The per cent frequency is given for wind direction over two 22½° sectors centered, for instance, on SE and NW. When summed over the eight directions shown in the bottom scale, the percentages add up to the total per cent frequency out of all wind observations, when wind speed exceeded the indicated limits. This total, for instance, is 55 per cent for winds over 10 mph; wind speed was above 10 mph 55 per cent and below 10 mph 45 per cent of the time. (After Samuel B. Solot.)

efficient and safe use of the airport during winter. Crosswinds arose when a cyclone traveled across the southern part of the Mediterranean Sea or along the coast of northern Africa from the west. Winds from southeast, sometimes of gale force, then blew in advance of the low-pressure center. When they reached the airport at Bengazi, these southeast winds had traveled across the sand desert. The heavy dust or sand loads they carried lowered the visibility and, with the crosswind, rendered airport operations especially hazardous.

Solot made a similar analysis at Abadan, Iran, at the tip of the Persian Gulf. There the main runway was oriented 325 to 145° on the 360° compass (Fig. 14.2). The question arose of whether or not a short and unserviceable runway oriented 280 to 100° should be extended. Solot found that the high winds blow mainly with northwest-southeast orientation, or at a crosswind angle of about 20 to 30°, from both the existing and proposed runways. Here, the construction would add little, if anything, to efficient airport operation.

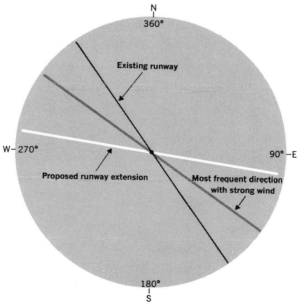

Fig. 14.2 Analysis of airport design at Abadan, Iran (30°N, 48°E), in July. (After Samuel B. Solot.)

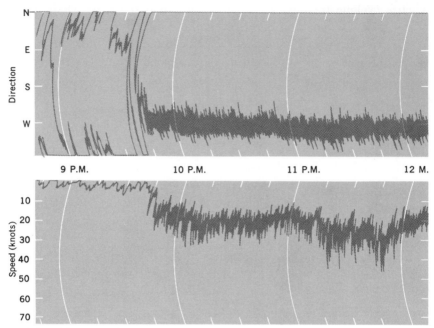

Fig. 14.3 *Wind direction (upper) and wind speed (knots, lower) at Colorado State University, just east of the Rocky Mountains, during the evening of January 16, 1964.*

PREDICTABILITY

Many demands are made for weather prediction; some of these can be satisfied and others not. What is predictable? We have a clear physical model of the daily temperature cycle. With this model, and statistical background on the daily temperature range at a station, we can predict daily high and low temperature within narrow limits as long as the model holds—that is, if no fronts pass or no overcast forms unexpectedly.

Consider, however, the wind record of Fig. 14.3. After some calm evening hours, a strong and gusty chinook wind set in suddenly about 9:50 P.M. Perhaps the motion of high- and low-pressure centers on the weather map might have suggested that a chinook would occur. But no method is known of predicting, within hours, when it will begin. Further, it would be impossible to say even 5 min in advance whether at 11:32 P.M. there will be a gust or a lull. The succession of gusts and lulls in Fig. 14.3 is very rapid; random processes determine the exact timing of the wind fluctuations. Similarly, the cumuli in the sky on a summer afternoon form from a random selection of impulses (Fig. 3.4), unless special terrain features determine their location. If only a few of these clouds rain out—the usual case—it is impossible to say whether a particular site will or will not receive a shower. A forecast of "scattered showers" describes the predictability of the situation well.

Figure 14.4 shows the seasonal march of average temperature at Chicago in winter and daily temperatures observed during the 1959–1960 winter. The mean seasonal march, of course, is related to the sun's changing altitude; it would be trivial to announce that winter will be colder than summer. Just like all winters, that of 1959–1960 was "unusual." The weather was cold early and late in the season, and warm in the middle. It may become possible to predict such a general pattern at the start of winter. But what can be

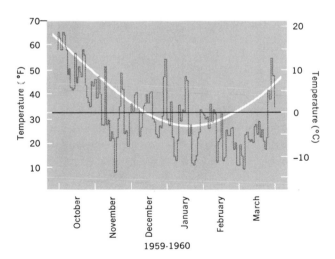

Fig. 14.4 Mean seasonal course of temperature at Chicago during winter, and daily temperatures for the 1959–1960 winter.

said about the daily temperatures? They appear to fluctuate in much the same way that wind speed does in Fig. 14.3. If so, the fluctuations, often predictable a day in advance, should be considered as random, or "noise," when we look ahead for several months.

This viewpoint is not universally accepted; there are those who maintain that a single day's weather can be foretold a year in advance. The interesting question arising here is to what extent the future state of the atmosphere is predetermined and to what extent it is governed by random processes. This question cannot be answered at present. The "state of the art" is such that prediction for tomorrow is likely to be most accurate if made today, and not yesterday or a week ago. Similarly, the best general outlook for next month is prepared this month.

DAILY WEATHER PREDICTION

In predicting tomorrow's weather, the first step is to find the most probable location and intensity of high- and low-pressure centers and their fronts at the surface, as well as that of the troughs and ridges with their jet streams in the upper air. Based on this information, a fairly successful forecast of temperature, precipitation, and other elements can usually be developed.

Since the 1950s, the future state of the weather is being calculated by numerical procedures, physical and statistical. The physical approach uses theorems such as that of conservation of vorticity and the changes in vorticity produced by convergence and divergence of mass. Over a large area covering the major part of a hemisphere or more, the evolution of wind systems and the temperature and pressure at the ground and in the upper air are computed in small time increments on electronic computers.

In statistical prediction, a specific important question is usually selected, such as this: will a cyclone form on the United States East Coast tomorrow? If so, where will it move? For solving such a problem, a large number of possible prediction factors is scanned over the historical weather record. These predictors may be pressure, temperature, upper wind, etc. The area scanned may range in size from the United States and its immediate surroundings to large portions of the Northern Hemisphere. The best predictors selected by statistical screening are combined into a prediction formula. This formula is tested with data not used in developing the equation. The test indicates how successful the formula may be in future situations, and the user of the forecast is advised how much confidence he can place in the outcome of the prediction.

Since no forecast is infallible, the confidence rating is very helpful to the user. He must make the decision of whether or not to accept the prediction. When danger to human life is involved, he may prefer not to take even a 1 per cent chance of a bad forecast. He may order protective measures, such as the evacuation of personnel from offshore installations, in the face of only a remote threat of a storm. In the case of economic risk alone, it is often possible to develop a numerical procedure specifying up to what point a forecast should be accepted. Many analyses relating weather prediction to the economy of operations have been made, and the following example will illustrate one approach to such problems.

The San Joaquin Valley of central California near the city of Fresno (37°N, 120°W) is a major center of the raisin industry. During fall, from late August to early October, grapes are dried on paper trays in the vineyards; the drying process takes 3 to 4 weeks. The longer the grapes can be kept on the vine, the higher their sugar content will be. Therefore it is desirable to begin drying the grapes as late as possible. With the advancing season, however, the threat of rain increases in California after the dry summer (Chapter 10). Precipitation of more than 0.25 in. causes extensive damage to the raisins; even smaller rains have unfavorable effects on the crop.

When rain threatens, the trays are rolled up and stacked. This protective measure costs about 3 per cent of the sales price, and it can be used only sparingly. On the other hand, if no protection were ever taken, chances are that the whole crop would be lost in 5 to 6 years out of 10. Since this solution is clearly not acceptable, a good weather forecast would be very welcome. Because of the mountainous terrain of California and uncertainties about the weather situation over the Pacific Ocean, where few weather data exist, it is very

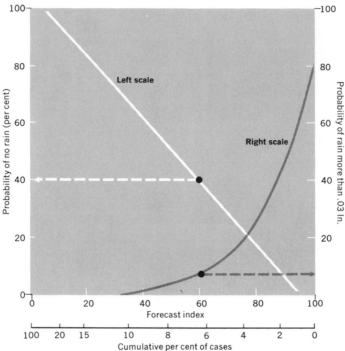

Fig. 14.5   Index for 24-hr rainfall prediction in the San Joaquin Valley of California during autumn (developed by D. L. Jorgensen, U.S. Weather Bureau). Probability that no rain will occur during the next 6 to 24 hours is obtained by going from the slanting straight line to the left scale. For instance, at an index value of 60 the chance for no rain is 40 per cent. The chance for rain greater than 0.03 in. is read by going from the curved line to the right scale. For the rainfall index of 60 this probability is 8 per cent. Bottom scale gives per cent frequency distribution of sample of 585 cases (cumulative) with forecast index. Eighty per cent of the sample had very low index, showing that California normally has good weather during the raisin-drying season. (After L. L. Kolb and R. R. Rapp, RAND Corp.)

difficult to predict tomorrow's precipitation reliably. Nevertheless, a rainfall index has been developed by the U.S. Weather Bureau, based mainly on winds and temperatures in the upper air. When the index is 0, the chance for rain is nil; when it is 100, rain is virtually assured (Fig. 14.5). With an index of 50, chances of no rain and rain are equal.

At what index value should the producer begin to protect? The lower scale in Fig. 14.5 shows that the vast majority of days—over 80 per cent—has an index of less than 10. On these days the grapes need not be protected. If the producer protects whenever the index is higher than 10, he will take his measures 20 per cent of the time—an average of 6 days during a 1-month drying season. His cost amounts to 18 per cent of the crop's value, unless several days with high index occur successively. If he waits to protect until the index reaches 50, in order to keep down the cost of the "weather insurance," the chance becomes very large that he will fail 1 in 10 years to protect against a damaging rain.

The best solution is intermediate: to protect at an index above 30. This value is attained 12 per cent of the time, so the producer will protect on 36 days per 10 years. Damaging storms are likely to occur only six times during the 10 years, but the producer is protected against all of them. His cost for the weather insurance will be 10 per cent of the sales price, still high, though much lower than the expense of other procedures. The forecast study has proven valuable since it has led to a procedure which is economically well defined: the producer pays a certain amount for weather insurance per year, but he is protected against economic disaster in any one year.

EXTENDED FORECASTS

Attempts have been made to predict weather for varying time intervals longer than 1 to 2 days. Since experience is most extensive with 5-day and 30-day forecasts, we shall examine the background of monthly forecasts.

During January, 1949, the upper-air flow at 500 millibars, averaged over the month (Fig. 14.6), departed drastically from the January mean. Normally, a ridge in the upper flow overlies the western half of the United States, and a trough the eastern half (Fig. 1.9). The inverse pattern prevailed in 1949. Cyclonic flow with cold air aloft predominated over the west, and anticyclonic flow with warm air over the east. Surface air temperatures reflected the upper-air conditions: it was warm to very warm in the east, cold to

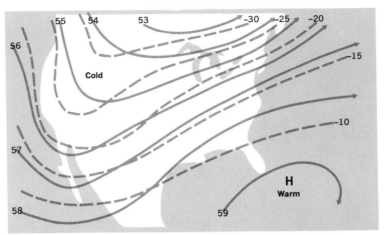

Fig. 14.6   Mean flow at 500 millibars during January, 1949. Height of the 500-millibar surface (solid lines) in 100s of meters; temperature (dashed lines) in °C.

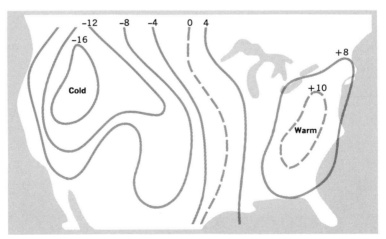

Fig. 14.7   Deviation of surface air temperature (°F) from the long period average during January, 1949. (After J. Namias, U.S. Weather Bureau.)

very cold in the west (Fig. 14.7). Virtually no major cyclones crossed the coasts of the United States (Fig. 14.8). Major storms formed in the southern Great Plains east of the upper-air trough (see model of Figs. 7.4 and 7.7). From there, they traveled northeastward across the Great Lakes to Canada, steered by the flow aloft from southwest. Accordingly, precipitation was far below average on the Pacific Coast and along parts of the Atlantic Coast; very heavy precipitation, with extensive flooding, occurred in the Mississippi and Ohio River Basins (Fig. 14.9).

In contrast, the average flow in January, 1958, at 500 millibars resembled the normal pattern (Fig. 14.10), but troughs and ridges were much more intense than normal. Warm air was thus drawn persistently into the Western states, while cold air moved far south in the East. As in January, 1949, temperatures departed from the mean in opposite directions in East and West. But this time it was warm in the West and cold in the East (Fig. 14.11). Further, across the entire northern belt of the United States and southern Canada the month was warm; cold weather dominated in the South. The north-south pattern indicates that the westerlies aloft were situated farther south than average, in fact by fully 10° latitude. We see that both east-west displacements of troughs and ridges of the long

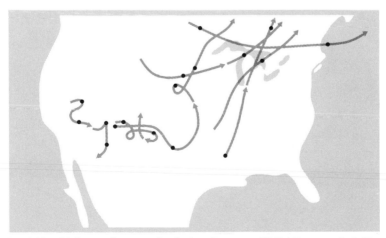

Fig. 14.8   Major cyclone tracks during January, 1949. Dots mark 24-hr positions, arrows show direction of movement.

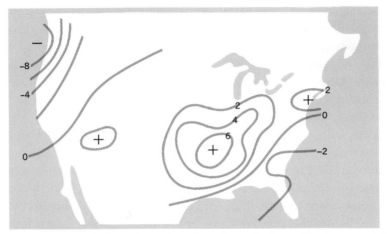

Fig. 14.9 Deviation of precipitation (inches) from the long period average during January, 1949.

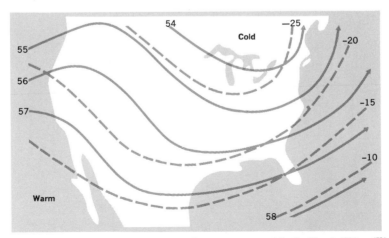

Fig. 14.10 Mean flow (solid) and temperatures (dashed) at 500 millibars during January, 1958. Units as in Fig. 14.6.

waves from their mean position and north-south shifts of the whole belt of westerlies affect surface air-temperature departures from long-term means.

Many cyclones accompanied the large-amplitude flow of January, 1958. Their paths at the surface reflect the upper current very clearly (Fig. 14.12). Cyclone tracks were concentrated along the Gulf and East Coasts of the United States. There, precipitation was well above average (Fig. 14.13). In contrast, the cyclones moving southeastward in the Central United States to the rear of the upper-air trough could not deliver even the meager average precipitation in many states.

If we compare the Januarys of 1949 and 1958, it is clear that the prediction of location and intensity of the long waves and the prediction of the latitude of the center of the westerly wind belt aloft are the keys to deciding whether next month will be warm or cold, dry or wet. We now return to a question raised at the start of this book. The winter of 1788–1789 was very cold in France, aggravating the differences between the people of France and their government. What causes temperatures of −18°F at Paris? Just as frequent strong outbreaks of cold air from Canada led to the very cold winter in the Southeastern United States in January, 1958, we expect that

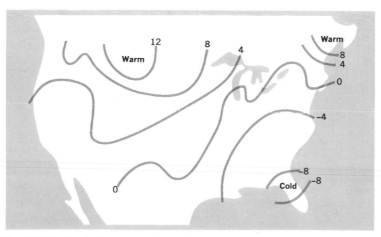

Fig. 14.11 Deviation of surface air temperature (°F) from the long-period average during January, 1958.

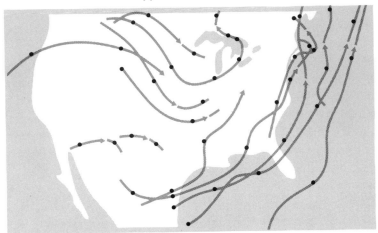

Fig. 14.12   Major cyclone tracks during January, 1958. Dots mark 24-hr positions, arrows direction of movement.

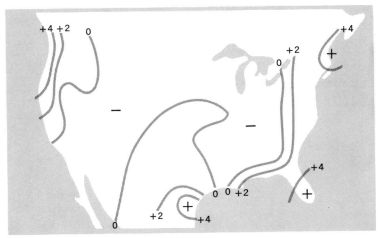

Fig. 14.13   Deviation of precipitation (inches) from the long-period average during January, 1958.

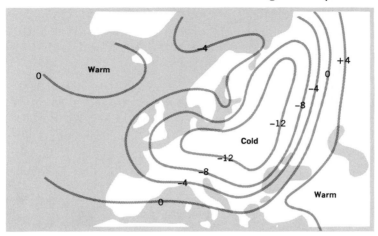

Fig. 14.14 Deviation of surface air temperature (°F) from the long-period average over Europe during January, 1963.

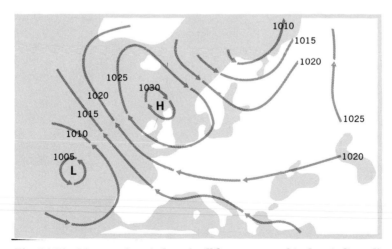

Fig. 14.15 Mean surface isobars (millibars, geostrophic flow indicated) over Europe and the eastern Atlantic Ocean during January, 1963, showing blocking of the normal westerly flow and prolonged transport of air from Russia westward.

western Europe will be very cold when polar air travels persistently westward from the Russian-Siberian cold-air reservoir. Such an air-mass movement from the east indicates a reversal of the normal westerly winds.

During January, 1963, western Europe experienced very severe cold. Temperatures averaged 5 to 6°C (9 to 11°F) below the mean for the month in northern France (Fig. 14.14). All Europe, down to the Mediterranean, was gripped by cold weather. The normal centers of action were reversed at the surface. A high-pressure center lay above the region of the Icelandic Low, a low-pressure center over the area normally occupied by the subtropical high-pressure belt (Fig. 14.15). Accordingly, the flow over western Europe was indeed from the east instead of from the west, and this brought on the severe winter. Since Fig. 14.15 is typical for cold European winters, we may conclude that this flow pattern probably prevailed during 1788–1789.

Reading of Weather Maps

In order to understand and follow weather, observations must be taken *at the same time* over very wide regions, such as the whole Northern Hemisphere, and exchanged internationally. Thus, when the observer on the United States East Coast makes an observation at 7 P.M. Eastern Standard Time, the observer in the Midwest makes it at 6 P.M. by his watch, the Rocky Mountain observer at 5 P.M. and the Pacific Coast observer at 4 P.M. These simultaneous observations provide the *synoptic* picture, the state of the weather at an instant of time.

The wealth of information must be presented so that the user of weather charts can learn the current situation almost at a glance. Pictorial presentation of weather data serves this purpose. The information at each station of a network, whether surface or upper-air, is arranged around a circle drawn at the location of the station. Analyses are performed depending on the purpose of the chart.

The following shows some of the most important symbols.

Cloudiness

	Clear	¼	½	¾	Overcast	Sky obscured
Amount of cloud cover	○	◔	◑	◕	●	⊗

Weather

Rain

Snow

Shower

Thunderstorm

Freezing rain

Fog

Blowing snow

Dust storm or sandstorm

The heavier rain or snow is, the more dots or stars are plotted, up to four.

∴ denotes heavy continuous rain.

Wind Direction and Speed

Wind direction is defined as the direction *from* which the wind blows. In modern practice direction is reported in degrees or tens of degrees on the 360°-compass (see opposite). Use of the 16-point compass, entered on the outside of the circle, is decreasing.

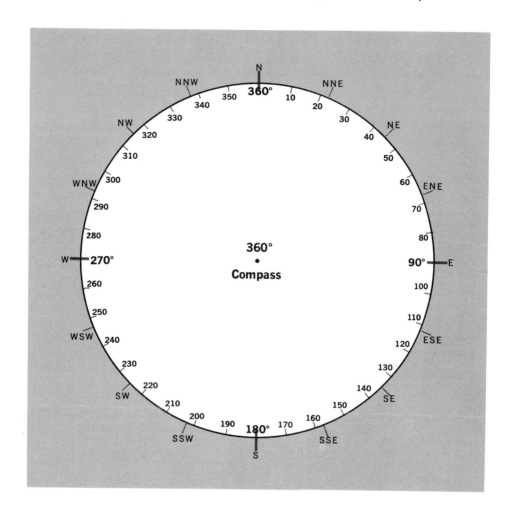

The principal unit for reporting wind speed is the knot (nautical mile per hour); Appendix II contains a table converting knots to other velocity units. The following table shows the old Beaufort scale, devised early in the nineteenth century by Admiral Beaufort of the British Navy for estimating wind at a height of 20 ft above the ground without instruments.

Beaufort	*knots*	*mph*
0	less than 1	less than 1
1	1–3	1–3
2	4–6	4–7
3	7–10	8–12
4	11–16	13–18
5	17–21	19–24
6	22–27	25–31
7 moderate gale	28–33	32–38
8 fresh gale	34–40	39–46
9 strong gale	41–47	47–54
10 whole gale	48–55	55–63
11 storm	56–65	64–75
12 hurricane	more than 65	more than 75

On weather maps a shaft, indicating the direction *from* which the wind blows, is drawn to end at the station circle. Wind speed is given in 5-knot increments. A short barb denotes 5 knots, a long barb 10 knots, and a heavy triangular barb 50 knots. Thus:

270° (W), 15   135° (SE), 30   250° (WSW), 75   320° (NW), 120

Weather Map Analysis

On surface charts isobars, or lines of equal pressure, usually are drawn. A convenient spacing is selected: 4 or 5 millibars outside the tropics, 1 or 2 millibars in the tropics. Centers of high and low pressure are marked *H* or *L*. On constant pressure charts of the upper air, contours of equal height of the pressure surface are drawn mostly in multiples of tens of meters, isotherms at intervals of 5°C or less.

Symbols used in analysis are as follows:

Cold front

Warm front

Occluded front

Stationary front

Frontless trough or
   wind shift line

Solid shading indicates areas where precipitation is currently falling.

Appendix II

Conversion Scales

Degrees Centigrade to Fahrenheit

Table 1   Temperatures C to F

°C	0	1	2	3	4	5	6	7	8	9
+40	104.0	105.8	107.6	109.4	111.2	113.0	114.8	116.6	118.4	120.2
+30	86.0	87.8	89.6	91.4	93.2	95.0	96.8	98.6	100.4	102.2
+20	68.0	69.8	71.6	73.4	75.2	77.0	78.8	80.6	82.4	84.2
+10	50.0	51.8	53.6	55.4	57.2	59.0	60.8	62.6	64.4	66.2
+ 0	32.0	33.8	35.6	37.4	39.2	41.0	42.8	44.6	46.4	48.2
− 0	32.0	30.2	28.4	26.6	24.8	23.0	21.2	19.4	17.6	15.8
−10	14.0	12.2	10.4	8.6	6.8	5.0	3.2	1.4	−0.4	−2.2
−20	−4.0	−5.8	−7.6	−9.4	−11.2	−13.0	−14.8	−16.6	−18.4	−20.2
−30	−22.0	−23.8	−25.6	−27.4	−29.2	−31.0	−32.8	−34.6	−36.4	−38.2
−40	−40.0	−41.8	−43.6	−45.4	−47.2	−49.0	−50.8	−52.6	−54.4	−56.2

Table 2   Differences °C to °F

°C	°F
1	1.8
2	3.6
3	5.4
4	7.2
5	9.0
6	10.8
7	12.6
8	14.4
9	16.2
10	18.0

Table 3   Lapse Rate: °C/km to °F/1,000 ft

°C/km	°F/1,000 ft
1	0.55
2	1.10
3	1.65
4	2.19
5	2.74
6	3.29
7	3.84
8	4.39
9	4.94
10	5.50

Length Conversions

Table 4   Centimeters to Inches

cm	in.	cm	in.
1	0.39	10	3.94
2	0.79	20	7.87
3	1.18	30	11.81
4	1.58	40	15.75
5	1.97	50	19.69
6	2.36	60	23.62
7	2.76	70	27.56
8	3.15	80	31.50
9	3.54	90	35.43
		100	39.37

Length Conversions (continued)

Table 5   Meters to Feet

m	ft	m	ft	m	ft
1	3.3	10	32.8	100	328.1
2	6.6	20	65.6	200	656.2
3	9.8	30	98.4	300	984.3
4	13.1	40	131.2	400	1312.3
5	16.4	50	164.0	500	1640.4
6	19.7	60	196.9	600	1968.5
7	23.0	70	229.7	700	2296.6
8	26.2	80	262.5	800	2624.7
9	29.5	90	295.3	900	2952.8
				1000	3280.8

Length Conversions (continued)

Table 6   Nautical Miles to Statute Miles and Km *

n. mi.	st. mi.	km	n. mi.	st. mi.	km
1	1.15	1.85	10	11.52	18.53
2	2.30	3.71	20	23.03	37.07
3	3.46	5.56	30	34.56	55.60
4	4.61	7.41	40	46.06	74.13
5	5.76	9.27	50	57.58	92.66
6	6.91	11.12	60	69.09	111.20
7	8.06	12.97	70	80.61	129.73
8	9.21	14.83	80	92.12	148.26
9	10.36	16.68	90	103.64	166.79

* Shift decimal points for larger distances.

Table 7   Inches of Mercury to Millibars

in. mercury	0.00	.01	.02	.03	.04	.05	.06	.07	.08	.09
0.00	0.00	0.34	0.68	1.02	1.35	1.69	2.03	2.37	2.71	3.05
0.10	3.39	3.73	4.06	4.40	4.74	5.08	5.42	5.76	6.10	6.43
0.20	6.77	7.11	7.45	7.79	8.13	8.47	8.80	9.14	9.48	9.82
0.30	10.16	10.50	10.84	11.18	11.51	11.85	12.19	12.53	12.87	13.21
0.40	13.55	13.88	14.22	14.56	14.90	15.24	15.58	15.92	16.25	16.59
0.50	16.93	17.27	17.61	17.95	18.29	18.63	18.96	19.30	19.64	19.98
0.60	20.32	20.66	21.00	21.33	21.67	22.01	22.35	22.69	23.03	23.37
0.70	23.70	24.04	24.38	24.72	25.06	25.40	25.74	26.08	26.41	26.75
0.80	27.09	27.43	27.77	28.11	28.45	28.78	29.12	29.46	29.80	30.14
0.90	30.48	30.82	31.15	31.49	31.83	32.17	32.51	32.85	33.19	33.53

Table 7   Inches of Mercury to Millibars (continued)

in. mercury	millibars	in. mercury	millibars	in. mercury	millibars
1	33.86	11	372.50	21	711.14
2	67.73	12	406.37	22	745.01
3	101.59	13	440.23	23	778.87
4	135.46	14	474.09	24	812.73
5	169.32	15	507.96	25	846.60
6	203.18	16	541.82	26	880.46
7	237.05	17	575.69	27	914.33
8	270.91	18	609.55	28	948.19
9	304.78	19	643.41	29	982.05
10	338.64	20	677.28	30	1015.92
				31	1049.78

Table 8   Knots to mph and m/sec

knots	mph	m/sec	knots	mph	m/sec	knots	mph	m/sec
1	1.2	0.5	10	11.5	5.1	110	126.7	56.6
2	2.3	1.0	20	23.0	10.3	120	138.2	61.8
3	3.5	1.5	30	34.5	15.4	130	149.7	66.9
4	4.6	2.1	40	46.1	20.6	140	161.2	72.1
5	5.8	2.6	50	57.6	25.7	150	172.7	77.2
6	6.9	3.1	60	69.1	30.9	160	184.2	82.4
7	8.1	3.6	70	80.6	36.0	170	195.8	87.5
8	9.2	4.1	80	92.1	41.2	180	207.3	92.7
9	10.4	4.6	90	103.6	46.3	190	218.8	97.8
			100	115.2	51.5	200	230.3	103.0

Table 9   *Standard Atmosphere*

Geometric height, m	Temp, °C	Pressure, millibars	Density, kg per cubic m
0	15.0	1013	1.23
1,000	8.5	899	1.11
2,000	2.0	795	1.01
3,000	−4.5	701	.99
4,000	−11.0	617	.82
5,000	−17.5	541	.74
6,000	−24.0	472	.66
7,000	−30.5	411	.59
8,000	−36.9	357	.53
9,000	−43.4	308	.47
10,000	−50.0	265	.41
11,000	−56.4	227	.36
12,000	−56.5	194	.31
13,000	−56.5	166	.27
14,000	−56.5	142	.23
15,000	−56.5	121	.20
16,000	−56.5	104	.17
17,000	−56.5	89	.14

Reference Books

Glossary of Meteorology, edited by R. E. Huschke, 638 pp., American Meteorological Society, 1959.

McGraw-Hill Encyclopedia of Science and Technology, edited by W. H. Crouse, McGraw-Hill Book Company, New York, 15 volumes and annual supplements from 1962.

Smithsonian Meteorological Tables, 527 pp., The Smithsonian Institution, Washington, D.C., 1951.

Data Sources

The Smithsonian Institution, Washington, D.C.:
"World Weather Records."
U.S. Weather Bureau, Washington, D.C.:
"Average Monthly Weather Resume and Outlook."
"Climates of the States."
"Climatological Data for the United States by Sections," monthly with annual summaries.
"Daily Series, Synoptic Weather Maps," surface maps, 500-millibar maps, synoptic data tabulations.
"Daily Weather Map."
"Monthly Climatic Data for the World."

Observations and Instruments

Handbook of Meteorological Instruments (part I: "Instruments for Surface Observations," 458 pp.; part II: "Instruments for Upper Air Observations," 209 pp.), Great Britain Meteorological Office, British Information Services, New York, 1956.

International Cloud Atlas, complete and abridged editions, World Meteorological Organization, Geneva, Switzerland, 1956.

Middleton, W. E. K., and A. F. Spilhaus, *Meteorological Instruments,* 3d rev. ed., 286 pp., University of Toronto Press, Toronto, Canada, 1953.

Surface Observation (manual), U.S. Weather Bureau, Washington, D.C.

U.S. Navy, *Marine Climatic Atlas of the World,* volumes on Atlantic, Pacific and Indian Oceans, Government Printing Office, Washington, D.C., published beginning 1955.

General and Special Subject Texts

Battan, Louis J., *Radar Meteorology,* 161 pp., The University of Chicago Press, Chicago, 1959.

Byers, H. R., *General Meteorology,* 540 pp., McGraw-Hill Book Company, New York, 1959.

Dunn, G. E., and B. I. Miller, *Atlantic Hurricanes,* 326 pp., Louisiana State University Press, Baton Rouge, La., 1960.

Flora, S. D., *Hailstorms of the United States,* 201 pp., University of Oklahoma Press, Norman, Okla., 1956.

Geiger, R., *The Climate near the Ground,* rev. ed., 494 pp., Harvard University Press, Cambridge, Mass., 1957.

George, J. J., *Weather Forecasting for Aeronautics,* 673 pp., Academic Press, Inc., New York, 1960.

Hess, S. L., *Introduction to Theoretical Meteorology,* 362 pp., Holt, Rinehart and Winston, Inc., New York, 1959.

Kendrew, W. G., *The Climates of the Continents,* 5th ed., 608 pp., Oxford University Press, Fair Lawn, N.J., 1961.

Landsberg, H., *Physical Climatology,* 2d ed., 446 pp., Gray Printing Co., DuBois, Pa., 1958.

Linsley, R. K., Jr., M. A. Kohler, and J. L. H. Paulhus, *Hydrology for Engineers,* 340 pp, McGraw-Hill Book Company, New York, 1958.

Neuberger, H., *Introduction to Physical Meteorology,* 271 pp., The Pennsylvania State University Press, University Park, Pa., 1951.

Neuberger, H., and F. B. Stephens, *Weather and Man,* 272 pp., Prentice-Hall, Inc., Englewood Cliffs, N.J., 1948.

Panofsky, Hans, *Introduction to Dynamic Meteorology,* 243 pp., The Pennsylvania State University Press, University Park, Pa., 1956.

Riehl, H., *Tropical Meteorology,* 392 pp., McGraw-Hill Book Company, New York, 1954.

Riehl, H., *Jet Streams of the Atmosphere,* 117 pp., Tech. Rep. No. 32, Dept. of Atmospheric Science, Colorado State University, Fort Collins, Colo., 1962.

Smith, L. P., *Farming Weather,* 208 pp., Thomas Nelson & Sons, London, 1958.

Sverdrup, H. U., *Oceanography for Meteorologists,* 246 pp., Prentice-Hall, Inc., Englewood Cliffs, N.J., 1942.

Trewartha, Glenn T., *An Introduction to Climate,* 3d ed., 402 pp., McGraw-Hill Book Company, 1954.

U.S. Dept. of Agriculture, *Climate and Man,* 1248 pp., U.S. Government Printing Office, Washington, D.C., 1941.

Willett, H. C., and F. Sanders, *Descriptive Meteorology,* 2d ed., 355 pp., Academic Press Inc., New York, 1959.

Popular

Stewart, G. R., *Storm,* 349 pp., Modern Library, Inc., New York, 1947.

Periodicals

Bulletin of the World Meteorological Organization.
Journal of Applied Meteorology, American Meteorological Society.
Journal of Geophysical Research, American Geophysical Union.
Monthly Weather Review, U.S. Weather Bureau.
Quarterly Journal of the Royal Meteorological Society.
Weather, Royal Meteorological Society.
Weatherwise, American Meteorological Society.

Monograph Series

Issued at irregular intervals on special topics by American Meteorological Society, American Geophysical Union, and World Meteorological Organization.

Societies

American Geophysical Union. House Organ: *Transactions AGU.* 1515 Massachusetts Ave., Washington, D.C.

American Meteorological Society. House organ: *Bulletin AMS.* 45 Beacon
     St., Boston, Mass.
Royal Meteorological Society, 49 Cromwell Road, London SW 1, England.

International Organization

World Meteorological Organization, Geneva, Switzerland.

Subject Index

Geographical Index